SCIENCE TEACHING IN THE SECONDARY SCHOOL

EDUCATION FOR LIVING SERIES

Under the Editorship of

H. H. Remmers

Science Teaching in the Secondary School

NATHAN S. WASHTON

Queens College

HARPER & BROTHERS

Publishers, New York

Library of Congress catalog card number: 61-8553

To my wife

Sylvia Irene Washton

CONTENTS

vii

Contents

EDITOR'S FOREWORD

The need for better science teaching at this juncture needs no emphasis or elaboration. Recent reminders of this have been frequent, loud, and often shrill and carping. In this book, Professor Washton, himself a leader among those concerned with science teaching in the secondary schools, provides an admirable teaching tool. In his educational philosophy he is, in my view, on the side of the angels in his insistence that science teachers must be not narrow specialists, but well grounded in the humanities and the social sciences as well as in the physical and biological sciences. He would, I judge, find himself in complete agreement with A. N. Whitehead's statement: "There is only one subject matter for education, and that is Life in all of its manifestations."

As already implied, the book is authoritative and well documented. It is both scholarly and eminently practical. The young prospective and beginning science teacher will, I believe, wish to keep it after it has served its purposes as a college textbook, for it contains highly useful resource material which in this regard makes it a kind of hand- and reference-book. The detailed lists of supplies and equipment, supply companies by regions, the sources of films and filmstrips, relevant scientific educational journals, excellent examples of instructional units, objectively scoreable thought questions, and valuable readings at the ends of chapters—these are some of the very useful and, in the best sense, practical contents of the book.

Since in some respects, particularly in science, the content of any college course soon becomes to some extent obsolete, Professor Washton includes the periodical government and other publications that the science teacher will need to keep abreast of the world of science, a world bound to be changing at an accelerated rate.

All too often science teachers suffer from budgetary anemia, and for this reason the sections of the book entitled "Improvising for Lack of Equipment" are valuable and welcome—especially to at least one thrifty-souled reader who would have prized such suggestions when he taught high school and premedical zoology laboratory a good many years ago.

Adding this timely book to the series for which I have editorial responsibility is distinctly gratifying. It will, I believe, serve importantly and constructively in the education of prospective teachers and of the boys and girls whom they will teach.

H. H. Remmers

PREFACE

During 1958, while preparing this book, the writer sent a letter to 250 leading science educators who are members of the National Association for Research in Science Teaching and of the National Science Teachers Association. The science educators were asked to suggest what should be included in a textbook on methods of science teaching. They were also invited to submit copies of their own studies and to propose other studies that should be included in such a text. Among the 150 replies received, most of the educators offered suggestions that were consistent with one another; a few listed some ideas that were contrary. In any case, the proposals were seriously considered by the writer, and many are incorporated in this book.

All prospective and beginning science teachers need some help. They need to know what to tell their students when the question is asked, Why should I study science? They need to understand the latest trends and effective techniques in teaching science based on educational research rather than on personal opinion or prejudice. They need to know where to go for help in selecting, organizing, and purchasing materials required for a topnotch science program. The science teachers are concerned with determining whether or not their students are learning science—evaluation. They must know how to prepare a daily lesson in science and how to plan a teaching unit in science. They want to know how to continue to improve their professional development. They must have access to the latest scientific information as well as the up-to-date approaches to teaching science effectively and economically. Science educators realize that they must always be students if they are to teach students.

It would be unfortunate if a science teacher tried one of the proposed methods and, finding such a method inadequate, abandoned it promptly. A given method or approach to teaching science needs to be refined for each teacher and each class. It may take many trial-and-error experiences before the science teacher masters a specific technique or approach to teaching a given topic or problem in science. This is especially true if he attempts to use the problem-solving method. It is also possible that a particular approach is more effective for some individuals and classes than others. Hence, the science teacher should "experiment" with his methods of teaching. It should be remembered that patience in trying out new techniques is a basic requirement of the scientist as well as the educator.

The science teacher must also be concerned with the majority of his students who will not become scientists. In an excerpt from Jean Rostand's address on the occasion of his accepting the 1959 Kalinga Prize for "outstanding contributions to the dissemination of scientific knowledge to the general public," April 21, 1960, he states:

Any distinction between the man of science and the ordinary man is no longer admissible, any more than a form of segregation based on an inequality of knowledge. Whether we like it or not, the laboratory henceforward opens right onto the street. Science not only affects us at any given moment of our day-to-day existence, it dogs us, it pursues us. Have we not, all of us, been transformed into involuntary guinea pigs ever since atomic fission, without asking our opinion, began to plant harmful particles in our bones?

The obligation to endure gives us the right to know.

The time is clearly coming when the man in the street will have his say with regard to the great social, national, international and moral issues latterly raised by certain applications of science; and it may be that the specialist himself, weary of bearing on his own the weight of his too-heavy responsibilities, will rejoice at finding understanding and support in public awareness.[1]

M. Rostand clearly indicates the need for teaching science for general education. Man is affected by science, and the major function of the science teacher is to help him understand and use his scientific knowledge intelligently. It is a real challenge to help our students interpret natural phenomena. This is vital to all—the slow, the average, and the gifted.

N. S. W.

[1] This excerpt appeared as part of the editorial, "Popularization of Science," *Science,* vol. 131 (May 20, 1960), p. 1491.

ACKNOWLEDGMENTS

Many thanks are due to Dr. Jerome Metzner, Bronx High School of Science; Dr. Abraham Raskin, Hunter College; Dr. William B. Reiner, Board of Education of the City of New York; Dr. Kenneth E. Anderson, University of Kansas; Dr. Herbert A. Smith, University of Kansas; Dr. George G. Mallinson, Western Michigan University; and Dr. Clarence M. Pruitt, University of Tampa, for most helpful suggestions and guidance which enabled the author to formulate the outline of the text.

The following colleagues were most cooperative in replying to the author questionnaire and in offering invaluable suggestions for which the writer is most grateful: Dr. Kenneth E. Anderson, University of Kansas; Dr. Arthur O. Baker, Cleveland Public Schools; Dr. Cyrus W. Barnes, New York University; Dr. J. Darrell Barnard, New York University; Dr. N. E. Bingham, University of Florida; Dr. Sam S. Blanc, Denver Public Schools; Dr. Stanley B. Brown, University of California; Dr. R. Will Burnett, University of Illinois; Dr. Kenneth B. M. Crooks, Grambling College; Dr. Ira C. Davis, University of Wisconsin; Dr. Will S. DeLoach, Florence State College; Mrs. Muriel Beuschlein, Chicago Teachers College; Dr. Warren M. Davis, Union County High School District #1; Dr. Donald G. Decker, Colorado State College; Dr. Ira Dubin, College of Education at Oneonta, New York; Dr. Albert F. Eiss, Indiana State College, Pennsylvania; Dr. Harley F. Glidden, Colorado State College; Dr. Harvey J. Goehring, Jr., University of Pittsburgh; Dr. Benjamin C. Gruenberg, New York City; Dr. James G. Harlow, University of Oklahoma; Dr. David A. Hilton, Highland Park School District, Michigan; Dr. Irene Hollenbeck, Southern Oregon College; Dr. Paul deH. Hurd, Stanford University; Dr. Willard J. Jacobson, Teachers College of Columbia University; Dr. Leland P. Johnson, Drake University; Dr. Philip G. Johnson, Cornell University; Dr. Haym Kruglak, Western Michigan University; Dr. C. A. Lawson, Michigan State University; the late Dr. R. W. Leffler, Purdue University; Dr. Vernon C. Lingren, University of Pittsburgh; Dr. William H. Lucow, University of Manitoba; Dr. Robert D. MacCurdy, University of Florida; Dr. W. Edgar Martin, U.S. Office of Education; Dr. John C. Mayfield, University of Chicago; Dr. Margaret McKibben, National Science Teachers Association; Dr. Morris Meister, Bronx Community College; Dr. Vaden W. Miles, Wayne State University; Dr. L. W. Miller, Chico State College; Dr. Ellsworth S. Obourn, U.S. Office of Education; Dr. Greta Oppe, Galveston Public Schools; Mrs. Archie MacLean Owen, Los Angeles Public Schools; Dr. Milton O. Pella, University of Wisconsin; Dr. James Perlman, San Francisco State College; Dr. Paul T. Rankin, Detroit Public Schools; Dr. John G. Read, Boston University; Dr. William B. Reiner, Board of Education of New York City; Dr. Francis St. Lawrence, Long Beach, California, Public Schools; Mr. Samuel Schenberg, New York City Public Schools; Dr. Edith M. Selberg, Colorado State College; Dr. Murl C. Shawer, Madison College, Virginia; Dr. Elizabeth A. Simendinger, Uniondale High School; Dr. Herbert A. Smith, University of Kansas; Dr. Herbert F. A. Smith, Southern Illinois University; Dr. Harold Spielman, College of City of New York; Dr. Robert Stollberg, San Francisco State College; Dr. Frank X. Sutman, Inter-American University of Puerto Rico; Dr. John Urban, College of Education at Buffalo, New York; Dr. William C. Van Deventer, Western Michigan University; Dr. Hanor A. Webb, George Peabody College for Teachers; Dr. E. J. Winters, New York University; Dr. Harold E. Wise, University of Nebraska; Dr. John H. Woodburn, Johns Hopkins University; Dr. G. Marian Young, University of Florida; and Dr. Herbert S. Zim, University of Illinois.

Thanks are due to the superintendents of schools and many of the administrative and teaching staffs of the following school systems for photographs that were supplied for use in the text: Detroit Public Schools; District Five Public Schools, Levittown, New York; Long Beach, New York, Public Schools; New York City Public Schools; Philadelphia Public Schools; Port Washington, New York, Public Schools; Northport, New York, Public Schools; and the Uniondale,

New York, Public Schools. Specific credit is given for each photograph as it appears in the text.

Thanks are also due to Dr. Margaret V. Kiely, Dean Emeritus of the faculty at Queens College, to Dr. Thomas V. Garvey, Dean of Administration at Queens College, and to Dr. Henry Gould of New York State Teachers College at Brockport for their invaluable assistance and encouragement.

My daughter Ruth rendered invaluable assistance in reading some copy to me, and my daughter Gale did some typing that helped get the manuscript in final form. My thanks to both of them as well as to my daughter Laura for helping in assembling the manuscript.

N. S. W.

February 1, 1961

SCIENCE TEACHING IN THE SECONDARY SCHOOL

1

INTRODUCTION

THE EDUCATION OF SCIENCE TEACHERS

Teaching Science Years Ago and Today

At the turn of the century it was a relatively simple matter to educate the science teachers for our secondary schools. At that time, the science teacher specialized in a particular science and lectured with the aid of specific objects to a very select group of high school students who were preparing for the ministry, law, medicine, engineering, or teaching. Very little was known about psychology or how adolescents learn. The teaching of science was simple. In his preface to *First Book of Zoology* in 1875, Edward Morse wrote, ". . . the pupil is expected to study, with the book in one hand, and the specimens in the other."[1] Principles and foundations of education, curriculum practices, and methods of teaching were confined to the three "l's"—*listening, looking,* and *learning.* There would be little need for professional training in education today if learning would occur for all students solely on the basis of listening and looking. But present-day science teachers in the secondary schools should acquire an understanding of how adolescents behave and learn.

What causes pupils to want to learn science? What makes them like or dislike science? How do students develop scientific attitudes, problem-solving skills, knowledge, interests, implications, and applications of science? How can these various kinds of learning be evaluated? What are the most recent and effective procedures of teaching science based upon current research in science education? To find the best available answers to these questions, sci-

---

[1] Edward S. Morse, *First Book of Zoology,* American Book Company, 1875, p. iii.

ence teachers today should obtain a thorough and carefully planned sequence of knowledge and experience in the area of teacher education.

Greater Responsibilities Today

Science teachers in American public schools have a greater responsibility today than in the days before atomic energy and space travel. These responsibilities will continue to increase as we advance in our search and research for scientific knowledge. Scientific discovery is no longer the concern of the scientist alone. If scientific discoveries were confined within the laboratory walls and employed only for the intellectual advancement of science, no one other than the scientists would be interested in such progress.

The 1956 election was a good illustration of how the social and political implications of science can affect our citizens. Unfortunately, our citizens did not comprehend too well the basic ideas of atomic energy or the implications involved. They were not able to judge too effectively whether or not they should support certain kinds of experimentation in atomic explosions that result in radioactive fall-out. The scientists were also in conflict in the use of atomic energy and the role they should play in promoting its use and control.

The American Association for the Advancement of Science recently considered the question of the social responsibility of science and asked its members to determine which one of the following alternatives should be adopted:

1. Scientific organizations should point out the scientific evidence that is relevant to a policy issue.
2. They should go farther and point out the implications of the scientific evidence.
3. They should go still farther and recommend the actions that seem, from the point of view of science, to be most desirable.[2]

It appears that the second alternative of pointing out the implications of the scientific evidence should constitute the function of

[2] American Association for the Advancement of Science, "Social Responsibility of Science," an editorial, *Science,* vol. 25 (January 25, 1957).

a group of scientists and science teachers. From a democratic viewpoint, it might become dangerous for any single group of citizens to dictate the course of action to follow.

Science teachers, therefore, have a responsibility over and above teaching science itself—they are also charged with teaching the socioeconomic and political implications of science in our present era. They can help young citizens understand how to vote intelligently without telling them how to vote on vital issues. Atomic explosions and radioactive fall-out constitute only one of the many scientific controversial issues. In some communities, there are controversies concerning such problems as the fluoridation of drinking water; the required injections of Salk vaccine; the control of smog; the physical location of airports; the use of germ warfare; state laws requiring pasteurization of milk; the degree of control of assigning radio frequencies; legislative action for the preservation and conservation of forests, wildlife, water, minerals, and other natural resources.

If citizens are to be able to discuss and vote intelligently on these issues, they must obtain the scientific knowledge necessary for understanding. Students should be taught how to evaluate critically the data and statements made by others before they arrive at a decision. This is another major responsibility of science teachers today—to teach for scientific thinking and scientific attitudes. In addition, the responsibility of science teachers includes the teaching of science, its implications, its applications, and the adjustments man must make in a changing society.

A College Program

Dr. Edmund W. Sinnott, Director of Sheffield Scientific School at Yale University, has said, "We must educate the minds of men in their totality. It is entirely possible that science alone may make monsters of men." It is for this reason that scientists and science teachers should possess an adequate background in the humanities and social sciences. If science teachers are to guide young people in understanding science and its impact upon man in his changing society, the teachers will need a good understanding of the principles of human behavior as well as the social, political, and

economic forces that affect our society. They can obtain this knowledge from studies in the areas of psychology, sociology, anthropology, history, political science, and economics. Some colleges
may offer a series of courses such as contemporary civilization to
achieve the same goals. Science teachers also need courses in oral
and written communication, literature, music, and art. They should
also study health and physical education. The science teacher is a
totally educated person who can make a worthy contribution
toward the further development of our cultural heritage.

Science teachers in the junior and senior high schools should
have a broad background in all of the basic sciences in addition to
specialization in one particular science. Specifically, all science
teachers should have at least an introductory college course in
biology, chemistry, physics, geology, and astronomy.

It would also be desirable to offer a seminar in which science
teachers study the interrelationships of two or more different sciences. For example, the topic of the physics and chemistry of the
cell might be a very appropriate area to pursue in a seminar. This
topic cuts across at least three basic sciences: physics, chemistry,
and biology.

A secondary school science teacher should be able to elect at
least 18 or more semester hours of advanced undergraduate courses
in one of the basic sciences and at least one or more courses in a
related science. The seminar should provide opportunities for individual and group creative thinking.

The science teacher who has an adequate background in the
sciences will be able to answer challenging questions and also
stimulate his pupils to seek further knowledge. He should be able
to inspire students to enjoy science. In addition to learning science,
pupils learn to like or dislike science, to enjoy or not to enjoy
school.

Since these by-products of instruction—a liking or disliking of
science and school, the willingness to learn or not to learn, the
various degrees of ability to learn science—are concomitant with
learning science, the science teacher should have a thorough
knowledge of what science to teach and how to teach it. Science

content cannot be separated from science methodology in teaching adolescents. Science teachers need to understand adolescents, their goals, drives, and problems. Achievement in science is highly dependent upon the emotional needs of the learner. In proposing an evaluation study for teacher training, Harry N. Rivlin states that preparation for teaching:

. . . should make adequate provision for students to know the subject matter they are going to teach—in fact, to be masters of subject matter.

. . . should provide opportunities which would increase each year of study for teacher candidates to work with children. First there would be just observation of children, then, in a graduated way, the candidate would assist the teacher, himself be a student teacher, then a teacher under supervision, and finally a full teacher. Each step would bring increasing experience, increasing independence.[3]

Science teachers will have a good deal more to learn within the next few years. We are in the infant stage of atomic energy and space travel. More knowledge is needed for esoteric value, for better health, for our national security and prosperity. With the wealth of knowledge which is yet to come, how can the science teacher be educated in totality in a few years? Compare the zoology textbooks of 1890—about 200 pages—with the biology textbooks of today—some 1000 pages—and remember that the teacher now must cover a text quintupled in size, but with no increase in the number of class hours. We should examine both what we teach science teachers and how we teach them so as to provide them with the knowledges, skills, and special abilities they need in order to fulfill their responsibilities.

SHORTAGE OF SCIENTISTS AND SCIENCE TEACHERS

In recent years, there has been much concern about the shortage of scientists, engineers, and science teachers. Conflicting studies and reports have appeared to indicate the need for scientists in various industries and the number of students who are majoring in the

[3] *New York Herald Tribune* (April 29, 1958), p. 9.

sciences in high schools and colleges. The launching of Sputnik, Explorer, and other earth satellites aroused even greater concern. In a pamphlet issued by the U.S. Office of Education, the following statement appears:

> Do the present shortage of specialized personnel and the attempts at improvement indicate that the schools have neglected to train students in science and mathematics? Some persons, in their concern for producing more scientists and engineers, have stated: "Fewer pupils take science and mathematics today than 50 years ago," and "Our schools are not doing a good job of teaching mathematics and science."
>
> For several years, the percentage of pupils enrolled in certain science and mathematics courses declined. The present study shows that between 1954 and 1956, *both percentage and numbers* increased. During 1956–1957 more pupils enrolled in high school science and mathematics than during any previous year in the history of our Nation.
>
> *If more pupils are taking science and mathematics,* why is there a concern about the shortage of specialized personnel in these areas? Is the quality of instruction inferior in science and mathematics? Perhaps the very excellence of the product which the high schools have produced has contributed to the shortage. The scientists who were trained in our Nation's schools invented and developed machines that require more specialized personnel to maintain them. From our schools have come the engineers who developed this machine age—the very machines that require more specialized personnel and the invention of more machines.[4]

This report does not list any single cause for the shortage of personnel. Among the many factors that contribute to this shortage of scientists and science teachers are: a period of low birth rate, a rapidly expanding technology and a greater demand for manpower, competition for skilled labor, and increasing military demands.

In a press release of February 1957, Frederick L. Fitzpatrick, who conducted the Teachers College Science Manpower Project, as-

[4] Kenneth E. Brown and Ellsworth S. Obourn, *Offerings and Enrollments in Science and Mathematics in Public High Schools, 1956,* Pamphlet No. 120, U.S. Department of Health, Education, and Welfare, 1957, p. 2.

serted that the scientist shortage is due to poor science teaching. The number of students our schools will send on to America's factories, laboratories, and drawing boards will be determined by whether the high school science teachers are interesting or dull, according to the 1000 Teachers College alumni opinions reported by Fitzpatrick.

An almost absolute relationship between good teaching and rising science enrollments was reported in the survey. Wherever growing interest and enrollment in physics, chemistry, and mathematics was found, the principal reason given was the influence and attraction of the science teacher or teachers.

On the other hand, in one out of three communities reporting decline in science enrollments, the teacher was named as the number one factor . . . Here the teacher was labeled as being "poorly prepared in the subject," "uninspired," or "uninteresting."

The Fitzpatrick study reported that outstanding and well-prepared science teachers are primarily responsible for attracting students to scientific careers. Some of the factors that make for poor science teaching are: teachers who are trained in fields other than science and who teach science, ill-equipped laboratories, teaching science for the select few, overcrowded classrooms, low salaries, and shortages of teaching staff or equipment.

IMPORTANCE OF SCIENCE TEACHING IN ATOMIC SPACE AGE

Science teaching will play a more vital role in the years immediately ahead than it has in the past. The ultimate conquest of space travel, the harnessing of hidden sources of energy from outer space, newer and greater uses of atomic energy, automation and related electronic devices, and additional developments in antibiotics and other biologicals serve as only a few illustrations of the greater demand for scientific and technical manpower. It is through effective science teaching that an adequate supply of future scientists may be obtained for our national security, health and prosperity.

Research in modern science is no longer the concern only of the specialists in the various fields of natural science. If scientific discoveries were confined within the laboratory walls of scientists and employed only for the intellectual advancement of science, no one other than the scientists would be interested in such progress. An understanding of science is every citizen's responsibility. Advances in science—and particularly the applications to the home, to industry, to agriculture, and to community living—have changed our environment.

Fig. 1.1. A ninth-grade meteorology project on weather caused by different fronts. Uniondale High School Science Fair, 1960. (Courtesy of Uniondale High School, Uniondale, N.Y.)

As a result, there are different ways and problems of living. Man is continually striving to adjust himself to an ever changing environment. Applied science is a vital factor in making man modify his behavior in modern society. Therefore, modern science is no longer to be thought of as cloistered academic knowledge on the part of pure researchers. Scientific phenomena and their understanding and uses by people affect everyday living.

SOCIAL IMPLICATIONS OF SCIENCE

The social implications of science are recognized by experts in political science, economics, sociology, psychology and by many other citizens as well. Science cannot make any contributions to society without demanding various adjustments of the denizens to the changed environment. Science and technology provided man with better materials for home construction, new foods, more effective means of communication and transportation, and devices that yield greater power and increase the efficiency of machines that speed up production. Mass production in turn affects consumption through the prices of commodities, labor, and wages. Applied science has given man new drugs, improved medicines, and better clothing. Thus, man is compelled to modify his behavior to meet the changes in society that are thrust upon him due to scientific implications and applications.

Many new economic institutions have been established as a result of scientific discoveries. For example, more than three out of four people are now employees rather than being self-employed. With the invention of the automobile, the horse and buggy era disappeared. The technological developments associated with the automobile employ a vast number of workers in the rubber industry and in the transporting, refining, and selling of oil and gasoline and allied industrial products.

New products and new markets are created. Today the automobile contains devices such as mirrors, radios, heaters, air conditioners, clocks, cigarette lighters, and other accessories, some of which are not basically essential for transportation, but people demand such luxuries. Some of these new products may be essential for safe driving. Hence, man adjusts himself to changes in the material environment that are made possible by producers and consumers.

Social, political, and economic implications may also be observed through the improvement of communication systems. The first means of long-range communication used by man was the messenger. Later, domesticated animals were employed. In some societies, smoke signals, drums, flaming arrows, and reflected sunlight were utilized for communication. Not until about 1837 was communication made convenient, speedy, and accurate through the discovery and use of the telegraph. It was the first successful method of transmitting signals electrically. Following the telegraph, new discoveries in science gave modern society the telephone, radio, radiotelegraphy, teletype, television, and radar.

During World War II, speedy and accurate communications were vital for any military task because communication meant control and was basic to successful military operations. The same relationship applies to living in the twentieth century. Commerce; international trade; political, diplomatic, and economic negotiations; and personal and social living demand several means of effective communication. What might happen to Wall Street if all of the "tape tickers," telephones, and telegraph and radio receivers were inoperative for an indefinite period of time? What adjustments would people be required to make under these conditions? How would our economy and society be affected? Herein is a clue to some of the implications of science only insofar as communication is concerned.

Instruments for communication today were made possible only through basic discoveries of scientific principles of electricity and magnetism. There is still a tremendous opportunity for research in this and other areas. What will be the findings of scientists tomorrow? How will these discoveries affect man and society? Since science will continue to change the environment, man will be required either to adjust himself to new changes or to learn how to control the environment.

SCIENCE AND WORLD RELATIONS

The one-world concept evolved largely through research and technological developments in communication and transportation. It no longer takes several days, weeks, or months to travel across the Atlantic or the Pacific oceans. Improved steam engines, internal combustion engines, diesel engines, and high-powered jet aircraft, as well as the principles of aerodynamics and related knowledges and their applications, make it possible to transport people; machinery; material for construction, clothing, and food to many parts of the world within a number of hours. International trade and interstate commerce are possible only as a result of rapid and safe means of transportation. Industry and agriculture are able to expand. Many billions of dollars worth of goods are exchanged annually with other countries. Scientific progress in transportation and communication provides the potentiality for international unity and peace. Space throughout the earth is "shrinking" with respect to travel time. We cannot remain isolationists. Science and technology demand that we learn how to adjust to our immediate environment as well as to the different people and nations throughout the world.

In promoting better relations of different people throughout the world, students should understand that science is international. The greatest scientific discoveries—that is, basic knowledge, not inventions—came from scientists throughout the world representing various nations, religions, and color. Students and teachers should be able to read at least one or two foreign languages and translate scientific information from foreign periodicals—in an almost hobby like fashion. New knowledge should be shared by all people, especially if this activity makes for a better world.

THE USE OF SCIENCE—FOR GOOD OR EVIL

The scientist is chiefly concerned with discovering fundamental knowledge regardless of how such knowledge is applied. Some people may argue this point. But scientists believe that they should not be told what to discover on the basis of how such knowledge is to be put to use. One of the major controversial issues is the possible curtailment of atomic test explosions because certain substances like strontium-90 produce radiations that are harmful to living organisms. Should it, therefore, be concluded that research in this area must cease?

In a democracy the search for truth and knowledge is of paramount importance to the scientist as well as to all citizens. This basic ideal is largely responsible for the intellectual curiosity and drive on the part of scientists who make the greatest discoveries. A scientist like other creative individuals must be free to search for knowledge. The historical progress of science gives evidence of how esoteric discoveries of basic scientific principles were applied many years after the fundamental ideas were known. As an illustration, the work by Oersted, Faraday, Helmholtz, and Clerk-Maxwell produced fundamental ideas pertaining to magnetism and electricity. Other earlier investigators like Galvani and Volta made important contributions in this area. After many years, the findings of these investigators were employed by engineers to invent or manufacture the electromagnet and finally the numerous appliances that operate electrically via motors.

It appears reasonable to assume that Galvani and other scientists did not desire knowledge for the specific purpose of making an electric vacuum cleaner or other electrical appliances. How scientific knowledge is applied, for good or for evil, should be determined by all citizens. Scientists, however, must enjoy continuous freedom in the search for basic understandings even though there may be no immediate applications, good or bad.

SUMMARY

Teaching science 50 years ago was very different from teaching science today. The number of pages in science textbooks doubled or tripled within 75 years, and the number of hours of science instruction in the classroom is unchanged. Methods of teaching science are no longer confined to listening and looking. Science teachers have greater responsibilities today. Socioeconomic and political implications of science need to be taught for our health, prosperity, and national security. Hence, the education of science teachers should go beyond the depths of science into related areas from social sciences and the humanities. This kind of education is essential in a world of peace where science can be employed to advance the welfare of people throughout the world.

EXERCISES

1. Discuss your formal education as a science teacher, and suggest ways of strengthening your background to qualify you for doing a more effective job of teaching science.
2. What factors were responsible in bringing about the required changes in teaching science during the past fifty years?
3. List several specific science topics that can influence better world relations, and discuss how they can be taught for this purpose.
4. "High school students should be taught the uses of science." Discuss how the uses of science may be for good or for evil.
5. How should the science teacher cope with the problem of ever expanding scientific information with relation to textbooks and classroom teaching?

2

TEACHING AND LEARNING
SCIENCE

WHY TEACH SCIENCE?

Science in Relation to School Curriculum

The following statement appeared over twenty years ago and is as appropriate today as it was then in a report of the Committee on the Function of Science in General Education:

Careful examination into the purposes and procedures of science teaching and its function in the education of the adolescent is appropriate for two reasons. The first of these is the increasingly significant effect which the sciences, their applications, and the scientific point of view are having upon social organization, cultural patterns, and consequently upon the life of the individual. The second lies in a prevailing confusion as to goals, functions, and procedures in the field of science teaching itself. Nor are these two sources of demand for re-examination and reformulation unrelated; clarification of purposes and programs must of necessity take place in terms of a conception of education consonant with the times, so deeply affected by developments in the sciences.

Instruction in the sciences has had an important place in the program of secondary education for many years. The role that it should be called upon to play today is undoubtedly more prominent and significant than ever before. Technological advances in means of production, transportation, and communication are having profound effects upon the material aspects of the culture. The problem of how best to use the results of these advances is ever before us. Man's way of thinking and his outlook upon life—particularly in relation to his conception of the universe and his place in it—continue to be deeply affected by advances in science. Further, the sciences have provided a great many tested methods and techniques which man can use with confidence and efficiency in attacking his problems. Yet, the use of these tools in solving the crucial problems of social living is, in large measure, only a promise for the future. These facts all point to a new and increasing responsibility for the science program of the school.[1]

This statement could have been made shortly after the launching of Sputnik. The confusion as to objectives, functions, and instructional procedures of a science curriculum is probably greater today among scientists, engineers, the general public, educators, and governmental representatives as a result of the hysteria produced by the earth satellites. Various "crash through" programs have been proposed in which the standard of achievement has been compared with the science curriculums in Russia.

If we are to benefit from the fruits of research, we should not permit a lag to occur between the discovery of knowledge and the time it takes for it to be used. Essentially, this is a major problem in science and science education. Almost 1000 research studies in science education were reviewed during the past two decades in several leading professional journals of science and science education. It is doubtful if more than a dozen of these doctoral studies were brought to the attention of the science classroom teachers. Hence, there is a great lag between educational research and its implementation for classroom use.

Recently, many school systems re-examined their science curriculums in terms of proposing changes or redesigning the science program to meet the newer developments of science and technology and the needs of their students. Paul DeH. Hurd lists four emerging points of view on science teaching:

1. Science should be a substantial part of general education. General education is not to be regarded as something for the nonacademically inclined, but basic for everyone.

[1] Progressive Education Association, *Science in General Education,* Report of the Committee on the Function of Science in General Education, Appleton-Century-Crofts, 1938, p. 3.

2. The importance of science is such that a continuous program of a general education nature from kindergarten through the fourteenth grade and of a pre-professional nature at the upper levels seems necessary.
3. Schools must recognize that science has become an intellectual and cultural pursuit in our generation. It is important that young people understand the attitudes and forces which are shaping contemporary society.
4. Science and the social studies must merge at some points in the curriculum. This view is expressed by those who see the widest ramifications of science—the scientists.[2]

In providing pupils with a general education in the junior high schools, the function is to advance their individual welfare as well as the welfare of the community. The general education program consists of the common knowledge, attitudes, and skills that are required for intelligent living in our democratic society. Through the organization and effective teaching of a junior high school curriculum which consists of a series of courses and/or experiences in English, citizenship education (social studies), mathematics, art, music, health and physical education, and general science, it is believed that the goals of a general education can be developed. Pupil interests and abilities, the techniques employed in motivating learning, the nature of the environment, evaluation procedures, and guidance represent a few of the major factors that determine whether or not better citizens are developed.

Content materials and appropriate student experiences should be carefully selected for all of the subjects in terms of specific objectives. For example, the teacher should ask the question, Why am I teaching this unit on weather? One purpose or objective is for pupils to develop an understanding of the basic scientific principles or concepts to help them interpret daily and periodical changes in the weather. Progress toward this objective can be made by teaching basic knowledge and providing pupils with various types of suitable experiences.

---

[2] Paul DeH. Hurd, "Critical Issues in the Teaching of Secondary School Science," *California Journal of Secondary Education*, vol. 33 (March, 1958), p. 135.

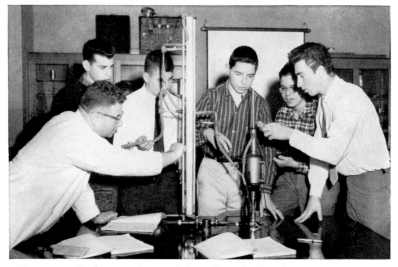

Fig. 2.1. Students make careful readings in learning the instrumental skills which are common objectives to all the physical sciences. (Courtesy of District Five Public Schools, Levittown, N.Y.)

How can the general science teacher make a worthy contribution along with teachers of other subjects in making better consumers of goods, leisure, and services? Better consumers do not develop automatically even though they can read a weather map in a daily newspaper.

The science teacher can discuss the effects of droughts and untimely frosts on the price of citrus fruits and other foods that are cultivated in farm areas. Prices of fresh foods and frozen foods can be compared with those of canned goods. Students can make community surveys of prices of various foods and other materials that may have been affected by extreme weather conditions. Weather and climate can be related to transportation and shipping. A variety of pupil activities will help uncover additional knowledge if community surveys, graphs, interviews and local or school weather stations are made.

It is possible to relate many scientific principles and applications to problems in the social studies or in mathematics. However, this does not imply that all of the scientific understandings or generalizations must be integrated with other subjects. There are many worthy objectives of teaching science for general education. The Report of the Harvard Committee states,

> Science instruction in general education should be characterized mainly by broad integrative elements—the comparison of scientific with other modes of thought, the comparison and contrast of the individual sciences with one another, the relations of science with its own past and with general human history, and of science with problems of human society. These are the areas in which science can make a lasting contribution to the general education of all students.[3]

Criteria in Formulating Objectives

Before a teacher states or lists the various objectives for a particular science course, it may be helpful to consider one's criteria in establishing such objectives. Perhaps a fundamental criterion might be whether or not a science teacher can evaluate the degree to which an objective is developed. The evaluation may be in the form of a pencil-paper test, observation by the teacher of pupil behavior and attitude, anecdotal record or another appropriate device for measuring or evaluating the degree of growth in the development of an objective.

The National Society for the Study of Education, in 1947 employed the following four criteria in formulating objectives: practicable, psychologically sound, attainable, and universal.[4]

Is the statement practicable for the classroom teacher? Is it usable? Does it develop logically from a simple step to the next step and so on? Does progress toward the development of the objective actually occur?

Is the statement of the objective psychologically sound? Is it based on accepted principles of learning?

Are the objectives possible of attainment under reasonable conditions? Are they suitable to the various levels of development in a class of heterogeneous learners?

Are the stated objectives universal for all groups in a demo-

---

[3] *General Education in a Free Society,* Harvard University Press, 1945, p. 155.
[4] National Society for the Study of Education, *Science Education in American Schools,* Forty-sixth Yearbook, Part I, University of Chicago Press, 1947, chap. 3.

cratic society? Are objectives avoided that are limited by geographical, religious, racial, and political considerations?

Significance of Objectives

Student teachers and beginning science teachers may underestimate the importance of formulating objectives both general and specific for a science course, a unit plan, or a daily lesson plan. In observing a science lesson, a supervisor very frequently may diagnose many of the shortcomings by examining the lesson plan's statements of objectives.

In "The Administrator Looks at Science Education Objectives," Harold B. Brooks and Clarence H. Woodruff write:

The administrator's first concerns in any field of learning are those of a competent newspaper reporter—what, when, where, why, and how. In science, he, with others, determines *what* shall be taught on the bases of texts, courses of study, current scientific discoveries and reports, the needs and interests of both pupils and the communities in which they live, and the combined opinions of teachers and scientists.

When general science, physics, chemistry, biology, or physiology shall be taught is governed by such factors as pupil growth and development, custom as established over a period of years, viewpoints of teachers and parents, and available facilities.

Where science shall be taught is being answered in ever broader terms. It is taught in classroom and laboratory, in the field, in museums, and in the home. But it is taught daily outside of school influence, too; for this is predominantly an age of science and of scientific information to young and old.

The *whys* of science teaching are almost endless. Most impressive reasons given are (1) the actual needs of individuals in their daily living, (2) the intense interests of pupils in all things scientific, (3) the opportunities opened up for scientific method in thinking, (4) the knowledge and understandings necessary for college entrance, and (5) the requirements of a well-rounded general education.

How science shall be taught is perhaps the most important consideration. Taught improperly, it can be a deadly recitation of memorized facts, with little or no meaning for the learner. Taught properly, it is a flexible, functional inquiry and exploration into a fascinating universe of facts, ideas, speculations, discoveries, and conclusions.

Science well learned is a basis for living and a philosophy of life, as well as a body of knowledge. *How* taught and *how well* taught, in the final analysis, will always depend upon the teacher's depth of knowledge, his enthusiasm, his technical skills, his love of youth, as well as his devotion to his subject, his breadth of view, and his experience.

. . . In summary may it be said that the principal who would build well in the field of science instruction must select his objectives, both general and specific, with care. He must be sure that they are sound in terms of educational philosophy, community understandings, and pupil needs and interests.[5]

To realize the attainment of certain objectives, it may be very useful to classify or categorize the various types before formulating them. Some courses of study list general and specific objectives. Others state them in terms of content, teacher aims, pupil attitudes, behaviors, or needs. For a more thorough preparation of daily lesson plans, unit plans, and syllabuses, the following categories may serve as a guide to the teacher:

A. Functional information or facts about such matters as:
   1. Our universe—earth, sun, moon, stars, weather . . .
   2. Living things—plants and animals.
   3. The human body—structure, functions, and care.
   4. The nature of matter—elements, compounds . . .
   5. Energy—sources, types . . .
   6. Contributions of science to the life of our times—radio, telephone, telegraph . . .
B. Functional concepts, such as:
   1. Space is vast.
   2. The earth is very old.
   3. All life has evolved from simpler forms.
   4. All matter is probably electrical in structure.
C. Functional understanding of principles, such as:
   1. All living things reproduce their kind.
   2. Changes in the seasons and differences in weather and climate depend largely upon the relation of the earth to the sun.
   3. Energy can be changed from one form to another.

[5] Harold B. Brooks and Clarence H. Woodruff, "The Administrator Looks at Science Education Objectives," *Bulletin,* National Association of Secondary School Principals, vol. 37 (January, 1953), p. 11.

    4. All matter is composed of single elements or combinations of elements.

    5. Living things in a given environment or locality are mutually interdependent.

D. Instrumental skills, such as ability to:

    1. Read science content with understanding and satisfaction.

    2. Perform fundamental operations with reasonable accuracy.

    3. Perform simple manipulatory activities with science equipment.

    4. Read maps, graphs, charts, and tables and to interpret them.

    5. Make accurate measurements, readings, titrations, etc.

E. Problem-solving skills, such as ability to:

    1. Sense a problem.

    2. Define the problem.

    3. Study the situation for all facts and clues bearing upon the problem.

    4. Make the best tentative explanations or hypotheses.

    5. Select the most likely hypothesis.

    6. Test the hypothesis by experimental or other means.

    7. Accept tentatively, or reject the hypothesis and test other hypotheses.

    8. Draw conclusions.

F. Attitudes, such as:

    1. Open-mindedness—willingness to consider new facts.

    2. Intellectual honesty—scientific integrity, unwillingness to compromise with truth as known.

    3. Suspended judgment—scientific control, withholding conclusions until all available facts are in, not generalizing from insufficient data.

G. Appreciations, such as:

    1. Appreciation of the contributions of scientists.

    2. Appreciation of basic cause-and-effect relationships.

    3. Sensitivity to possible uses and applications of science in personal relationships and disposition to use scientific knowledge and abilities in such relationships (attitude).

H. Interests, such as:

    1. Interest in some phase of science as a recreational activity or hobby.

    2. Interest in science as a field for a vocation.[6]

[6] National Society for the Study of Education, *op. cit.*, pp. 28–29.

Perhaps the groups B and C above may be classified in one major heading, *Functional Understandings,* to include concepts, principles, laws, and generalizations that are broad. This would be distinguished from specific facts in group A above. Facts are needed to help us arrive at a generalization. Both types of objectives are needed if we are to see the "trees and the woods."

Fig. 2.2.   The use of a Geiger counter requires both scientific information and skill. (Courtesy of Board of Education, City of New York)

Since many changes in science occurred in recent years, the objectives of teaching science should also change. Hurd indicated in 1958 that the greatest attention had been given to the following objectives during the preceding year: (1) Understandings of the impact of science on society, the methods and attitudes of science, and the basic principles, concepts, ideas, and generalizations of science; (2) appreciation of their contribution to human thought; (3) acquiring verbal and quantitative skills of communication used by scientists; (4) developing lifelong interests, recreational activities, hobbies, an appreciation of science, and its achievements in relation to human welfare.[7]

Another major objective of science teaching which is frequently overlooked is the possible correlation between science education and improved human relations. Students may learn scientific knowledge and perhaps desirable scientific attitudes such as open-mindedness and freedom from prejudice during the course of a science experiment but fail to transfer these attitudes and behaviors outside of class to other citizens. Williams writes: "The impact of science, at times subtle, at times brutally direct, has become a vital political force dominating the action of statesmen and threatening the stability of the social organization to which we are dedicated."[8]

Science teaching, per se, cannot develop better human relations. But if all knowledge from all of the fields of endeavor were to accept better human relations as a vital objective in a school program, and if there were a concerted attempt to teach for the development of this objective, it is possible that this aim might be realized. It is no longer adequate to say that a particular scientist was a Frenchman, German, Russian, Catholic, Negro, or Jew. How did eminent scientists of various nationalities, religious beliefs, and skin color actually relate to fellow scientists and other human beings in ultimately achieving their great discoveries? How did they actually behave to different groups? Perhaps a series of case studies of leading scientists with heterogeneous backgrounds should be introduced in the science curriculum. This academic approach should be translated into action by the students in daily living with their fellow students.

Objectives of teaching science are most significant in determining the selection of course content and in guiding the science teacher in the development and organization of learning activities. Without them, the science teacher may merely be presenting an array of isolated facts without meaning and understanding. Objectives are essential to the teacher to answer the question, Why

---

[7] Hurd, *op. cit.,* p. 136.

[8] Simon Williams, "A Tool for Effective Science Teaching: The Study of Human Relations," *Science Education,* vol. 37 (April, 1953), p. 151.

teach science? Lists of questions or student activities do not replace the need for and the development of objectives. A study by Blackwood throws some doubt on the validity of the assumption that an analysis of a problem area primarily stated as questions will serve the identical function as an analysis in terms of objectives.[9] Blackwood also reports that individual teachers do not tend to write questions which correspond with or match their own statements of objectives. Hence, it is also essential to formulate clear-cut objectives in constructing or modifying a science curriculum.

Objectives for Science Courses

In 1958, the New York City Board of Education reorganized the Course of Study and Syllabus in General Science for Grades 7, 8, and 9. Five considerations were stated as a guide in accepting the objectives that had appeared in the Forty-sixth Yearbook of the National Society for the Study of Education.

1. Consider the nature of the child. Individual students have many wide variations with respect to ability, interests and needs, previous experiences, and maturity, both in and outside of the school environment.
2. Consider the overall purposes of education at the junior high school level. Many of the educational activities at this developmental stage, in which the pupil is expanding his conception of the environment and of his universe, are largely exploratory.
3. Consider the relation of the study of general science to the total educative process. There should be a close relationship between the aims of general science and those of general education.
4. Consider the approach that should be recommended in teaching the general science course of study. This approach is problem centered and is directly related to pupil interests. It should be purposeful and directed to the learning process.
5. Consider general science as an introduction to science for young adolescents, as a specialized area for uniquely organized experi-

9 Paul E. Blackwood, "An Analysis of the Statements of Objectives, Questions, and Activities Proposed by Teachers for the Study of Two Problem Areas," Ed D. project, Teachers College, Columbia University, 1953.

ences. Previous pupil science experiences are being reoriented into a more mature pattern of understanding and interpreting the natural phenomena.[10]

The following objectives were adapted from the list in the Forty-sixth Yearbook:

1. Growth in functional understanding of scientific phenomena that are part of the child's environment
2. Growth in development and understanding of scientific concepts and principles that function in children's experiences and help to explain them
3. Growth in the use of the manipulative, experimental, and problem-solving skills which are involved in investigations in the area of science
4. Growth in the development of vocational and avocational interests in science
5. Growth in such desirable habits and attitudes as open-mindedness, intellectual honesty, suspended judgment, and respect for human dignity
6. Growth in appreciation of the contributions and potentialities of science for the improvement of human welfare and in appreciation of dangers through its misuse
7. Growth in those moral and spiritual values which exalt and refine the life of the individual and society[11]

These are general objectives for a general science program as well as for courses in biology, chemistry, physics, and earth science. Through the use of previous studies, questionnaires, consultants, and reports, the writer formulated the following criteria of general education which were used as objectives of biology:

To provide students with the necessary knowledge, skills, and attitudes in order that they may:

Understand the world of nature, physical and biological, and be able to interpret natural phenomena.

[10] Reprinted from "General Science, grades 7, 8, 9," by permission of the Board of Education of the city of New York, *Curriculum Report* (January, 1958).

Have some appreciation of the background of the civilization which is our heritage.

Understand the social, economic, and spiritual forces at work in society and develop a sense of social responsibility.

Gain a better understanding of the meaning and purpose of life and a truer sense of values.

Participate more effectively in solving problems of contemporary society.

Maintain and improve their health and share in the responsibility for protecting the health of the community.

Attain an emotionally stable personality and make a worthy social adjustment.

Utilize a scientific approach in solving problems dealing with society and human welfare.

Be better fit for family and marital relationships.

Communicate effectively through oral and written expression.

Develop a code of behavior based on ethical principles consistent with democratic ideals.

Recognize the interdependence of the different peoples of the world.

Recognize and accept one's personal responsibility for fostering international understanding and peace.

Appreciate the best in literature, art, and music, including drama, the dance, radio and motion pictures.

Discover their own abilities, aptitudes, and interests and choose a vocation.

To understand the place of the consumer in society and to learn to become an intelligent consumer of goods, services and time.[12]

The above objectives are stated primarily in terms of behavior changes that students are expected to undergo in a gradual manner as they acquire additional knowledge, skills, and attitudes. Specific objectives should be formulated in the preparation of unit and daily lesson plans. Samples of specific objectives will be given in Chapter 4, "Selecting and Organizing Science Materials."

Burmester and Noll developed a splendid technique for synthesizing and evaluating objectives for a biology course on the college

[12] Nathan S. Washton, "A Syllabus in Biology for General Education," *Science Education,* vol. 35 (March, 1951).

level, and the same technique may prove to be very helpful to high school biology teachers. Essentially, it consists of preparing a rating sheet of objectives and distributing them to students, biology faculty, and other staff members in the college for their opinions on relative importance.

It is interesting to note from the data in Table 1 that the students consider factual knowledge related to healthful living most important, whereas this objective was ranked at $12\frac{1}{2}$ by the staff and at 4 by the biology faculty. Objectives classified as appreciations and interests were generally ranked among the lowest 10 by almost all groups. Perhaps one of the major problems is the inability at the present to evaluate the appreciations and interests of students by means of well-constructed tests that can be used in the biology classroom.

If one of the vital objectives of teaching biology is to enable students to improve and maintain their health and to assume responsibility for bettering community health, then reading and listening may be insufficient in the development of this objective. Evans employed a vast array of procedures in studying a community problem such as health.[13] Community surveys by students, gathering of information through consulting experts, visiting health officials and agencies, pupil participation in assisting health agencies and other learning activities should be utilized along with reading assignments, supplementary reading, and experiments if pupils are to benefit from instruction in biology for better health.

Objectives for teaching biology and other science courses have been obtained by many secondary school teachers in studies of communities in which they teach. These science teachers based the objectives around the contemporary problems that face youth and adults in a given community. Laton and Powers describe the technique for obtaining these objectives in their book, *New Directions in Science Teaching* (see Suggested Readings). Essentially, it consists of a workshop approach in a series of meetings with science teachers from different geographical areas, the use of consultants,

---

[13] Hubert M. Evans, "Science Education and the Study of Community Problems," doctoral dissertation, Teachers College, Columbia University, 1946.

TABLE 1. Rankings of Objectives by Three Groups, in Order of Importance
of Objectives to Students

Objectives	Students	Faculty	Staff
Healthful living	1	4	$12\frac{1}{2}$
Basic laws	2	8	$5\frac{1}{2}$
Accurate observations	3	2	1
Open-mindedness	4	1	$3\frac{1}{2}$
Suspend judgment	5	3	$3\frac{1}{2}$
Social good	6	9	9
Interpret facts	7	6	$5\frac{1}{2}$
Man to environment	8	12	$14\frac{1}{2}$
Organize facts	9	14	3
Scientific method	10	11	7
Cause and effect	11	5	9
Philosophy	12	$7\frac{1}{2}$	$18\frac{1}{2}$
Intellectual curiosity	13	10	$12\frac{1}{2}$
Structure to function	14	19	21
Formulate hypotheses	15	20	$14\frac{1}{2}$
State problems	16	16	9
Fact from theory	17	13	$16\frac{1}{2}$
Freedom from prejudice	18	15	11
Unsolved problems	19	17	$16\frac{1}{2}$
Accuracy of science	20	22	$23\frac{1}{2}$
Freedom from superstition	21	27	22
Vocabulary	22	21	25
Apply laws	23	18	$18\frac{1}{2}$
Plan experiments	24	23	20
Scientific apparatus	25	24	32
Economic values	26	25	26
Professional fields	27	26	31
Avocational reading	28	32	$29\frac{1}{2}$
Aesthetic values	29	29	$29\frac{1}{2}$
Avocational interests	30	31	$27\frac{1}{2}$
Biological literature	31	30	$27\frac{1}{2}$
Graphs and tables	32	28	$23\frac{1}{2}$

SOURCE: Mary Alice Burmester and Victor H. Noll, "A Synthesis and Evaluation
of Objectives for a Course in College Biology," *Science Education,* vol. 38 (March,
1954), p. 149.

community surveys of needs of youth and adults, and the use of studies and resource materials. Educational research and literature clearly indicate that the trend is toward utilizing a group of experts made up of teachers with varied backgrounds in science and specialists in educational research to seek objectives in terms of individual and community needs rather than having one person assume the task of determining why he is to teach a specific science course.

The Grand Rapids Public Schools adopted the following scientific attitudes as part of the objectives in teaching biology.

1. A lively curiosity about the world in which we live
2. The firm belief that nothing, not even the strangest and most mysterious occurrence, ever does happen or could possibly happen without a cause
3. The belief that truth itself never changes, but that our ideas of what is true are certain to change in many respects as our knowledge becomes more exact and complete
4. An unwillingness to accept any statements as facts unless they are supported by sufficient proof
5. The determination not to believe in *any* superstitions
6. The determination not to try to solve our problems in a careless or hasty way, but to make and carry through complete and careful plans for solving them
7. The determination always to make our observations carefully and accurately
8. A willingness to weigh all the evidence and to try to decide whether it really relates to the matter under consideration, whether it is sound and sensible, and whether it is complete enough to justify a conclusion
9. A determination not to jump to a conclusion or to base a conclusion upon one or a few observations, but to seek evidence as long as may be necessary in order to find a true answer to a problem
10. A preference for gathering our own facts by experimenting and observing, but a willingness to use the results and facts obtained by others
11. A willingness to change an opinion or a conclusion if later evidence shows it to be wrong

12. The intention to respect other people's ideas, opinions, and ways of life that are different from our own
13. The determination not to allow our judgments to be influenced by our likes and dislikes[14]

Examples of some pupil activities dealing with the topic *behavior* that could be directed toward the development of scientific attitudes include:

1. Study newly born puppies, kittens, hatched birds, or chicks. Students can make a list of all discoveries made in observing the behavior of one of these newly born animals. A written record should be made for periodic intervals such as one hour, one week, two weeks, and the like.
2. Attempt to develop a conditioned reaction in a pet. A record of animal responses should be kept and a report made to the class.
3. If there is a meat packer in the community, inquire which of the endocrine glands are removed from animals and what products are made from them.

These activities should be guided not only for the acquisition of understandings and facts but also for the development of scientific attitudes. It cannot be assumed that these attitudes will develop automatically. The science teacher should guide learning directly for these objectives.

With the exception of the basic principles of a specific science and the unique instrumental skills to be learned, the general objectives of teaching physics, chemistry, and earth science are common. "The objectives of courses in physics and chemistry should extend far beyond a minimal comprehension of the basic facts and principles. . . . The appreciation of the scientific method, the ability and willingness to change beliefs and opinions after careful weighing of new evidence, and the development of the habit of critical thinking are the intangible but most important outcomes of the study of these sciences."[15]

[14] Francis D. Curtis and John Urban, *Biology in Daily Life,* Ginn & Co., 1953, p. 571.
[15] New York State Education Department, *Chemistry and Physics,* 1957, p. 7.

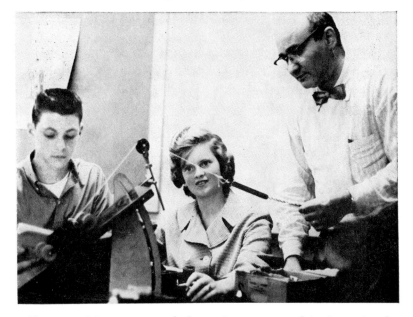

Fig. 2.3. Measurement and observation are stressed in the study of a simple machine, the inclined plane. (Courtesy of District Five Public Schools, Levittown, N.Y.)

WHY SHOULD STUDENTS LEARN SCIENCE?

Most parents and teachers know that students in the junior or senior high school do not necessarily accept a proposal made by adults on the basis that it is good for them. If science teachers perform demonstrations and experiments in class to show that smoking or drinking alcoholic beverages can produce harmful effects, adolescents raise the question, why do teachers, parents, and other people smoke cigarettes and drink whiskey? Students and adults are confused about learning facts that are not put into practice. For some individuals a danger point is reached where fear is the cause in changing one's behavior such as "no more smoking."

Do students really learn how to select foods wisely for better health? They may temporarily possess the knowledge in terms of what is good for them, and yet thousands of them will go on eating ice cream and soda as a complete luncheon.

There exists a gap between the objectives of science teaching as viewed by the teacher and by the student. An attempt is made to "bridge this gap" by stating the objectives in relation to functional or daily living activity, now or in the future, by adding the words "How does _____ affect you?" For example, instead of stating the topic, fish, we modify and state the problem, How do fish affect you? or How are we dependent upon fish? or How do we use fish for better health? For economics or industry?

An attempt is made to utilize a few of the psychological principles of learning (e.g., pupil experience, interest, or need) in order to cause students to want to learn about fish or weather or another topic. We think this procedure may motivate pupil learning in science. It is one of several steps in the right direction to stimulate students if they become interested or have a need to learn about fish or the weather. However, not all students have the same need at the same time. This is one of the bottlenecks to learning.

At this point, it is suggested that the teacher find out what the pupil interests are in order to relate instruction to these interests. The hope is that these pupil interests will arouse a need or desire to learn the basic concepts and skills. The teacher discovers that the pupil interests and needs are not the same for all of the students in the class. To make matters more complex, research in the psychology of learning during the past quarter-century indicates that student personality and emotional needs are vital factors that determine the nature and degree of learning.

Hence, the following types of principles for guiding learning can be formulated: Each student is an individual with unique interests, needs, emotional make-up, aptitudes, cultural background, social and economic values, and intellectual ability. Therefore, adequate provisions should be made for students to learn science as individuals—there should be learning activities for the slow learner, the average student, and the gifted. These provisions are usually made by varying the curriculum or by assigning specific projects to individual students. New courses are proposed in the attempt to satisfy the "needs" of students with varied intellectual ability.

If sufficient science experiences are offered to these students according to their "state of readiness" to learn, why should they learn science? If a student asks a question, How can I repair my faulty electrical circuit to make my bicycle light go on? he is ready to learn and has a need to learn specific scientific information and skill to help him solve his problem. Unfortunately, a common topic or problem for class discussion does not have immediate readiness or need for each of the pupils at the same time. The teacher therefore endeavors to plan problems, projects, and topics that are of contemporary social, economic, recreational, and healthful import to the students. A psychological principle of learning suggests that this can be accomplished more effectively through joint planning by pupils and the teacher.

The noble objectives of teaching science cannot be developed unless each student can answer the question, Why should I learn science? For some students, it is merely a matter of passing the examinations to obtain satisfactory grades. For others, the goals or purposes of an education have been clearly established, and they recognize that they must obtain high grades in order to gain admission to college for a chosen profession. For a very large group of students, unfortunately, science is uninteresting, and they do not know why they should memorize the valences, atomic numbers, and formulas pertaining to work and energy and the classification of plants and animals. The teacher response that students are required to learn this material because it will appear on an examination does not necessarily promote real learning for the majority of the students. It is reasonable to assume that some students avoid taking advanced courses in science in the senior high school because previous work in science was dull and unimportant and might cause them to lower their academic average.

"Students want to learn science because it satisfies their curiosity about natural phenomena" might be a correct interpretation for some students at different intervals. The task of the teacher is to offer professional guidance to all students, along with the formal and informal science activity in the classroom, through individual and group activity so that the students will ultimately realize the need for learning science. The sooner the student can answer the problem, Why learn science? the more efficient will the educative process become. Through guidance, the teacher will recognize that one student's answer will be different from that of another. Learning science is a highly individualized process. No one scientist is competent in all areas of a specific science. Curiosity about natural phenomena will differ among individuals. Some adolescents enjoy making explorations about living things but are not always curious about the causes of erosion or the melting of snow at the required learning period.

There are students who enjoy learning science because they are fond of the science teacher. They want the teacher and their classmates to think well of them. The science teacher indirectly and accidentally teaches pupils to love or hate science and school. The social climate of the classroom will influence students to learn science. Pupil-pupil relations and teacher-pupil relations make up the social climate of a classroom. The degrees of competition or cooperation among students, aggression or hostility, recognition by the peers as well as the teacher, psychological reassurance by the teacher when pupils make mistakes, teacher dominance and authoritarianism, democratic classroom activity, mutual respect, and purposeful pupil activity constitute vital factors in determining whether students learn science.

From the student's point of view there is no one answer to the question, Why should students learn science? In planning daily lessons, therefore, the teacher should not only consider objectives but give serious thought to motivation.

Science for General Education

Since the majority of high school youth do not continue their studies in colleges or universities, they need guidance and motivation to learn science. The junior high school science teacher plays a vital role in guiding young adolescents to evaluate careers both in scientific and nonscientific professions. An inspiring junior high school teacher could very well be responsible for causing "the spark to ignite" in young people who decide to become scientists. A good instructional program of science for general education can prove itself to be invaluable both to the future scientist and nonscientist. Page reports that junior high school science is highly significant in determining at which level high school seniors decide to specialize in science.[16] Competent and qualified science teachers, encouragement by parents who provide suitable reading materials, pupil hobbies that are related to science, and out-of-school science jobs affected pupil interest and the decision to specialize in science.

Wendt lists four major aspects of science: research, knowledge, applications, and the social force. He states:

. . . education for citizenship requires sufficient awareness of the first three to permit evaluation of the fourth, the social power of science, while education for earning a living must open for each youngster the door to his suitable specialty in scholarly knowledge or in its useful applications; and the genius for research must be found and developed wherever, by strange accident of birth, it appears . . .

Science education in the secondary school can enliven and focus the native research mind both by revealing the great vista of desirable knowledge and by encouraging the pupil to find the answers for himself, if only by library research. If this be done by inspired teachers, by voluntary science clubs, or by such devices as science fairs or a "talent search," the gifted pupils will emerge, ready for selection into careers of scientific research that will keep this country in the forefront of progress. This is one important goal of secondary education. But equally important is the larger result that other pupils too, nonscientists, learn to respect the habit of research, to keep open minds, and to face the problems of life optimistically with the conviction that problems are meant to be solved and that research thinking can solve them. To welcome a problem instead of fearing it is half the battle of life.[17]

Students come to science classes with fixed opinions and attitudes

[16] Allen D. Page, "A Study to Determine How High School Seniors Become Interested in Science," doctoral dissertation, University of Wisconsin, 1954.
[17] Gerald Wendt, "The Role of Science Education in a Democracy," *Bulletin,* National Association of Secondary School Principals, *op. cit.*

about science, scientists, and scientific careers. Motion pictures, radio, and television programs help establish the image of the scientist in the minds of youth. Mead and Métraux in a study of about 35,000 high school students indicate pupil opinions and attitudes as revealed in their views of scientists.[18] It is interesting to note that the responses ranged from views of the scientist as a highly intelligent man, characterized as almost a genius, dedicated, patient, devoted, and having other desirable traits, to views at the other extreme of the scientist as a dull person who neglects his family. The study recommends that there should be less passive watching of repeated experiments and demonstrations in the classroom. Especially in general science, students should be encouraged to be active and should be made to feel that they are performing experiments. Individual and group projects and cooperative teamwork should be emphasized.

How can students be assisted in finding out their attitudes and opinions about science and scientists? Teachers can administer a questionnaire to their pupils at the beginning and at the end of the science course to evaluate possible changes in attitudes. Wilson developed the following questionnaire in studying student opinions in relation to the nature of science and its purpose in society.

Mark the following statements with an A if you agree that they are essentially true and with a D if you disagree or think they are essentially false. Please give your reaction to all statements.

1. Scientists as a group are more intelligent than those in other lines of work such as law, business, and farming.
2. Scientists are likely to be more logical in their approach to problems, even those outside their field of work, than are other professional men and women.
3. The exactness and impartiality of the scientist in performing and reporting laboratory experiments is probably due in large part to the knowledge that his work will be examined by other competent workers rather than to the fact that scientists are more impartial and objective than other men.

[18] Margaret Mead and Rhoda Métraux, "Image of the Scientist Among High School Students," *Science,* vol. 126 (August 30, 1957), pp. 384–390.

4. Scientists have advanced knowledge by consistently following, step by step, a definite method called the problem-solving formula.
5. Scientists often make errors and waste much time exploring "blind alleys."
6. A scientist is likely to be unbiased and objective, not only in his own field of work, but in other areas as well.
7. The great scientists of the past often made use of lucky guesses or "hunches."
8. History will show that when scientists make mistakes they are quick to admit their errors when these errors are pointed out to them.
9. Training in science will definitely help one to make more logical decisions in other fields, such as politics for example. Thus, the study of science is the best education for those who wish to be impartial in their thinking.
10. Great progress would be made in all fields of human activity if scientific methods were applied to them.
11. A rapid expansion of scientific programs such as that of the Atomic Energy Commission will make us secure against attack.
12. Science and scientific research have become essential to modern progress. Since scientists are specialists in this field we should accept their judgment in matters of public policy related to science rather than attempt to educate the public to make decisions on scientific matters.
13. Science is a difficult subject and can really be pursued profitably only by those of better than average ability.
14. The fundamental theory which made possible the release of atomic energy was developed in the United States.
15. The one primary purpose of science in human society is to increase man's control over nature and to increase his ability to use natural resources so as to make life more comfortable.
16. Science is responsible for much of the evil in the world today because of its application to the production of weapons of war.
17. Many of the scientific theories of the past have been discarded or modified as they have been found inadequate. However, the theories and laws of modern science are essentially accurate and are likely to endure in their present form.
18. The scientist can obtain a direct answer to any simple question

concerning nature by means of a carefully designed experiment.

19. Advances in science consist of the accumulation and classification of accurate data.

20. The observations and measurements involved in scientific experiments are seldom erroneous, and the interpretation of results involves little chance of error.

21. The real advances in science consist of the production of such useful things as radios, automobiles, and drugs.

22. Science is a highly organized social activity the very existence of which depends upon the ability of experimental scientists to communicate rapidly with each other.

23. Due to the high cost of scientific research and to the importance of science as a factor in national survival it may be desirable for the federal government to assume responsibility for the financing and direction of all scientific research.

24. Since scientific research is very expensive it would seem wise to curtail research directed solely toward advancing knowledge and to concentrate on engineering development and the application of scientific principles to practical problems.

25. It is quite possible that a policy of secrecy regarding scientific research, such as that now in force in the Atomic Energy Program, might work to the long-range advantage of science in this country since if scientists in other nations do not have access to our findings we will soon outstrip them in the race for new knowledge.

26. Science is valuable only to the extent that it benefits the whole of society in a practical way, and thus scientific research should be planned and directed to meet the immediate needs of society.[19]

The function of teaching science for general education is to provide pupils with the common attitudes, knowledge, and skill to enable them to live more effectively and intelligently in a democratic society. Several investigations by Blair, Geyer, Hancock,

[19] Leland L. Wilson, "A Study of Opinions Related to the Nature of Science and Its Purpose in Society," *Science Education,* vol. 38 (March, 1954), pp. 159–164. See also R. W. Heath, M. H. Maier, and H. H. Remmers, "Science, Education, and Civil Liberties," *Report of Poll No. 51 of the Purdue Opinion Panel,* Purdue University, March, 1958.

and McMelly have shown that it is possible to teach general science with the aims of developing scientific attitudes and removing superstitions that ninth-grade pupils have, if science is taught directly for these objectives.[20] Among the common misconceptions, fallacies, and superstitions that remain with many individuals are: Green apples when eaten will cause a belly ache. Eating pickles and ice cream will make you sick. When blood is transferred from one person to another, the people concerned must be of the same race or religion. A reading of the horoscope will predict the future. Breaking a mirror will cause one to have seven years' bad luck. All snakes are harmful. It is cruel to keep live lobsters on ice. Holding toads in your hand will cause warts. A soap is pure because it floats. A leaking rowboat (wood) will sink. Rainbows after storms mean good weather. The man determines the sex of of the offspring.

Merely telling the students that the above statements are untrue is inadequate as instructional procedure. Attitudes and misconceptions are the result of many vicarious experiences. Hence, the science teacher should provide such experiences as will enable his pupils to modify attitudes, behavior, and ideas. How can students read the horoscope and apply this information to daily life in order to conclude that another person cannot forecast the future for another individual? One suggestion might be to have students keep records of their activities over a period of time and compare the outcomes with the horoscope. Among the student experiences that may help develop the objective of science attitudes are keeping records; analyzing daily activities; participating in discussions; taking a pupil science attitude inventory which includes superstitions, misconceptions, and fallacies; and completing a self-evaluation check list of changes in attitudes and behaviors. To dispel the idea that holding toads will cause warts, it would be more effective to provide pupils with the experience of holding toads to determine if they will get warts than to state the correct concept without providing firsthand experience.

[20] See Suggested Readings at end of chap.

Fig. 2.4A. Plant growth projects help students seek careers in biology and chemistry.

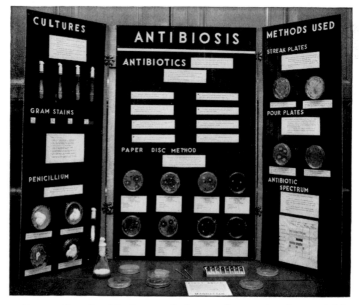

Fig. 2.4B. Antibiosis may influence future chemists and biologists.

Fig. 2.4. The projects depicted here have stimulated students to seek

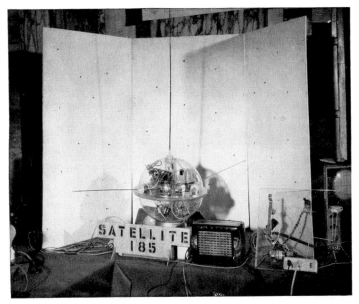

Fig. 2.4C. Making a miniature satellite may help develop a future physicist, astronomer, or geologist.

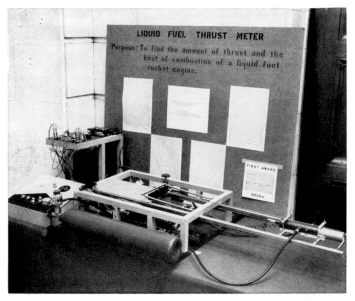

Fig. 2.4D. A study of liquid fuels in rocket engines influenced students to become scientists.

careers in science. (Courtesy of Board of Education, City of New York)

Guidance

If pupils are provided with a vast array of good learning activities in and out of the science classroom, they may develop new interests and abilities in science. Some of these science experiences may encourage or discourage pupils from considering careers in the scientific professions. The teacher makes a vital contribution in guiding adolescents in terms of vocational choice. Group and individual reports on various kinds of careers that are either directly or indirectly related to science may be introduced in classroom discussion and student projects when new topics are taught: astronomy, electricity, chemistry, meteorology, botany, zoology, geology, space travel, health, and other areas of science.

Students will want to learn science if they can determine, with the help of the teacher, whether or not science offers them stimulating and rewarding careers. Occupational information such as educational requirements, working conditions, the need of special skills or talent, salary, promotional opportunities, the working environment, and the degree of personal and social success would be most helpful. Pupils can acquire most of this information through reading selected books, pamphlets, and leaflets. See the leaflets on Guidance and Science Careers published by the U.S. Government Printing Office.

Inspirational learning experience can be gained through individual, group, and class excursions to nearby science industries; manufacturers of biologicals, pharmaceuticals, and scientific instruments; airports; military installations; weather stations; local colleges and universities that have excellent scientific equipment; hospitals; research centers; and governmental agencies. In addition, career information can be obtained by individual pupils or the class during the field trip. Outside speakers representing various types of scientific industries and careers can be invited to speak in a class, school assembly, or club after school hours. These speakers should be encouraged to perform demonstrations that illustrate basic scientific principles applicable to a particular industry. Time should be available to the students for discussion and a question-answer period. This activity is just as rewarding for junior high school students as for those at the senior high school level where it is used almost exclusively. In this regard, it may be recalled that students' experience with junior high school science plays an important part in determining the level at which seniors decide to specialize in science.

The science club offers more than a meeting of pupils with common interests. It provides an opportunity for sharing ideas, for carrying out scientific projects, and for realizing the joy that comes with accomplishments which are recognized by one's peers. It is a place where opportunity is offered to future scientists as well as to young people who are uncertain of careers in science. The interplay of student personalities and interests can be a stimulating experience for each participant. Many of these future scientists pretend to be scientists and fulfill adolescent dreams by imitating great scientific ideas and scientists. Many good friends develop in science club activities. The result usually produces some fine scientists and people. Throughout each of the varied activities in a science club, there is a genuine opportunity for the science teacher and outside participants to administer guidance, either toward or away from careers in science.

The pupil sense of satisfaction from these activities in the science clubs is transferred to the classroom. Science teachers have found that many of the procedures employed outside of class are equally effective during the classroom period. When the pupils have clarified their goals, understand the importance of science in their daily routines, see the relationship of science to their other interests and needs, and obtain pleasure and accomplishment from working in science, they want to learn science. The following statement by Clem and Dudleston is just as correct today as it was when it appeared more than 25 years ago: "Pupils who are members of high school science clubs excelled nonmembers in scientific knowledge."[21]

---

[21] Orlie Clem and J. Dudleston, "Factors Influencing the Common Science Knowledge of High School Pupils," *Science Education*, vol. 17 (December, 1933), pp. 267–272.

Science for Specialization

In the previous sections of this chapter, it was indicated that teaching science can make a vital contribution to the general education of youth. Not all of the students should become scientists; nor is it the function of the teacher to make scientists out of all of the pupils. However, it is the responsibility of the teacher to encourage "budding" scientists and to "nourish" the desire to learn science to the maximum potentiality. The motives for learning science are well established when students seek careers in medicine, dentistry, engineering, and related areas. In general, students who plan to attend a college will be motivated to learn science and the other subjects. The science teacher can stimulate learning science in the college preparatory student who does not seek a career in science. On the junior high school level, general science is taught primarily to achieve the objectives of a sound general education program. Although the same point of view applies to the teaching of the biological and physical sciences in the senior high school, several kinds of provisions should be made for the slow learner, the average student, and the pupil who seeks a career in science. These proposals are discussed in the following chapter pertaining to the preparation of a science curriculum.

SUMMARY

Man's place in the universe is changing drastically as a result of technology and advances made in scientific research. The teaching and learning of science are not merely desirable; they are almost mandatory for intelligent living. Science courses should be continually re-examined to determine if they are in accord with the stated objectives and with our changing times.

Principles of science constitute only a part of the overall purposes of science. Skills, scientific attitudes, appreciations and extending interests are also important objectives in teaching science. The objectives of science instruction are most important in determining what kind of science modern man needs in our changing civilization. How science can modify man's overt behavior is still one of the riddles that needs to be solved.

EXERCISES

1. Discuss the role of the science program with respect to the total curriculum in the junior or senior high school.
2. How does science make a unique contribution to the program of general education?
3. List the basic criteria that can be employed in formulating the objectives of teaching a science course.
4. How does a science teacher deal with the pupil's question, "Why should I learn science?"
5. What are the basic objectives of teaching any course in the natural sciences or a course in general science?
6. How can a science teacher determine pupil interests, needs, and abilities?
7. What is the significance of objectives in planning a science program of instruction?
8. How can objectives of science teaching influence pupils in selecting a career in science?
9. What possible effects can be predicted as a result of the role played by parents, science teachers, science clubs, and science fairs on students?
10. What type of activities should potential scientists be given in and out of the science classroom?

SUGGESTED READINGS

American Council of Science Teachers, National Committee on Science Teaching, *Redirecting Science Teaching in the Light of Personal-Social Needs,* Washington, D.C., National Education Association, 1942.

American Council of Science Teachers, National Committee on Science Teaching, *Science Teaching for Better Living,* Washington, D.C., National Education Association, 1942.

Anderson, Kenneth E., "Summary of the Relative Achievements of the Objectives of Secondary School Science in a Representative Sampling of Fifty-Six Minnesota Schools," *Science Education,* vol. 33 (December, 1949), pp. 323–329.

Barnard, J. Darrell (chmn.), *Rethinking Science Education,* Fifty-ninth Yearbook, National Society for the Study of Education, Chicago, University of Chicago Press, 1960.

Barnard, J. Darrell, "Teaching Scientific Attitudes and Methods in Science," *Bulletin,* National Association of Secondary School Principals, vol. 37 (January, 1953), pp. 178–182.

Barnard, J. Darrell, *et al.,* "Problems Related to the Teaching of Problem Solving That Need To Be Investigated," *Science Education,* vol. 34 (April, 1950), pp. 180–184.

Bernal, J. D., "Science Teaching in General Education," *Science Education,* vol. 29 (December, 1945), pp. 233–240.

Bingham, N. Eldred, "A Direct Approach to the Teaching of Scientific Method," *Science Education,* vol. 33 (April, 1949), pp. 241–249.

Blair, Glenn M., and Goodson, Max R., "Development of Scientific Thinking Through General Science," *School Review,* vol. 47 (November, 1939), pp. 695–701.

Brown, Stanley B., "A Consideration of the Learning Process in Science Teaching," *Science Education,* vol. 42 (February, 1958), pp. 79–86.

Burnett, R. Will, *Teaching Science in the Secondary School,* New York, Rinehart & Company, Inc., 1957, chaps. 1, 2.

Burnett, R. Will, "The Science Teacher and His Objectives," *Teachers College Record,* vol. 45 (January, 1944), pp. 241–251.

Burton, William H., *The Guidance of Learning Activities,* New York, Appleton-Century-Crofts, Inc., 2d ed., 1952.

Caldwell, Otis, and Lundeen, Gerhard E., "A Summary of Investigations Regarding Superstitions and Unfounded Beliefs," *Science Education,* vol. 20 (February, 1936), pp. 1–4.

Cohen, I Bernard, *Science: Servant of Man,* Boston, Little, Brown & Company, 1948.

Cole, William E., *The Teaching of Biology.* New York, Appleton-Century-Crofts, Inc., 1934, chaps. 3, 11.

Educational Policies Commission, *The Unique Function of Education in American Democracy,* Washington, D.C., National Education Association, 1937.

Educational Policies Commission, *Education for All American Youth —A Further Look,* Washington, D.C., National Education Association and the American Association of School Administrators, 1952.

Finkel, Maurice, "A Study of the Factors Affecting the High School Student's Choice Regarding a Science Career," unpublished doctoral dissertation, University of Denver, 1956.

Geyer, Warren F., "Functional Chemistry in the Junior High School," *Science Education,* vol. 24 (December, 1940), pp. 264–269.

Hall, Thomas S., "Implications of General Education for the Teaching of Biology," *Journal of General Education,* vol. 2 (January, 1948), pp. 107–116.

Hancock, Cyril H., "An Evaluation of Certain Popular Science Misconceptions," *Science Education,* vol. 24 (April, 1940), pp. 208–213.

Harris, Chester (ed.), *Encyclopedia of Educational Research,* New York, The Macmillan Company, 1960.

Harvard Committee, *General Education in a Free Society,* Cambridge, Mass., Harvard University Press, 1945.

Heiss, Elwood D., Obourn, Ellsworth S., and Hoffman, Charles W., *Modern Science Teaching,* New York, The Macmillan Company, 1950, chaps. 1, 2.

Humphreys, Lloyd G., "Transfer of Training in General Education," *Journal of General Education,* vol. 5 (April, 1951), pp. 210–216.

Hunter, G. W. and Spore, LeRoy, "The Objectives of Science in the Secondary Schools of the United States," *School Science and Mathematics,* vol. 43 (October, 1943), pp. 633–647.

Jacobson, Willard J., "Science Education and the Development of Abilities to Cope with Problematic Life Situations," *Science Education,* vol. 37 (April, 1953), pp. 172–182.

Laton, Anita D., and Powers, S. Ralph, *New Directions in Science Teaching,* New York, McGraw-Hill Book Company, Inc., 1949.

MacCurdy, Robert D., "Superior Science Students and the Subgroups," *Science Education,* vol. 40 (February, 1956), pp. 3–24.

McMelly, Cal., "An Experiment in the Use of Free Reading in General Science," *Science Education,* vol. 25 (January, 1941), pp. 7–9.

Meister, Morris, "On Becoming a Scientist," *Vital Issues in Education,* Washington, D.C., American Council on Education, 1957, pp. 26–33.

Mikhail, Monir K., "Contributions of Science to Selected Problem Areas Proposed for a Program of General Education in the Secondary School," *Science Education,* vol. 39 (October, 1955) pp. 300–304.

National Association for Research in Science Teaching, "Problem Solving as an Objective of Science Teaching," *Science Education,* vol. 33 (April, 1949), pp. 192–195.

National Society for the Study of Education, *Science Education in American Schools,* Forty-sixth Yearbook, Part I, Chicago, University of Chicago Press, 1947, chaps. 2, 3, 11.

Neivert, Sylvia S., "Identification of Students With Science Potential," unpublished doctoral dissertation, Teachers College, Columbia University, 1955.

Noll, Victor H., "Teaching Science for the Purpose of Influencing Behavior," *Science Education,* vol. 20 (February, 1936), pp. 17–20.

Preston, Carleton E., *The High School Science Teacher and His Work,* New York, McGraw-Hill Book Company, Inc., 1936, chap. 3.

Progressive Education Association, *Science in General Education,* Report of the Committee on the Function of Science in General Education, New York, Appleton-Century-Crofts, Inc., 1938, chaps. 1–7.

Reiner, William B., "The Interactions of Society and Science," *Science Education,* vol. 42 (February, 1958), pp. 37–42.

Richardson, John S., *Science Teaching in Secondary Schools,* Englewood Cliffs, N.J., Prentice-Hall, Inc., 1957, chap. 1.

Stice, Glen, Torgerson, Warren, and Molenkopf, William G., "A National Study of High School Students and Their Plans," reported in Charles C. Cole, Jr., *Encouraging Scientific Talent,* New York, College Entrance Examination Board, 1956, pp. 139–169.

Washton, Nathan S., "A Syllabus in Biology for General Education I," *Science Education,* vol. 35 (March, 1951), pp. 84–92.

Washton, Nathan S., "What Science Course for General Education?" *Association of American Colleges Bulletin,* vol. 35 (December, 1949), pp. 509–518.

3

DEVELOPING AND PREPARING
A SCIENCE CURRICULUM

THE DEVELOPMENT OF SCIENCE COURSES

A Historical Summary

It is extremely difficult to determine at what date in the history of civilization man became interested in science education. Many textbooks referred to Aristotle as "the father of biology" because of his keen interest and ability in observing natural objects. Perhaps this was the major influence in teaching nature study and biology at the beginning of the twentieth century for developing "powers of observation." Socrates and other philosophers speculated on the nature of the continuity of matter such as water, sand, and other objects which are considered by some historians in science as the origin of the nature of matter—atomic structure. Some of the early Greek philosophers believed a drop of water to be made up of great numbers of tiny particles.

It may be reasonable to assume that the beginning of science education dates back to such times as when man showed a curiosity to explore natural phenomena, living things, and their surroundings. Forbes writes:

It is often little realized that the fundamental discoveries and inventions on which our modern civilization is based were made before the dawn of history. History is usually said to begin with the advent of written documents, and writing was first conceived in the ancient Near East in the latter half of the fourth millennium B.C. We can trace man's activities before that time only by the remains found by the archeologist. We can only try to reconstruct his beliefs, theories, and reasonings from those remains, for we possess none of his documents, assuming that there were any. Hence we can only state that he employed this or that tool or method at such a period, and are left to guess at the steps that led to its discovery or invention.[1]

Singer states, "Scientific knowledge begins with the people who came to call themselves the Hellenes, but whom we know as the Greeks."[2] It is reported that the earliest medical school was established in about 600 B.C. on the Island of Cos and that the most eminent member of the school was Hippocrates who is frequently referred to as "the father of medicine."

We shall begin arbitrarily with Bacon (1561–1626) and Comenius (1592–1670). They believed that the best way to study nature is to go straight to nature and use one's own senses and powers of observation. Comenius said,

"Are not we as well as the old philosophers placed in Nature's garden? Why then do we not cast about our eyes, nostrils, and ears as well as they? Why should we learn the works of Nature of any other master rather than of these our senses? Why do we not, I say, turn over the living book of the world instead of dead papers? In it we may contemplate more things and with greater delight and profit than any can tell us."[3]

Bacon and Comenius influenced the development of the inductive method of reasoning which plays a vital role in the problem-solving approach to teaching science. As a result of applying their abilities in observing nature or natural phenomena, they were able to formulate generalizations (inductive reasoning). Pestalozzi (1746–1827) and Froebel (1782–1852) followed the major ideas proposed by Bacon and Comenius. Pestalozzi once said, *Ich will den menschlichen Unterricht psychologisieren*—"I wish to psychologize human instruction." Froebel also used natural objects during the course of instruction. Pestalozzi, Froebel, and others also showed much concern for human growth and development, and Rousseau

---

[1] R. J. Forbes, *Man the Maker,* Henry Schuman, 1950, p. 14.

[2] Charles Singer, *A History of Biology,* Henry Schuman, 1950, p. 1.

[3] From Comenius, Preface to *Naturall Philosophie* reformed, English translation, 1651, as quoted by Robert H. Quick, *Essays on Educational Reformers,* D. Appleton and Company, 1902, p. 149.

(1712–1778) probably influenced the modern approach to teaching biology. Pestalozzi and Rousseau believed in the worth of outdoor observations and field trips and placed great emphasis on things and not on words alone. They saw the relationships of children and the environment and the impact on the growth of the total individual (mind and body). However, their ideas were not adopted by the schools in America until the early part of the twentieth century.

There seems to be a lag of from 30 to 300 years between educational practice and educational research or theory. This gap varies with the teacher and the school. For example, America's first organized secondary school, established in Boston in 1635, was the Latin grammar school which offered a college preparatory curriculum consisting essentially of Latin, Greek, and theology. A private school for the wealthy, it did not teach any of the sciences but placed emphasis on the ability to write and read Latin verse and prose. Some of the remnants of the curriculum still prevail in some schools where the same ability is stressed. For about 200 years, most of the graduates of the Latin grammar school entered the college primarily to become ministers. It is interesting to note that up until the turn of the present century, most of the graduates from public high schools in America entered a college with the purpose of becoming either a physician, minister, lawyer, or teacher.

The beginning of science teaching in the schools occurred in the Academy of Philadelphia, established in 1751 as a result of the efforts of Benjamin Franklin. The purpose of the academy as conceived by Franklin was to give students a practical, real-life education. Not only college preparatory students but students who did not plan to enter a profession or a college were admitted. The academy curriculum comprised subjects in English, Latin, arithmetic, and some of the natural sciences. It was estimated that the peak of the development of the academies was in 1850. At that time, science instruction was introduced as natural philosophy which at first was chiefly physics and later was chemistry and astronomy. By the beginning of the nineteenth century, botany, zoology, and geology were established.

The lack of widespread communication facilities made it extremely difficult to share the discoveries by scientists of the period —Dalton, Faraday, Lavoisier, and Priestly. Hence, the teaching of science was very fragmentary and unsystematized. Students memorized isolated "bits" or "gems" of knowledge. Although the teaching of science was supposed to be practical in terms of the environment, knowledge was taught for storage of facts with the hope that it could be used at the time of probable need. The methods of teaching science consisted primarily of verbalization by the teacher and the student. The ideas of Comenius and Pestalozzi were finally introduced: objects came to be used in order to make concrete the visual images. Ultimately, the teachers learned to demonstrate scientific principles through the use of crude equipment. This was the initial stage in the demonstration method of teaching science. Hunter classifies the development of natural science as follows:

I. The Period of the Natural History Method; botany, 1800–1860; zoology, 1825–1870.

II. The Period of Comparative Anatomy and Plant Analysis of Asa Gray; a period in which botany, especially, flourished, 1870–1890.

III. The Period of Laboratory Study of Types, 1890–1900; a period in which the emphasis was placed particularly on plant or animal morphology worked out in the laboratory; the beginning of modern plant physiology.

IV. The Period of Plant and Animal Physiology, 1900–1910; a period in which there was a predominance of plant and animal physiology taught by the laboratory method and the beginning of correlation between plant or animal biology and human physiology.

V. The Period of Correlation and Application of Biology, 1910–1920; the period of correlation and human application of biological subject matter with rather complete emphasis on the side of human interests, both social and biological. A further tendency toward correlation was seen in the rise of general science as an introduction to the study of science.

VI. Rise of General Science, 1920–1930; the period of the rise and elaboration of general science, and the development of unitary concept in science.

VII. The Rise of Junior High School Science, 1930 to date; a period of the rise of the junior high school science and the testing of modern courses of study and of psychological applications in teaching.[4]

Integration of Biology

Zoology was incorporated in the school curriculum about 1825. At that time, botany and zoology were taught for their use, religious and aesthetic feelings, and recreation. Inadequate textbooks were employed, and students were required to observe specimens with the view of verifying their readings in the textbook. The Linnaeus system of classification was used, and students were required to memorize the taxonomic features of specimens. Toward the end of the nineteenth century, there was a shift in emphasis from taxonomy to morphology to physiology of plants. At the beginning of our century, a very drastic departure took place—courses in biology were offered. The biology courses in the secondary schools in the early 1900's were not integrated courses; they consisted essentially of three parts: botany, zoology, and physiology. Two college biology textbooks influenced the integration of biological principles and their applications on the secondary school level: Sedgwick and Wilson's *General Biology,* 1895, and Parker's *Elementary Biology,* 1897. Basic principles of biology were taught for better health, understanding the environment and living things in relation to their environment, and the applications of heredity to eugenics.

The General Science Movement

The early biology courses required the dissection of a representative species from most of the phyla in the plant and animal kingdoms. But many high school students were dissatisfied with memorizing the anatomy and physiology of these organs found within the organisms. The morphology of the grasshopper, spider,

[4] George W. Hunter, *Science Teaching,* American Book Company, 1934, pp. 24–25.

earthworm, fern and other living forms—as taught most usually in the early elementary ninth-grade biology course—did not inspire most of the students. Around 1899 some of the pioneers of the general science course appeared in the Oak Park, Illinois, High School and in the Springfield, Massachusetts, High School. The general science course in the ninth grade began to replace the morphology-oriented elementary biology course. At Springfield, the following units of instruction were offered in the general science course: foods, health, electrical appliances in the home, houses we live in, cleansing and dyeing, our neighbors in space, and weather.

From 1895 to 1909, the first general science courses were introduced in the states of Pennsylvania, Illinois, Massachusetts, and California. According to several studies, the number of schools that offered general science increased tremendously during 1910 through 1915.[5] Until 1940—and even today in many schools—the general science courses were largely compartmentalized segments of specialized sciences: astronomy, meteorology, geology, biology and health, physics, and chemistry.

During the early part of the twentieth century, the junior high school movement gained much momentum, and with it the number of general science courses increased from Grades 7 through 9. It was believed that general science would be diversified enough to appeal to pupil interests, needs, and environmental experiences. It was also believed that general science would stimulate interest in some of the specific sciences and that students would be encouraged to elect advanced courses in biology, chemistry, or physics. Some of the basic functions of the junior high school were orientation and exploration; the same concepts applied in the teaching of general science. Students were to be given those experiences during the instruction of general science that would enable them to determine whether or not they should take advanced courses in the natural sciences in the senior high school.

<hr>

[5] J. H. Rusterholtz, "The Present Status of General Science in High Schools in Pennsylvania," *General Science Quarterly*, vol. 1 (May, 1917); E. E. Lewis, "General Science in Iowa High Schools," *School Review*, vol. 24 (1916); E. R. Downing, *Teaching of Science in the Schools*, University of Chicago Press, 1925; Aravilla M. Taylor, "The Extent of Adoption and Attitude Toward General Science," *School and Society*, vol. IV (1916).

In some cases, students were discouraged from continuing with science for many reasons. In recent years, many students have avoided the election of advanced courses in the senior high schools for a variety of reasons, including the shortage of trained science teachers, lack of adequate science facilities and equipment, teachers qualified in other subjects but assigned to teach science even though they were uninterested in teaching science,[6] the reputation that some science courses in the senior high school are very difficult and few students achieve high scores, competition for college admission based upon cumulative high school average, uninspirational teaching, and lack of engaging pupil interests and suitable activities.

Nevertheless, more students are enrolled in general science throughout the country than any other science course. This is chiefly due to the fact that general science is a required subject for most of the junior high school students.

Two independent studies which traced the historical development of general science in the junior high schools were conducted by Blanc and Haupt. Blanc found the general science course to be the result of the junior high school movement and the many social and scientific forces at work during the preceding 300 years.[7] Haupt reported trends toward exploration, differentiation, socialization, and articulation in junior high school general science between 1920 and 1954.[8] He also indicated that there is less agreement as to the aims and methods of science education today than previously.

Development of Physical Science Courses

During the past 140 years, the teaching of high school physics presented many complex problems. Colleges and universities greatly influenced the high schools in (1) the teaching of new

---

[6] Nathan S. Washton, Paul Brandwein, Brenda Lansdown, William Goins, Jr., Abraham Raskin, and Harold S. Spielman, "What Should Be the Subject Matter Competency of Science Teachers?" *Science Education,* vol. 40 (December, 1956), pp. 392–395.

[7] Sam S. Blanc, "The Development of Science Education in the Junior High School," *Science Education,* vol. 36 (March, 1952), pp. 107–113.

[8] Walter N. Haupt, "The Historical Background of Science Teaching in Junior High Schools Since 1920," master's thesis, Boston University, 1954.

discoveries of basic knowledge of physics and the formulation of laws and their applications; (2) the degree to which students were expected to master fundamental mathematical skills and concepts; (3) the emphasis on laboratory procedures and techniques. The early development of the physics course was outlined by Rusk: "In 1821, the first public high school was opened in Boston, and physics was included in its curriculum. In 1823 a course of experimental lectures in natural philosophy was mentioned as a part of the curriculum, and four years later the school announced the purchase of some apparatus for the demonstration of physical phenomena. . . . In 1857 the state of Massachusetts passed a law requiring public high schools to give courses in natural philosophy."[9] By 1900, laboratory instruction was an integral part of the physics course in the high schools as a result of college requirements and the influence of the report of the Committee of Ten in 1892 which elevated standards by demanding more mathematical physics. "Again in 1900," Hunter recorded, "still more formal requirements were made, hedged about with the doctrine of formal discipline. It is little wonder then that registration in physics has been steadily declining during the past three decades."[10] According to a study by Brown and Obourn, the percentage of total high school students enrolling in physics courses declined from 19 to 4.4 between 1900 and 1956.[11] It should be noted, however, that for the same period the number of students in physics increased from 98,846 to 309,600 as a result of more adolescents attending public high schools in America.

Chemistry became an acceptable course for meeting college admission requirements in 1872. Tracing the growth of chemistry courses, Powers wrote: "The Academy first fostered the teaching of chemistry to adolescents. Reference to curricula and advertising material published by the earlier schools shows that there were at least four academies which gave instruction in chemistry previous

9 R. D. Rusk, *How To Teach Physics,* J. B. Lippincott Company, 1923, p. 26.
10 Hunter, *op. cit.,* p. 45.
11 Kenneth E. Brown and Ellsworth S. Obourn, *Offerings and Enrollments in Science and Mathematics in Public High Schools, 1956,* Pamphlet No. 120, U.S. Department of Health, Education, and Welfare, 1957.

to 1820; at least 15 that began such instruction not later than the period of 1830–1840."[12] Until about the 1860's, chemistry was taught as a book course and often as part of natural philosophy in connection with physics. Gradually, laboratory work emphasizing the ability to follow instructions and perform specific laboratory skills was incorporated as part of chemistry instruction. Again, the colleges exerted much influence in changing the nature of the teaching of chemistry as they did for physics. Hunter wrote in 1934:

> The evil of college domination is, however, still with us. Instead of popularizing chemistry, the result was to emphasize the techniques of laboratory procedure, to make the memorization of factual material the chief aim of the student and to deaden initiative by requiring a certain number of exercises, all of which had to be submitted as evidences of having satisfactorily completed the requirements for college.
>
> Fortunately for chemistry teaching two factors have changed the point of view of the secondary school chemistry teacher and to some extent the college control. The Great War [World War I], which toward its close placed so much emphasis on the discoveries of chemistry and the demand of the common people to know more practical chemistry directed to the needs of human betterment—these factors have to some extent changed the secondary school chemistry courses.[13]

Physics, Chemistry, and Physical Science

In many chemistry courses, the teachers do emphasize the practical aspects through the use of household chemicals, soaps, powders, toothpaste, cosmetics, salts, the water purification system, and related topics. Yet the laboratory activity in most schools consists of a cookbook approach, as many of the manuals direct. In a later chapter, suggested approaches and methods of ultilizing laboratory instruction in chemistry and physics based upon several experimental studies will be discussed. Since chemistry and physics are

---

[12] S. R. Powers, "The Teaching of Chemistry in the Early American Secondary Schools," *School and Society,* vol. 24 (October 23, 1926), pp. 497–503.

[13] Hunter, *op. cit.,* p. 43.

usually elective courses in the eleventh and twelfth years, the problem might be, How can general science courses in the earlier grades stimulate students to elect chemistry and physics courses later? Brandwein observes: "There is some evidence that where General Science is taught poorly—in a nonfunctional, chalk-talk way, with emphasis on rote memory rather than upon investigation and experimentation—registration in later courses is reduced."[14]

Chemistry and physics are frequently elected by students who plan to attend a college. Of these, the larger percentage usually hope to become scientists, engineers, and physicians. Hence, the college is still a vital factor in determining the course content of chemistry and physics. To what degree this should be the case is a controversial subject that should be examined very critically and experimentally.

In recent years, however, a physical science course has gained in popularity in many high schools among nonscience majors and pupils who may not necessarily continue in college. In a few instances, the physical science course consists of a condensed, superficial, two-semester course in which half was devoted to chemistry and the remaining half to physics. But the well-integrated physical science course selects some of the major principles and applications from each field and treats their relationships to man and his changing environment. Such a course serves as a terminal science course for the nonscience majors and for the college-bound student who does not intend to specialize in the natural sciences. It may also serve as an introductory course for the future scientists.

There is a problem of grade placement and reorganization of science courses from Grades 7 to 12. According to Mallinson and Buck,

Earlier grade-placement has proved to be eminently more successful, as evidenced by experimentation with the course in a number of high schools, notably among them Arlington Heights Township High School, Arlington Heights, Ill. In schools such as this, where there is an organized program of elementary school science, it has become

---

14 Paul F. Brandwein, *The Gifted Student as Future Scientist,* Harcourt, Brace & Company, 1955, pp. 74–75.

apparent that many of the materials formerly taught in general science at the junior high school level are being taught successfully in the lower grades. The resulting repetition of topics of general science in junior high school has proved to be deadening to the students. In these schools the general science program has been developed as a sequence for grades on through eight, and general biology has been moved from the tenth grade to the ninth grade. The move has been found to be very satisfactory insofar as the achievement of the students is concerned. The tenth grade has thus been left free for the introduction of general physical science.[15]

The eleventh and twelfth years are available for students to elect any two of the following courses: one year of chemistry, one year of physics, one year of advanced courses in such areas as electronics, radio, and aviation. In a few high schools, advanced biology courses are available in the eleventh and twelfth years.

The educational research pertaining to integrated courses in the physical sciences was recently summarized by Smith and Washton.[16] Their report noted the studies described below.

The status of integrated physical science courses in senior high schools was investigated by Ray who queried 100 secondary schools in cities of 5000 or more population in 24 states.[17] Of the 70 schools responding, 40 offered a physical science course, chiefly in Grades 11 and 12, which integrated physics, chemistry, geology, meteorology, and astronomy. Findings showed an increase in the number of such courses as well as the enrollments in them. The courses were usually substituted for the traditional chemistry or physics courses by students not planning to go to college.

Mudge undertook a similar but less extensive study.[18] He concluded that the senior science-survey course was widespread and that attempts were made to gear the subject to the community and

[15] George G. Mallinson and Jacqueline V. Buck, "The Coming of General Physical Science," *The Clearing House,* vol. 28 (November, 1953), p. 160.

[16] Herbert A. Smith and Nathan S. Washton, "Science in the Secondary Schools," *Review of Educational Research,* vol. 27 (October, 1957), pp. 350–351.

[17] Sister M. Amadeus Ray, "Nationwide Status of Integrated Courses in Physical Sciences," master's thesis, Boston University, 1953, p. 34.

[18] John E. Mudge, "The Feasibility in Present Usage of the Senior Advanced General Science Course in High School," master's thesis, Cornell University, 1952, 84 pp.

its youth. Consumer education was frequently emphasized; some courses appeared to be designed to occupy the uninterested student's time. The courses were comparatively new. Flannigan's findings were much the same.[19]

The teaching of soil and water conservation was investigated by Glidden.[20] He selected 66 principles which might be included in the school curriculum and had asked two groups of specialists to evaluate them. On the basis of a statistical analysis undesirable items were eliminated. An examination testing the remaining principles was administered to seniors in selected high schools. Test scores were considered low, and curriculum changes were suggested to overcome the deficiencies.

Miles contributed a study that should help the organization and teaching of a physical science course on the high school level.[21] A large number of principles of physics, chemistry, and geology were found to be feasible objectives for courses in the physical sciences, and many experiments already in use in the high school science courses were deemed adaptable for use in the physical science courses. This study as well as others indicated that individual laboratory experiences can be made suitable for the development of the understanding of basic principles of the physical sciences.

In accordance with the several research studies dealing with the teaching of a physical science course, it is recommended that secondary schools seriously consider a science program which includes a physical science course. According to many science teachers, it appears that the Grade 10 may be most suitable for placement. Possibilities of moving biology into the Grade 9 and of retaining chemistry and physics in Grades 11 or 12 should also be

[19] Norman A. Flannigan, "A Study of High School Science Courses in Grades 9–12 Designed for General Education," doctoral dissertation, Cornell University, 1954, 210 pp. Abstract: *Dissertation Abstracts,* vol. 15, no. 1 (1955), pp. 62–63.

[20] Harley F. Glidden, "The Identification and Evaluation of Principles of Soil and Water Conservation for Inclusion in the Secondary School Curriculum," *Science Education,* vol. 40 (February, 1956), pp. 54–78.

[21] Vaden W. Miles, *A Determination of the Principles and Experiments Desirable for a High School Course of Integrated Physical Science,* Edwards Brothers, 1950, 430 pp.

explored by secondary schools. This proposal would be effective if it were coordinated with science instruction from kindergarten through Grade 8. Topics should be selected for grade placement to avoid duplication and better articulation.

Specialized and Vocational Science Courses

Many schools throughout the country offer advanced courses in chemistry, physics, biology, electronics, aviation and other sciences to meet the needs of students and the community. In rural areas, a special course in agriculture is offered. In several high schools, students may arrange either to be excused from an introductory college science course or to be granted credit on the college level. This curriculum modification should be made only after the colleges concerned have been consulted in order to prevent misunderstandings of transfer credit.

At present, it is not possible to make a generalization about offering some advanced science courses, equivalent to college level, in the senior high schools. Some college faculty members believe that it is not the function of the high school to offer college work. They insist that the high school should give the basic background and stimulate interest in order that college freshmen will elect science courses.

Science teachers have found that special projects for science fairs and individual research by students after class hours may play a greater role toward influencing future scientists than the offering of advanced courses beyond the high school curriculum. There are, however, a few very large specialized science high schools that have provided for the needs of the talented pupils through an enriched program of instruction that offers several advanced courses equivalent to college level.

Applied science or vocational-type science courses, especially in agriculture, were introduced in the schools and colleges as a result of Federal legislation, including the Hatch Act of 1887, the Adams Act of 1906, the Smith-Lever Act of 1914, and the Purnell Act of 1925. Vocational education in the public schools was aided by the Smith-Hughes Act passed by Congress in 1917. The Smith-

Hughes Act and the George-Dean Act of 1936 provided funds for teacher salaries and for research in vocational subjects. As a result, many technical science courses were developed for vocational high schools, trade schools, and comprehensive high schools. Courses such as radio and electronics, aviation, applied physics, applied chemistry, and agriculture constitute an important part of the high school curriculum for vocational or trade school students. Specialized or technical courses such as fundamentals of electricity, direct current, alternating current, and related courses are usually offered by technical high schools, primarily for pre-engineering students. The applied, vocational science subjects are usually pursued by terminal students who seek jobs prior to or immediately after graduation from the vocational or trade high school. The emphasis in trade school science subjects is on the practical aspects such as radio and television repair mechanics and factory work in radio and electronic industries. In addition to elementary theory, students are required to master specific skills in the use of laboratory and factory equipment. Teachers of trade courses in the sciences should have some journeyman experience or appropriate industrial experience.

Enrollment and Course Offerings in Science

During the past decade there has been a continuous increase in pupil enrollment in the public elementary and secondary schools. In 1958, the estimated total pupil population was 33,508,814 which is about 40 percent greater than the pupil population of 10 years earlier (see Table 2).

"In percentages, secondary school enrollments are now going up faster than elementary school enrollments. The increase of this year over last year was 4.4 percent in secondary grades and 3.6 percent in elementary grades."[22]

Many people are concerned with the enrollments in science courses in the secondary schools. In 1957, the United States Office of Education provided the data in Table 3.

---

[22] National Education Association, Research Division, *Research Bulletin*, vol. 36 (February, 1958), p. 9.

TABLE 2. Enrollments in Public Elementary and Secondary Schools

Year	Enrollment	Percent of increase over previous year	Percent of increase over 1947–1948
1947–1948	24,101,300	—	
1948–1949	24,653,383	2.3	2.3
1949–1950	25,185,436	2.2	4.5
1950–1951	25,794,510	2.4	7.0
1951–1952	26,711,656	3.6	10.8
1952–1953	27,532,435	3.1	14.2
1953–1954	28,916,703	5.0	20.0
1954–1955	29,966,052	3.6	24.3
1955–1956	31,141,338	3.9	29.2
1956–1957	32,268,459	3.6	33.9
1957–1958	33,508,814	3.8	39.0

SOURCE: National Education Association, Research Division, *Research Bulletin,* vol. 36 (February, 1958), p. 9.

TABLE 3. Percentage of Pupils in the Last Four Years of Public High Schools in Certain Science Courses: 1890 to 1956–1957

Year	General science	Chemistry	Physics	Biology
1890		10.1	22.8	
1900		7.7	19.0	
1910		6.9	14.6	1.1
1915		7.4	14.2	6.9
1922	18.3	7.4	8.9	8.8
1928	17.5	7.1	6.8	13.6
1934	17.8	7.6	6.3	14.6
1949	20.8	7.6	5.4	18.4
1954	—	7.3	4.6	19.6
1956	21.8	7.5	4.4	20.5

SOURCE: Kenneth E. Brown and Ellsworth S. Obourn, *Offerings and Enrollments in Science and Mathematics in Public High Schools, 1956,* Pamphlet No. 120, U.S. Department of Health, Education, and Welfare, 1957.

Although the proportion of students enrolled in chemistry remained almost constant at about 7.4 percent, the actual number enrolled, according to the study, "has increased nearly 13-fold or from 40,084 in 1900 to an estimated 519,900. . . ." This becomes evident upon comparison of the data in Tables 2 and 3. It is also noted that fewer students are enrolled in physics and chemistry than in general science or biology. The study furnishes data which indicates that with the exception of biology all science courses enroll more boys than girls. There are limitations in terms of making national generalizations from this survey. Questionnaires were sent to 10 percent of the public high schools in the United States; 90 percent of the questionnaire returns were usable. There were variables such as semester versus full-year science courses. The data is very helpful, however, in determining trends or patterns of science programs which should cause science teachers and administrators to evaluate science curricula.

THE PREPARATION OF THE SCIENCE CURRICULUM

The Science Syllabus in the Metropolitan School System

In most of the large cities, school systems usually have a curriculum research office with a group of consultants in science and education who work very closely with a teacher committee. The teachers are encouraged to make recommendations for improving the science syllabus. Usually, teacher representatives from most of the schools are designated to attend the meetings scheduled by the curriculum committee. Before the modified syllabus is prepared, committee members examine research in education and in science and scrutinize professional literature pertaining to objectives, methods of teaching, instructional material, audio-visual aids, and techniques for evaluation. Teachers exchange views and share experiences in making specific proposals. Some members may survey community and individual pupil needs and interests. Community resources for the improvement of science teaching are occasionally explored. After considerable thought and study, a tentative science syllabus is prepared and used for experimental purposes in a few selected schools.

Evaluating the New Syllabus

One of the weakest areas in science curriculum construction is the failure to design an adequate technique for evaluating the goals or objectives of the new syllabus. This may partially be due to the inadequate type of testing program and the lack of sufficient instruments for measuring change in pupil attitudes and behavior as a result of science instruction.

Another problem in evaluating a new science course of instruction is the inability to trace or diagnose in the classroom the various potential causes for failure or underachievement. Do students know how to study and work in science effectively? Howell makes the following recommendations which have strong implications for a good evaluation program:

1. Every teacher should become a teacher of such study skills as pertain to his own subject.
2. Every librarian should participate in this program by cooperating with all teachers to make available the materials of the library. Furthermore, the librarian should have regularly scheduled classes in which he teaches the skills that are unique to his area of the educative process.
3. The student's attitude toward study must be improved.
4. Study procedures to be emphasized in how-to-study courses are note-taking; outlining; reviewing; preparing for examinations; learning the principles of study, including memorizing and remembering; selecting and organizing subject matter; increasing knowledge of word meaning; improving reading comprehension; adapting speed of reading to the materials and the purpose involved; preparing a term paper, theme, or report; identifying and expressing cause-and-effect relationships; using general reference books; using study procedures appropriate to different areas of study.
5. Students should be helped to work out and observe a study schedule.
6. As students progress through the secondary school, they should be taught to work independently at maximum efficiency.
7. Practical clinical procedures should be used by the guidance counselor to help students learn and use helpful study skills. . . .
8. Audio-visual aids, such as sound films, maps, charts, graphs, and

strip films, are necessary and valuable for satisfactory pupil accomplishment in study skills.

9. Since the parents can help immeasurably in establishing proper work habits by providing an atmosphere in the home conducive to proper study habits, they should be informed of the best conditions for study. Pupils must be taught the study skills by the school before homework can become an effective experience.

10. Teachers, administrators, and counselors should be familiar with the tests of work-study skills in order to direct adequate clinical research.[23]

Importance of Grade Placement and Attitudes

In modifying an existing or developing a new science syllabus, consideration should be given to how the elementary science program is articulated with the junior high school, and with the senior high school sciences. This is essential to avoid undue and needless repetition. Serious attention should be given to grade placement of topics or problems in science and to appropriate pupil experiences in terms of pupil readiness, motivation, and interests.

In referring to Snygg and Combs,[24] Howell writes: ". . . the learning of any skill or item of subject matter is accompanied by the formation of attitudes (which may be desirable or undesirable) by the pupil toward the subject, toward school, toward his teacher, toward adults, toward society, and toward himself. As a result, *how* subject matter is taught may be even more important than *what* is taught."[25] Few syllabuses suggest various approaches to the *how* or methods of teaching. Rather, the usual syllabus or handbook is made up of an outline of the content, demonstrations or experiments, references, audio-visual aids, equipment needed, and the objectives or goals of the units.

The syllabus is an outline of a course with much emphasis on the content to be taught. It may suggest pupil and teacher learning activities, references, and other aids to learning such as demonstra-

[23] Wallace J. Howell, "Work-Study Skills of Adolescents in Grades VII–XIV," *School Review*, vol. LXI (May, 1953), p. 281.

[24] Donald Snygg and Arthur W. Combs, *Individual Behavior*, Harper & Brothers, 1949.

[25] Howell, *op. cit.*, pp. 277–278.

Fig. 3.1. It is important to teach attitudes as well as biological information such as the skeleton. (Courtesy of Board of Education, Port Washington Public Schools, Port Washington, N.Y.; photograph by Irvin Simon)

tions and experiments. A teacher's handbook is a compilation of detailed materials based on a syllabus and is a guide to instruction for the teacher. The syllabus can similarly be used as a guide where the teacher can implement and supplement instruction in science based upon pupil and teacher experiences, interests, needs, and abilities.

A Sample Teaching Unit

In 1958, the Board of Education of the City of New York proposed a General Science—Grades 7–8–9—Course of Study and Syllabus which lists the following units.

Getting Acquainted with Yourself
Getting Acquainted with Your World

Increasing and Improving Our Food Supply
Increasing and Improving Our Use of Natural Resources
Making Work Easier
Speedier Transportation
Improving Communication
Prolonging Your Life
Our Atomic World

A portion of the fifth unit is given below as a sample:

MAKING WORK EASIER

OBJECTIVES OF THIS UNIT:

In this unit, students are introduced to an understanding of the kinds of energy that man uses and the transformation of one form of energy into another. Students should gain an understanding of how energy is made available and how the world's work is facilitated by the use of machines.

Through an analysis of machines commonly encountered by the children, the basic principles of operation of all machines are derived.

There is opportunity in this unit for pupil practice in simple laboratory skills, in reading scales, in deriving mathematical relationships and using basic mathematical procedures, in organizing data, in making hypotheses, and in making and checking conclusions.

The major problems to be developed in this unit are as follows:

Problem 83.1 How does the energy available to man affect his standard of living?

Problem 83.2 How do machines enable man to perform difficult tasks more easily?

Problem 83.3 In what other ways can machines help man?

Problem 83.4 How can electricity make work easier?

PROBLEM 83.1   HOW DOES THE ENERGY AVAILABLE TO MAN AFFECT HIS STANDARD OF LIVING?

Suggested Approaches and Activities:

a. What are some common sources of energy available to man? Place a ping-pong ball on the table. Ask the class how the ball can be moved without touching it. Elicit several ways: blowing, squirting it with water, forcing a jet of steam against it, etc. Indicate that each of these devices are sources of energy. Develop a definition of energy as the ability to do work—to make things move. Ask the pupils what was common to each of the sources of energy just presented. Define kinetic or *mechanical* energy as the energy of moving objects. Discuss applications of mechanical energy provided by nature: windmills, sailboats, hydroelectric plants, water wheels, etc.

Explore with the children other ways in which objects may be made to move; i.e. other sources of energy. Place about one inch of water in a metal "pop" bottle (Fig. 83–1), and set it on a tripod. Heat with a Bunsen flame until the water is boiling vigorously. Remove the flame, insert a cork (CAUTION: just tap the cork down with a finger) and reheat. What caused the cork to pop out? Define a fuel as a material which is burned to provide energy. Elicit other types of solid, liquid, and gaseous fuels, and their particular advantages and disadvantages. Develop the concept that the *chemical* energy of the fuel is converted to heat in the process of combustion. Trace the means by which the heat actually makes the cork pop. Develop the concept that the fuel is a form of stored-up energy to be used when desired.

Operate a radiometer, using sunlight, a heating coil, or a lamp as a source of energy. Vary the distance from the source to the radiometer. Repeat with an opaque object. Develop the concept of *radiant* energy, consisting in this case of light energy and heat energy. With some pupils, you may wish to investigate other forms of radiant energy. Recall the use of radiant energy from the sun in photosynthesis. Students may report on other practical uses of radiant energy from the sun.

Operate a small electric motor. Elicit that the motion of the motor is derived from *electrical* energy.

Raise a ball from the table top. Ask the children if the ball has energy (is capable of making an object move) in its raised position. Let the ball drop on the raised end of a ruler pivoted like a see-saw, on the lower end of which is a coin. Develop the concept that a raised object has a form of stored-up energy. Discuss the pile-driver hammer as an application.

Develop the differences between *potential energy* (as in coal, dynamite, a raised hammer, etc.) and *kinetic energy* (as in a steam engine, exploding dynamite, a falling hammer, etc.).

Summarize, and elicit further applications of the common sources of energy. What other sources of energy are available to man? (Nuclear energy will be studied in the 9th year.)

See New York State Handbook, Part III: 3240, 3557, 3558.

b. How can one form of energy be transformed to another? Assemble a model generating station, consisting of a water motor (or electrically driven steam engine) and a 6-volt generator. Connect the pulleys on the motor and the generator with a large rubber band to serve as a drive belt. Use the output of the generator to light a 6-volt lamp. Trace the energy conversions involved.

Demonstrate as many of the following as possible.

Apparatus or Process	Energy Conversion	
Incandescence—heat a wire with a Bunsen burner until it glows	heat	to light
Steam turbine	heat	to mechanical
Thermocouple	heat	to electrical
(green plants)	radiant	to chemical
Absorption of radiation—expose sheets of black and white paper to a bright light. Check changes of temperature	light	to heat
Radiometer	light	to mechanical
Photoelectric relay or solar battery	light	to electrical
Camera film	light	to chemical
Friction—rub palms of hands together	mechanical	to heat
Strike flint on steel	mechanical	to electrical
Static electricity, hand magneto	mechanical	to light
Electric iron, toaster, etc.	electrical	to heat
Neon lamp	electrical	to light
Electric motor	electrical	to mechanical
Electroplating	electrical	to chemical
Burning	chemical	to heat and light
Explosions (State Handbook: 3320)	chemical	to mechanical
Dry cell	chemical	to electrical

Develop the idea that each of the above devices or processes begins with a source of energy and results in the output of a different form of energy. Point out the need for an intermediary device in each of these conversions. Try to elicit from the children the need for converting energy from one form to another.

Have children report on machines or devices which involve several conversions, e.g., a gasoline engine (chemical to heat to mechanical), an incandescent lamp (electrical to heat to light), etc.

With some classes, point out that heat is "low-grade" energy; it is most easily formed and most difficult to convert to another form. Our loss in efficiency of machines is due primarily to the formation of unusable heat energy.

See New York State General Science Handbook: Part II: 2410, 2501–2503, 2507–2509; Part III: 3215, 3216, 3243, 3320, 3454.

c. How is energy used by man? How has man improved his way of life by discovering and using new sources of energy? Students may report on the progress of man's use of energy for such purposes as farming, transportation on land, transportation on water, lighting, and building. Develop the idea that man uses nature to provide energy to supplement or replace that provided by his own muscles, and that machines are needed to make this energy readily useful to man.

What are the prospects for an unlimited supply of energy? The following questions may serve as guides for class discussions or reports:

1. How much energy do we have? Our available and anticipated supplies of petroleum may not last through this century; our supply of other fossil fuels (coal and gas) is limited in supply and availability.
2. How much energy do we get from the sun? More energy is received on the earth each day, through sunlight, than that produced by all the atomic and hydrogen bombs ever exploded. Similarly, the energy in a hurricane (derived from the sun) is equivalent to thousands of hydrogen bombs.
3. How cheap is atomic energy? Energy obtained from nuclear fission cannot compete (in the United States) with energy obtained by burning fossil fuels at the present time. However, our supply of nuclear fuels may last for centuries.
4. How much energy can be obtained from nuclear *fusion?* If nuclear fusion (thermonuclear reactions) can be controlled, the oceans will become our chief source of energy.

5. How will the standard of living of all the peoples on the earth be affected by the universal availability of "free" energy?

See New York State General Science Handbook, Part III: 3552–3554.

Understandings:

1. Energy exists in many forms—heat, light, mechanical, chemical, electrical, nuclear.
2. Energy may be transformed from one form to another more usable form.
3. Our present civilization depends on our ability to harness an ever increasing supply of energy.
4. The energy sources of the future may be those from thermonuclear reactions and the direct utilization of sunlight.

Problems and Projects for Individual and Committee Work:

1. Make a chart which includes diagrams or pictures to illustrate the conversion of one form of energy (e.g., electricity) to another (e.g., heat).
2. Make a chart showing the energy conversions which are involved in bringing electricity into your home. Use diagrams or pictures of the apparatus utilized to make these energy changes.
3. Investigate and report to the class on the methods by which the efficiency of a machine can be measured.
4. Investigate and report on energy sources of the future.
5. Construct one of the following:
   a. A model of an electric power plant.
   b. A model of a nuclear power plant.
   c. A thermocouple.
   d. A photoelectric relay.
6. Demonstrate the lead storage cell, and explain the energy conversions involved in charging and in using the cell.

PROBLEM 83.2   HOW DO MACHINES ENABLE MAN TO PERFORM
DIFFICULT TASKS MORE EASILY?

Suggested Approaches and Activities:

   a. What is meant by work? What is meant by force? Place a book on the table, and have a child move it toward or away from him.

Identify his efforts as a push or pull. Roll a cart toward the pupil, and ask him to stop it (by pushing). Roll a cart away from the pupil, and ask him to stop it (by pulling). Roll a ball on the table, and ask the child to change its direction (by a push or pull). Elicit the definition of a *force* as a push or pull which tends to *change motion* (speed or direction).

Have a child lift one book from the floor to the table. Another pupil lifts five (identical) books from the floor to the table. Who is using more effort (force)? How much more force?

How are forces measured? Place a weight on a diet scale, and have the students note the reading on the scale. Point out that the weight is pushing down on the scale. Suspend the same weight from a spring balance, and have the students note the reading. A pull (against gravity) is being applied here. Elicit that forces can be measured in units of weight; that is, by comparison with the force of gravity. Elicit some of the common units in which forces are measured. Be sure to make clear that forces can be measured in any direction, not only vertically, as with that of gravity.

How can we measure work? Have the pupils identify the factors (force and distance) involved in moving the books. Define work as the product of force and distance. Ask a pupil to lift five books from the floor to the table. Another pupil lifts five books from the top of the table to a box about one foot high. Who has done more work? Why? Assume that each book weighs one pound, that the distance from the floor to the table is 3 feet, and the distance from the top of the table to the top of the box is one foot. Calculate the amount of work done in each case. The unit "foot-pounds" may be used with some classes. Provide drill through practical illustrations.

Have a child push against the blackboard. How much work is being done? Allow a student to hold a book. How much work is being done? Determine the work needed to lift a cart to a height of two feet and to move the cart two feet along the table. Is the same amount of working being done? Why? Compare the work required to walk ten feet and to climb a ten-foot ladder; to roll a bicycle on its wheels and to lift the bicycle. Develop the concept that work is accomplished only when an object is displaced (moved) and that the force used in calculating work is that actually needed to overcome other forces (gravity, friction, etc.) which try to keep the object from moving.

See New York State Handbook, Part I: 1301–1304, 1307.

b. How do machines enable us to do work with less effort? Wrap some strong clothesline around two window poles. Have the (Fig. 83–2) two strongest pupils in the class hold the window poles, as shown, and try to prevent the smallest child in the class from pulling them together. Elicit that the smaller child was using a machine to multiply her efforts.

Set up an inclined plane which is 3 feet long and 1 foot high (Fig. 83–3). Determine the weight of a cart and calculate the work required to *lift* it to a height of one foot. This is the work output— the work the machine is to do. Have a pupil measure the effort needed to move the cart up the incline. Calculate the work put into the machine. Compare work input and output. Emphasize that the incline made it possible to lift the weight with less effort, but at the expense of increased distance.

Repeat this demonstration with the incline set at heights of 6″, 9″, and 18″. Tabulate the data and ask the pupils to interpret the results. Which position of the incline required least effort? How does the ratio of length to height of the incline compare with the ratio of resistance to effort? Define mechanical advantage as the number of times the effort is multiplied by the use of the machine. Present applications of the inclined plane—ramps, railroad grades, for loading trucks, etc.

Set up the apparatus as shown (Fig. 83–4). One end of the meter stick rests on the diet scale, which is adjusted to read zero. Push down at end E, and read the forces recorded on the diet scale (effort) and on the spring balance (resistance). Estimate the vertical distances moved by each end of the meter stick. Elicit or explain that this device is a lever. Demonstrate pliers, metal shears, a crowbar, etc. Show that the advantage gained in effort requires an increased distance over which the force must be applied.

In some classes, committees may be able to report on other kinds of levers, and the relationship of effort arm and resistance arm to mechanical advantage.

Set up the pulley system shown in the diagram (Fig. 83.5). Use a weight of 300 grams as the resistance, and counterbalance it with a 100-gram weight as the effort. How many times has the effort been multiplied? How many strands are holding the resistance? Lift the weight (resistance) 4 inches. Over what distance has the effort moved? By what factor has the distance been increased? Compare work input with work output. Illustrate further with other pulley systems, and with practical applications.

Demonstrate the wheel and axle with a commercial or student-constructed model. The major learning here, as in the previous examples of simple machines, should be that effort is gained at the expense of distance. Explore applications of the wheel and axle: faucet handles, screw drivers, capstans, automobile steering wheels, etc.

Some pupils may be asked to report to the class on other simple machines (wedge, screw, gear train), or to analyze more complex machines or instruments (auto jack, derrick, steam shovel, etc.).

See New York State General Science Handbook, Part I: 1308–1315, 1320; Part III: 3301–3304, 3338–3344.

c. How can we reduce wasted effort in a machine? What are the effects of friction? Have the children in the class rub their hands together firmly and quickly, and then put their hands to their cheeks. Ask them to press their hands together more firmly while rubbing. Generalizations can be made regarding the effects of friction in producing heat and in slowing down motion. Show that friction also wears down surfaces by demonstrating the use of sandpaper or a nail file.

Ask the pupils to give instances where friction is desirable for each of the effects elicited above. Similarly, derive illustrations of the undesirable and harmful effects of friction.

How can friction be increased? Attach a string to a chalk box containing stones or weights, and measure the force needed to move it uniformly along a smooth table top or sheet of glass, and then along a plank of wood which has been covered with sandpaper. Add weights to the box, and again measure the force needed to pull it along the smooth and rough surfaces. Elicit that friction can be increased by increasing the roughness of the surface and by increasing the force applied to the surface. (Friction also depends on the nature of the surfaces in contact.) Apply this knowledge to automobile safety—compare stopping times when the automobile is traveling over ice, dry concrete, and sand. More force must be applied to the brake pedal if we want to slow down faster. Bags of sand are carried in the trunk compartment in winter time, both to add weight and to be spread out over ice or snow when necessary. Apply to other situations

—rubber-soled athletic shoes, spikes on shoes, making a quick stop on ice skates, etc.

How can friction be reduced? Deduce the converse of the above. Smoother surfaces and less weight make for less friction. Repeat the demonstrations with the weighted chalk box on the sandpapered surface. Measure the force required to move the box on rollers (sections of glass rod). Rolling friction is less than sliding friction. Show samples of ball and roller bearings from skate wheels, bicycles, engines. Again ask the pupils to rub their hands together. Have several pupils wet and soap their hands, and then rub them together. Elicit the effect of lubrication in reducing friction. Emphasize that different materials require different lubricants. Oil or grease is suitable for most metals; paraffin or soap can be used for wood; vaseline or water can lubricate rubber.

Discuss the importance of reducing friction in machines. Stress that some of the force applied to a machine is used to overcome friction and therefore produces no useful effect. We never get back in useful form all the energy (work) that we put into a machine, because some is lost as heat. Friction reduces the *efficiency* of a machine. Reducing friction increases the efficiency of a machine.

See New York State General Science Handbook, Part I: 1328–1340.

Understandings:

1. A force is a push or pull which tends to change the motion of an object.
2. Work is done when an effort is applied to an object over a distance. Work is measured as the product of the force and the distance.
3. Machines enable us to do a job, not with less energy (work input), but with less force or effort. This advantage in effort is made up by a corresponding increase in the distance through which the effort must be moved.
4. Many machines which we use are combinations of simple machines such as the inclined plane, lever, pulley, and wheel and axle.
5. Friction causes the loss of energy as heat.
6. Friction may be reduced by the use of rollers or ball bearings, and by proper lubrication.

Problems and Projects for Individual and Committee Work:

1. Find out and explain to the class why little or no force is required to keep a rocket ship moving in space.
2. Construct a display or make a chart showing pulley systems (or inclined planes or wheel and axle) with mechanical advantages from one to five.
3. Construct a display or make a chart showing various simple machines, each with a mechanical advantage of 4.
4. Find out and report to the class on the characteristics and grading systems of lubricating oils and greases. Report on the uses of special lubricants.
5. Investigate and report to the class on the history of "Perpetual motion" machines.[26]

The above sample of a part of a teaching unit from the New York City General Science Syllabus is an excellent illustration of the results of cooperative effort in the construction of a curriculum. It also represents a recent trend in the preparation of science syllabuses to include more of instructional procedures, specific demonstrations, and pupil activities. School administrators, supervisors, and science teachers have found that this type of syllabus is most helpful especially for the beginning science teacher and for the teacher who is asked to teach science but was trained in another subject. Since many people not fully equipped to do so are teaching science in the junior and senior high schools, it has become necessary to produce a more specific kind of syllabus which contains aids to teaching and learning science.

A careful examination of the problems presented in the unit will indicate to the reader that the word *elicit* appears frequently. The science teacher stimulates learning by presenting various problems, situations, demonstrations, and pupil experiences with the view of getting the pupils to formulate principles and applications of science. This method of eliciting thought on the part of pupils is a major part of the developmental method of teaching which will be discussed fully in Chapter 7. Essentially, the pupil is encouraged

[26] Reprinted from "General Science, grades 7, 8, 9," by permission of the Board of Education of the City of New York, *Curriculum Report* (January, 1958).

to perform both deductive and inductive reasoning. The science teacher may be compared with a conductor of a symphonic orchestra. The conductor who wishes harmony must know when, where, and how to utilize the various talents of the musicians in various sections. The science teacher directs or guides learning by calling on different pupils for their abilities in observing, interpreting, evaluating, reporting, investigating, constructing, drawing, and concluding in order that they may come to understand basic scientific ideas pertaining to natural phenomena. The teacher cannot expect to master this method in one easy lesson. Careful planning and work by teacher and pupils are essential to make progress toward the development of the objectives or goals stated as understandings, concepts, attitudes, interests, or abilities such as problem solving. All of these goals cannot be achieved by merely presenting a "neatly packaged" demonstration in which pupils are asked to observe and state a conclusion. The teacher needs skill in stating good thought-provoking questions that require students to perform deductive and inductive reasoning.

Maintaining a Science Curriculum That Meets the Need

In planning science curriculums, it is important that science teachers in the secondary schools and specialists in curriculums and science education re-examine existing courses of study with a forward look and not wait until some emergency occurs. A temporary crash-through program may prove exceedingly weak and costly. Not only is it important to keep abreast of the numerous and varied developments in science and the educational research in the teaching of science; it is equally important to fit these developments into the science curriculum. It is also essential that the science curriculum be carefully scrutinized periodically without waiting for a Sputnik or an emergency to occur before modifications are made to meet the needs of our changing society. In 1942, Webb stated: "In the present emergency for national defense the discovery has been made that far more time is required to train a scientist than a pilot or soldier. Adaptations of science courses for immediate use are only makeshifts. The revision of a science curriculum is a long-distance matter. Curriculum planners must look far ahead."[27] This statement, although made in 1942, is pertinent today and will be for many years to come.

Several studies discuss various forces that affect secondary school curriculum development.[28] State legislatures that make scholarship funds available to future scientists, local boards of education, pressure groups (such as those favoring conservation or anti-vivisection), ideological differences, religion, professional groups, individual scientists—all comprise the social forces that influence what science should be taught in the public secondary schools.

It is evident that no one syllabus in science can meet the needs of all groups, individuals, and geographic areas. Although there are basic scientific principles universally accepted by scientists, the applications of these principles should be carefully selected to meet the needs of specific localities and individuals. In our American democracy it is important that controversial topics be included along with noncontroversial subject matter. If, however, some parents object to certain instruction as contrary to their religious beliefs—some, for example, may not wish to have their children instructed about diseases that are caused by germs—they may request that their children be excused from this instruction. But the basic principles of science should be taught.

County, Suburban, or Small School System

There are advantages and limitations in the preparation of science curriculums for both the large high schools and the smaller ones with an enrollment of less than 300 pupils. Although the metropolitan school systems may have high schools with enrollments of several thousands of students and can therefore, offer a greater variety of science courses each year, they usually have large-size classes that make individualized instruction for students very difficult. The smaller high school with fewer students in each

[27] Hanor A. Webb, "Impending Changes in the Science Curriculum," *Education,* vol. 62 (January, 1942).

[28] Dan W. Dodson, "Factors Influencing Curriculum Development," *Review of Educational Research,* vol. 27 (June, 1957), pp. 262–269.

class enables the science teacher to guide individual students more effectively, assuming all other factors are equal. High schools with student populations of under 300 seldom offer all of the basic sciences each year. It is also unlikely that fully qualified teachers of all of the basic sciences are available in these schools. Salary schedules in rural areas frequently are lower than those of the urban regions with the result that they attract few qualified science teachers. The same problem applies to the larger school systems where there is competition with industry to attract the most capable science teachers. Recently, however, many school systems have recognized the importance of increasing salaries and are paying teachers more.

Funds for sorely needed science equipment and facilities are still lacking in rural high schools and, to a lesser degree, in the metropolitan school districts. In both types of situations, resourceful science teachers are able to improvise some equipment for demonstrations and experiments. There is an inadequate supply of science books other than textbooks in the school library. Anderson found the following ratings in sampling 56 of the 483 high schools in Minnesota: 26 percent of the teachers rated the reading material for science as a good supply; 44 percent as a fair supply; 30 percent as a poor supply.[29] Biology and chemistry courses are "far from ideal" was one of the conclusions made in Anderson's study.[30] There is a lack of specialized curriculum materials to meet the needs of groups whose interest and abilities vary. In discussing "Science Education in Small High Schools," Schulz writes:

> In each science class, there is great variety in mental abilities, backgrounds, interests, and goals. About four of every ten graduates will leave their home community for areas of more ample opportunities. The graduates will become farmers, professional people, tradesmen, and homemakers; but high school will be the terminal education for most of them. It is for this reason the objectives of factual knowledge

[29] Kenneth E. Anderson, "Adjuncts to Science Instruction," *School Science and Mathematics*, vol. 49 (June, 1949), pp. 475–476.

[30] Kenneth E. Anderson, "Summary of the Relative Achievements of the Objectives of Secondary School Science in a Representative Sampling of 56 Minnesota Schools," *Science Education*, vol. 33 (December, 1949), pp. 323–329.

and preparation for college should be carefully re-examined and modified.[31]

It should not be concluded that only poor students become science teachers. There are many dedicated, inspirational, and highly capable science teachers in the secondary schools. In recent years, one problem has been how to retain these people; another has been how to recruit additional topnotch future science teachers for the small and large high schools in America. Unless excellent teachers of science and other qualified specialists work as a team, it will not be possible to prepare a science program to meet the needs of our youth in our ever changing society.

Guiding Principles for Constructing a Science Curriculum

The following questions may serve as a guide to the personnel confronted with the design, modification, or evaluation of a science curriculum:

1. How does the science program meet the needs of both the academic and nonacademic students? Are there two or more separate or parallel courses or multitrack programs in science or differential subgrouping in a single course? For example, is physical science required for all students, or is it an elective course for noncollege preparatory students in place of physics and/or chemistry? A single-track program implies that there is no choice—only chemistry or physics is offered; there is no provision for other science courses.

2. Is the science curriculum functional and organized in terms of personal development, civic responsibilities, human relationships, and occupational proficiency? Does this functional program promote the mastery of selected theoretical content that is usually memorized?

3. How does the science program provide for individual laboratory experiences for pupils? Is it a key experience in which students discover for themselves, using laboratory methods and skills in solving problems? This is very different from the cookbook type of laboratory manual which primarily aims at getting students to learn how to read and execute the directions plus some manipulative, laboratory skills. Is one point of view emphasized to the exclusion of the other?

[31] Richard W. Schulz, "Science Education in Small High Schools," *Bulletin,* National Association of Secondary School Principals, vol. 37 (January, 1953), p. 35.

4. Does the course of study provide for teacher-made demonstrations with the emphasis on skill as an incentive to inspire young people to do the same in the classroom as well as in the laboratory?

5. How are community resources utilized in the construction of the science program? Are field trips suggested to such places as nearby museums, industrial plants, a planetarium, farms, swamps, water purification plants, woodlands, sewage disposal plants, airports, public agencies for health, conservation, defense, and nearby research centers? Are these direct, field experiences related to reading and teaching materials?

6. What provisions are made for individual pupil projects and group work both in and out of the classroom? Does the course of study suggest specific learning activities in science that promote better individual and cooperative effort as required in group work?

7. Does the course of study include teaching materials that are obtained easily? Do these materials make up a major part of the course, and do they serve to illustrate the basic scientific principles via demonstrations? Are various kinds of equipment available as suggested by the syllabus to enable students to apply scientific principles to the environment: dry cells, motors, auto jacks, old clocks, living plants, animals, electric pumps, telephones, and the like?

8. How adequately does the syllabus provide for student activities in science?

Is the science program organized in terms of units that represent major topics, central themes, or problems that have many related facts and meaningful experiences for the student rather than in a day by day series of isolated assignments?

10. Are provisions made for student evaluation of their own work? Does the syllabus provide for pupil opportunities in making judgments of the work of their fellow students?

11. Does the science curriculum suggest ways in which the teacher can evaluate student changes in attitudes, skills, and knowledge?

12. Are units of instruction in the syllabus based on both pupil needs and interests? How are these needs and interests determined?

13. How does the science program encourage students to challenge authority in terms of experiments and other activities that prevent pupils from accepting blindly or without a sound, scientific attitude, the statements made by other people.

14. Does the curriculum contain scientific applications and impli-

cations of contemporary, social import for everyday living? Are such problems as fluoridation of water, control of radiation and fall-out, new antibiotics, and new discoveries included and added?

15. How does the science program recognize the various levels of pupil maturity? Do students have responsibilities in preparing bulletin boards, forecasting daily weather in the school, cleaning up after laboratory periods, operating audio-visual aids, caring for livestock and equipment?

16. Does the syllabus suggest the use of resource personnel, hobbyists, and specialists from the community?

17. Does the course of study list a wide array of references both for teachers and students? Are these references such as textbooks, supplementary readings, and periodicals employed in making topic assignments instead of assigning pages day by day in the textbook alone?

18. Is there an adequate list of audio-visual aids, films, filmstrips, and equipment for each unit in the course of study?

19. Does the science program suggest and encourage teachers to use the materials in a flexible manner? Does the teacher feel free to substitute demonstrations and learning activities for assigned units other than those that appear in the syllabus?

20. Are good thought-provoking questions in addition to challenging problems stated for each of the units?

21. Are the understandings or principles of science listed for each of the units? Are they to be developed as a result of stimulating learning activities, or are they offered for students to memorize?

22. To what degree does the science program make for provisions for atypical students: slow learners and the intellectually gifted?

23. Are safety precautions stated wherever necessary?[32]

Single- Versus Multiple-Track Programs of Science

In recent years, much criticism has been launched against high school science programs. Claims have been made that the intellectually gifted students are neglected in the sciences. Some educators have claimed that the science curriculums are geared for the slow student. Shortly after Sputnik was launched, many school systems

[32] See Commonwealth of Pennsylvania, Department of Public Instruction, *Course of Study in Science for Secondary Schools*, Bulletin 400, 1951, pp. 60–62.

decided to use a double-track program under which talented students might take advanced college-equivalent science courses in the senior year of high school. This program was made possible by moving biology into the ninth grade and offering chemistry and physics in the tenth and eleventh years.

The Oak Park and River Forest High School in Chicago announced that beginning in September, 1958, 100 freshmen were to be selected on the basis of the recommendation of the public and parochial elementary school teachers and principals and intelligence and reading test data. Standardized science tests were to be administered to these pupils. For this group, a minimum of two years of laboratory science would be required for graduation. It was expected that most of these students would want four full years of high school science. In a press release dated March 27, 1958, Superintendent of Schools, Kenneth W. Lund stated: "This is the first step in the reorganization of our science curriculum which has been under discussion. . . . During the winter, joint meetings of the biological and physical science departments were held, and the new plans were evolved for providing a sound program in science which recognizes the level of learning attained in the elementary schools and will challenge our students in this important area of learning."

This new curriculum calls for reorganization of science content in several courses as well as ability grouping of students. It is an accelerated program of science content under which selected students are able to learn faster and probably master more skills, information, and science understandings than in the previous science courses. Up until now, results appear to be encouraging. However, this reorganization of the science program calls for a modification of the "track" for average students, that is, for those who do not show special aptitudes or abilities in the sciences. The trend has been to offer two years of science for general education in the senior high schools: one year of biology and one year of general physical science.

Some high schools offer more than two tracks of science curriculums. In a few of the comprehensive high schools of more than 1500 students, special courses of a vocational nature such as applied physics, radio and electronics, aviation mechanics, and applied chemistry are offered in a third track for vocational and terminal students who do not attend a college.

Another approach to meeting the needs of some students and communities is to offer advanced courses in a specific science not necessarily on the college level. In some high schools a third-semester elective course in chemistry is offered to all students who complete one year of chemistry in the eleventh year. This type of course which emphasizes consumer chemistry and is of interest to most of the students will be discussed in Chapter 4. Some chemistry teachers have found it most desirable to include consumer problems in the first course in high school chemistry.

Science teachers and other school personnel who are concerned with improving the science program of instruction should design effective methods of determining which students are talented in science as well as procedures for setting up special courses or a multitrack curriculum.

In seeking out the potentially gifted science students it may prove helpful to administer a battery of standardized tests. The test series may include MacCurdy's "Scientific Aptitude Inventory" which consists of 300 items and can be administered in one to two hours.[33] Other test scores of pupils to be carefully interpreted are: high school achievement, intelligence, and reading ability. Teacher grades in science and mathematics should likewise be analyzed in selecting potential future scientists. No one factor should be the complete determinant. For example, some people believe that scientists must have an unusually high intelligence quotient. In examining the IQ's on high school records of 89 physical scientists who earned the Ph.D. degree, Samuel Strauss reported the following data:[34]

---

[33] Robert D. MacCurdy, *Scientific Aptitude Inventory,* College of Education, University of Florida, 1957.

[34] Samuel Strauss, "Looking Backward on Future Scientists," *The Science Teacher,* vol. 24 (December, 1957), pp. 385–387.

From 96 through 100	3%
From 101 through 110	6%
From 111 through 120	29%
From 121 through 130	36%
From 131 through 140	17%
From 141 through 165	9%

The high school records revealed that the physical scientists were ranked in their high school graduating classes as follows:

In top 1% of class	10%
In top 2% of class	22%
In top 5% of class	43%
In top 10% of class	64%
In top 15% of class	79%
In top 25% of class	92%
In top 33% of class	97%
In top 50% of class	100%

Although most of these students included much high school mathematics in their programs, they did not necessarily attain high marks.

The studies by Strauss and by Bloom show that a high IQ is a desirable but not a determining factor in screening potential scientists.[35] In studying the Science Talent Search winners in three New York City high schools, Bloom concluded: (1) Proper selection and motivation do encourage students in science careers. (2) It is essential to identify early those students with above-average capacities and scientific leanings. (3) The cooperation and sympathetic understanding of many teachers are necessary. (4) Manipulative laboratory skills, indoctrination into methods of science, and ability to observe and record are also important factors in the individual's development. (5) It is desirable to provide opportunities for exploration through participation in extracurricular activities such as science clubs.

In preparing a curriculum for the gifted or slow learner in science, organizational or mechanical devices do not completely answer or solve the problem. Good skill and artistry in teaching are fundamental for all students. The double- or multiple-track

[35] Samuel W. Bloom, "The Search for Science Talent," *Science Education*, vol. 38 (April, 1954), pp. 232–236.

program of science instruction may help some pupils in a few of the schools. Provisions must be made for transferring pupils from one track to another. The assumption should not be made that homogeneous grouping is static. Pupil interests change, and so do their abilities. Hence, the teacher should be prepared to provide individual projects, homework assignments on several levels, and multilevel supplementary science readings to meet the individual abilities and needs of students. The new course of study in science in many school systems lists many varied pupil activities to help the teacher in proposing learning activities on different levels of abilities and interests.

Assuming that a homogeneous grouping of students were made in a given science class according to reading ability, chronological age, and the IQ, the individual pupil interests, abilities, and needs will still vary within a science topic or from one science topic to the next. In developing a science curriculum, therefore, reading assignments, the nature of research, and pupil activities are proposed in accordance with these variations. For example, the Junior High School Science Curriculum of the Indianapolis Public Schools treats the unit on light as follows.

Problem Area

What is light?

Understandings

Activities of this unit should lead to the pupil's understanding that:
Light is the direct result of heat.
Light, like heat, is a form of *radiant energy*.
Heat causes the tiny particles (molecules) which compose the object to move around so rapidly that they set up a disturbance (possibly a vibration) in the area around them.
Objects which give off light are said to be luminous. Any object can become *luminous* if it becomes hot enough.

Pupils May

Read *Wonderworld of Science,* Book VIII, pp. 37–44, about radiations which cause light.

Also read about light energy in *Introduction to Science,* pp. 596–597.

Read *New Ideas in Science,* pp. 238–243. Look into the furnace and see the burning coal giving off light and try to explain why.

Turn on an electric light bulb and watch the wire inside begin to glow. Use a clear glass bulb. With a thermometer record the amount of heat given off in all directions equal distances from the bulb.

Make a list of the things which give off their own light and are luminous. Also list nonluminous objects.

Place a piece of *phosphorous* on a *porcelain* plate. Look at it in a darkened room. (Do not handle phosphorous with bare hands.)

Place a book between a lighted candle and a burning alcohol lamp. Notice the difference in the amount of light given off by each. Now place a piece of nickel-chromium wire from a burned out electric heater element in the alcohol flame, and note what happens. Explain.[36]

Not all of the students will perform all of these suggested activities. Some pupils may elect to perform some of these activities because of personal interest or motivation; others may elect to do different activities that may be proposed by the science teacher. The curriculum, therefore, is a guide for the teacher to use in making science instruction inspirational and effective. Some activities may be omitted because the teacher may initiate or create more stimulating learning experiences for a given class or student.

In addition to preparing an appropriate science curriculum for the gifted student in science, the teacher should take other factors into account. Future scientists who are junior and senior high school students are to be regarded as normal human beings who make a good adjustment to people and their environment. They participate in social and extracurricular activities just as do students who do not seek careers in the sciences. They come from all levels of socioeconomic status. The potential scientist in the high school has a very strong drive to succeed. This drive may stem from unusual frustrations, anxieties, or undue hardships in the home.

[36] Indianapolis Public Schools, *Science, a Guide for Teachers,* Junior High School Curriculum Bulletin No. 20, 1955. The above is an excerpt from a unit.

Although these students are not antisocial, they display a non-conforming type of behavior from time to time. For example, they may find it extremely difficult to accept the *one* method of solving a problem. They seek other ways which may offer them a greater challenge in solving problems. They respond extremely well to encouragement by the teacher and outsiders. The outsider might be a college professor, an industrial scientist, a pharmacist, an engineer, or a government official. The encouragement is more than verbal if it is to have a real impact upon the future scientist. The highly interested or gifted science student appreciates a chemical or a particular type of scientific object that is related to his interest. He enjoys telling an expert what he thinks about doing experiments and performing some interesting research work. The first meeting and discussion is not the last one. A genuine interest in a student's work in science by parents and outsiders may be the real basis for the development of a future scientist. The teacher takes each of these factors into account and attempts to relate these factors to a sound science program of instruction.

Using the case history approach, Bull determined the activities and backgrounds of 100 high school students identified by teachers as having dominant science interests.[37] Major findings were: (1) The large majority of these students were superior in scholastic ability to the other students in the same schools. (2) Three-fourths of the group studied had a preference for physical science (3) nearly all the students tended to have good social poise and were not classified as unusual in social behavior. (4) Approximately 60 percent of the students were inclined to avoid the usual physical activities found in the typical secondary school. (5) All members of the group were readers of science literature. (6) The students had been encouraged by parents or science teachers in their interests and hobbies.

In discussing the factors affecting the gifted student as a future scientist, Brandwein writes:

[37] Galen W. Bull, The Activities and Backgrounds of Pupils with Dominant Science Interests," doctoral dissertation, University of Missouri, 1954, 366 pp. Abstract: *Dissertation Abstracts,* vol. 15, no. 1 (1955), p. 61.

Three factors are considered as being significant in the development of future scientists: a Genetic Factor, with a primary base in heredity (general intelligence, numerical ability, and verbal ability); a Predisposing Factor, with a primary base in functions which are psychological in nature; an Activating Factor, with a primary base in the opportunities offered in school and in the special skills of the teacher. High intelligence alone does not make a youngster a scientist.[38]

In addition to the use of multiple-track science curriculums, science clubs, and related extracurricular activities in the typical or comprehensive high school, larger cities have established special high schools for the talented student in science. The Bronx High School of Science in New York City administers a special admission test to prospective students. Besides offering the usual basic science courses, the curriculum includes more specialized courses such as clinical laboratory techniques, nutritional science, field biology, electronics, aeronautics, historical development of science, motor engines, qualitative analysis, science laboratory techniques, and other advanced courses. Many of the graduates from the Bronx High School of Science enter college with advanced standing as a result of the Placement Program of the College Entrance Examination Board.

Special classes based on ability grouping or interests in which a modified syllabus is used for the same, or almost the same, titled course may be observed in a few of the larger high schools. For example, Biology I is the usual biology course for all students except the talented. Biology IA or a similar designation may be employed for the special students. The IA course may include content that approaches college freshman level. A greater variety and more intensive materials are used in this course. Teachers and administrators are able to justify the pros and cons of this approach depending upon their local situation. There is no evidence based upon research to substantiate either claim. For a detailed account of two different ways in which high schools attempt to

[38] Paul F. Brandwein, *The Gifted Student as Future Scientist*, Harcourt, Brace & Company, 1955, p. xi.

meet the needs of the gifted student, the reader is referred to Paul F. Brandwein, "The Selection and Training of Future Scientists: A Plan for High Schools," and James H. Getty, "The Individual Project Method."[39]

Slow learners should present a challenge to the science teacher as the students in special or accelerated classes. In many junior high schools, students are grouped into classes according to their IQ's and/or reading ability scores. In some schools, mathematical ability may be another criterion in establishing homogeneous classes. The science teacher is faced with the problem of teaching science to a seventh- or eighth-grade class of youngsters where the IQ range may be from 80 to 95. It is reasonable to assume that the science syllabus for these classes should be less difficult and not as complete as the faster learners. But it is possible to make some rash assumptions that follow the previous one, for example, that a student with an IQ of 90 or 95 cannot learn the same science taught to the students in a class where the IQ range may be from 100 to 130. Another fallacious assumption might be that these slow learners are slow in learning all subjects. The implication here is that drive and pupil interest are insignificant. It would be incorrect to state that slow learners do not develop new interests in science or that because of some unusual stimulating learning activity that these pupils actually become interested in science. It is possible that a slow learner in English or social studies may become a fast learner in a topic or subject such as science. Many teachers have found that a youngster who has been slow in the beginning of the course has become one of the more talented students. It is therefore dangerous to label students with a stigma in which no intellectual or very little intellectual growth in science will occur.

In preparing a science curriculum for slow learners, average students, and the gifted, the teacher should observe that the curriculum, as good as it may be in meeting the needs of diversified groups, is no stronger than the teaching skill and artistry

[39] In R. Will Burnett (ed.), *Selected Science Teaching Ideas of 1952*, National Science Teachers Association, 1953.

displayed by the teacher. Curriculum and methods of teaching science are inseparable. The effective teaching techniques will be discussed in subsequent chapters. Samples of science curriculums will be presented in the following chapter.

Educational research in science suggests the serious limitations of grouping and teaching students on the sole basis of IQ. Although an adequate testing program by the school guidance counselor and the science teacher may be employed in screening and classifying slow, average, and fast learners, the teacher still needs to observe these pupils study, work, and learn if an effective program of science is to be taught. The teacher should be ready to modify the curriculum and instructional techniques to allow for pupil growth and development in understanding science. It may be true that there is no one best science curriculum for all students in one school or for all schools. Hence, we are ready to explore the basis for selecting and organizing a science program in the following chapter.

SUMMARY

The development of science courses may be traced from natural history with emphasis on "powers of observation" to natural sciences with emphasis on scientific thinking and problem-solving. At the turn of this century, general science was initiated in many states. Shortly thereafter, biology became a regular course which replaced individual courses in botany, zoology, and physiology. Later, physics and chemistry were integrated into a physical science course, especially designed for the nonscience majors. At present, many schools offer advanced science courses for the interested and talented student in science as well as applied science for students in vocational high schools.

In preparing science curriculums to meet the needs of youth today, objectives should be seriously considered, and appropriate content and learning experiences should be adopted. Emphasis should be placed on scientific problems and understandings that affect the individual in our contemporary society. Attempts should also be made to integrate and articulate the science curriculum from kindergarten through the twelfth grades. Evaluation of these new programs should also be made.

EXERCISES

1. Explain the various factors that were responsible for introducing courses such as general science and physical science in place of the more specialized individual science.
2. Discuss the advantages and limitations of teaching general science.
3. How have enrollment trends in the secondary schools influenced the enrollment in science courses?
4. What procedures should a school follow in designing or planning a new science curriculum?
5. How can a school and a science teacher in particular provide for the varied abilities and interests of students?
6. What are the criteria or guiding principles to be used in constructing a science curriculum?

SUGGESTED READINGS

Anderson, Kenneth E., "Adjuncts to Science Instruction," *School Science and Mathematics,* vol. 49 (June, 1949), pp. 475–476.

Barnard, J. Darrell (chmn.), *Rethinking Science Education,* Fifty-ninth Yearbook, National Society for the Study of Education, Chicago, University of Chicago Press, 1960.

Bloom, Samuel W., "The Search for Science Talent," *Science Education,* vol. 38 (April, 1954), pp. 232–236.

Brandwein, Paul F., *The Gifted Student as Future Scientist,* New York, Harcourt, Brace & Company, 1955.

Brandwein, Paul F., Watson, Fletcher G., and Blackwood, Paul E., *Teaching High School Science: A Book of Methods,* New York, Harcourt, Brace & Company, 1958, chaps. 8, 9, 10, 18.

Brown, Kenneth E., and Obourn, Ellsworth S., *Offerings and Enrollments in Science and Mathematics in Public High Schools, 1956,* Pamphlet No. 120, U.S. Department of Health, Education, and Welfare, 1957.

Burnett, R. Will, *Teaching Science in the Secondary School,* New York, Rinehart & Company, Inc., 1957, chaps. 3, 6, 14.

Burnett, R. Will (ed.), *Selected Science Teaching Ideas of 1952,*

Washington, D.C., National Science Teachers Association, 1953.

Dodson, Dan W., "Factors Influencing Curriculum Development," *Review of Educational Research,* vol. 27 (June, 1957), pp. 262–269.

Glidden, Harley F., "The Identification and Evaluation of Principles of Soil and Water Conservation for Inclusion in the Secondary School Curriculum," *Science Education,* vol. 40 (February, 1956), pp. 54–78.

Harris, Chester (ed.), *The Encyclopedia of Educational Research,* New York, The Macmillan Company, 1960.

Heiss, Elwood D., Obourn, Ellsworth S., Hoffman, Charles W., *Modern Science Teaching,* New York, The Macmillan Company, 1950, chap. 2.

Hunter, George W., *Science Teaching,* New York, American Book Company, 1934, chaps. 2, 11.

MacCurdy, Robert D., *Science Aptitude Inventory,* Gainesville, College of Education, University of Florida, 1957.

Miles, Vaden W., *A Determination of the Principles and Experiments Desirable for a High School Course of Integrated Physical Science,* Ann Arbor, Mich., Edwards Brothers, 1950, 430 pp.

New York City Board of Education, Bureau of Curriculum Research, "General Science—Grades 7–8–9, Course of Study and Syllabus," *Curriculum Report* (January, 1958).

Richardson, John S., *Science Teaching in Secondary Schools,* Englewood Cliffs, N.J., Prentice-Hall, Inc., 1957, chaps. 3, 9.

Smith, Herbert A., and Washton, Nathan S., "Science in the Secondary Schools," *Review of Educational Research,* vol. 27 (October, 1957), pp. 343–355.

Strauss, Samuel, "Looking Backward on Future Scientists," *The Science Teacher,* vol. 24 (December, 1957), pp. 385–387.

4

SELECTING AND ORGANIZING SCIENCE MATERIALS

CRITERIA FOR SELECTING MATERIALS

What kind of science content, materials, and experiences should students be given in the secondary schools? In many schools, the science teacher is given a syllabus or course of study to use as a basis for selecting and organizing the content in science. Most of these syllabuses and courses of study suggest that the teacher should feel free to augment and enrich the proposed curriculum. And yet, in several situations, the teacher may feel restrained and forced to follow the syllabus, almost word for word, topic for topic, which is not necessarily the most effective means of science teaching.

The degree of rigidity in a classroom or in a school frequently influences the flexibility employed by the teacher in selecting suitable science materials for instructional purposes. Published materials such as textbooks, syllabuses, periodicals, pamphlets, and other reading materials may serve as the basis for the teacher's selection of science content. Uniform or standardized examinations promote rigidity in teaching, especially if they are employed regularly and periodically. Highly specialized scientific interests based upon the training of the teacher may overemphasize certain aspects of the curriculum to the inadequate treatment of other science topics. For example, a biology major who is teaching general science may stress the biological content in the general science course and perhaps delete some of the principles in the physical sciences. Contemporary events (Sputnik, for example), newspaper headlines, pressure groups such as professional engineers, and other agencies may cause undue stress in terms of what the science teacher should select for everyday teaching. As a result, one can find nuclear equations introduced in the general science syllabus for youngsters in the eighth or ninth grades. Some individuals and groups are determined to teach many of these technical concepts regardless of whether all of the pupils are capable of learning these principles and facts on this grade level.

Even if a teacher feels compelled to follow the text and/or syllabus, the science teacher is still faced with the problem of day-to-day selection and organization of learning materials. During the past 40 years, several studies were conducted to help the teacher use a few guiding principles or criteria in selecting learning materials. A teacher should examine the objectives of teaching science, the needs of individual students, the needs of the community and the nation, student interests, and geographical factors.

Selection in Terms of Objectives

Chapter 2 contains several statements to explain why teachers teach science and why students should learn science. Chapter 3 traces the historical development of science courses in American secondary schools. There we found that at the beginning of the present century high school students who completed all of their graduation requirements entered a college or university. The science content was largely determined by the colleges. Most of the students who graduated from high schools were preparing for the ministry, law, engineering, medicine, or teaching. At the turn of this century, youngsters were not compelled to attend a senior high school. Many of them did not enter a junior high school. Hence, the students in the secondary schools of America then were highly selected students who knew their purpose was to enter a college and prepare for one of the professions. They were therefore able to accept whatever content was taught in science on the basis that it was required for admission to college. Reeder writes:

Today, practically every child of elementary school age is enrolled in school, but there is a large drop-out at the end of the elementary school. A large percentage of pupils who complete the elementary school do not enroll in secondary school, and of those pupils who enter secondary school only about two-fifths finish secondary school.[1] Since the majority of high school students do not enter college for lack of financial or intellectual ability or motivation, the college-preparatory objective of science education—which was true for almost all of the secondary school students in 1900—is no longer the major objective for all students.[2]

In teaching biology, botany, or zoology in the early 1900's it was most appropriate to have students spend hours in the classroom merely observing, classifying, and taking notes of their observations of a snail, a grasshopper, or a butterfly. Within the past 50 years, the biological scientists moved from taxonomic to experimental approaches in solving biological problems. Students in high school biology classes are required to learn more than the "powers of observation" today. Not all of the students are expected to become scientists. Yet science can make a real contribution toward better living for all citizens.

As a guide in selecting content and suitable learning experiences for senior high school courses in biology, chemistry, and physics, the Kalamazoo Public Schools adopted the following general objectives:

To help children gain ideals, understandings, and skills essential to becoming good citizens in a modern scientific world by developing:

Understandings of
Man's relationship in his environment.
How man changes and controls his environment.
Relationship of science to the health and safety of the world.
Materials needed and the services used by modern society.
Responsibility of modern society toward conservation of world's physical resources.
Value of science in successful vocational and avocational interests.

[1] Ward G. Reeder, *A First Course in Education,* New York, The Macmillan Company, 1958, p. 18.
[2] See Francis H. Horn, "Liberal Education Re-examined," *Harvard Educational Review,* vol. 26 (Fall, 1956), pp. 303–314.

Skills

Reading, writing, and arithmetic essential for gaining necessary information.

Seeing things accurately.

Listening intelligently.

Speaking effectively.

Sensing problems and solving them scientifically.

Developing thinkers—fair in judgment—accurate—free of prejudice and superstition.

Planning, executing, and evaluating experiences.

Attitudes

Appreciation of beauty in natural surroundings, in plant life, and in animal life.

Responsibility for preservation of wildlife—trees, flowers, and birds.

Willingness to use reliable resources and evaluate those resources.

Open-mindedness to new ideas and opinions of others.

Harmonious group activities toward a desired end.

Careful investigation and observation before drawing conclusions.

Relying on evidence rather than propaganda, tradition, hearsay, or superstitious beliefs.[3]

In attempting to determine the objectives of science education as a result of an extensive analysis of articles and sections of books, Feaster Wolford in his doctoral study, "Methods in Determining Types of Content for a Course of Study for Eighth-Grade Science in the High Schools of the Southern Appalachian Region," concluded:

1. Educators seem universally agreed . . . that the objectives of education should be based upon an analysis of the activities of life, but there is a difference of opinion as to what to include in the analysis. Most educators would use as a basis the things individuals do, but some would have as a basis what individuals should do in a well-ordered society.

2. Several authorities seem to emphasize the utilitarian value of

[3] Kalamazoo Public Schools, Curriculum Department, "Tentative Resource Guide in Science, Senior High School Biology, Chemistry and Physics," mimeographed bulletin (September, 1955).

education by emphasizing the development of knowledges and skills in order to perform the activities met in everyday life. Others emphasize the importance of developing the personality of the individual through the creating of proper attitudes, habits, interests, standards, and ideals.

3. There is no general agreement as to the character of objectives for science in the junior high school, but most authorities emphasize the ideas of exploration, stimulation, guidance, and adjustment to the environment. There appears to be no conclusive method of evaluating objectives. . . .

4. In courses of study the specific objectives for science are not always in harmony with the general objectives.[4]

Although this study was made in 1935, similar conclusions would probably be formulated if such a study were to be repeated today. Wolford's study raises the important question of the needs of individual students in terms of what they actually do or what they ought to do, now or in the future.

Needs of Individual Students

If a student has a bicycle, he may have a need for learning that gases expand upon heating. The real fulfillment of the student's need does not occur until an application of this scientific concept is made to a pupil's problem. One morning when the temperature has dropped to zero, a student notices that his bicycle tires are almost flat. Does he know that the sudden drop in temperature has caused a change in the pressure and volume of the air in the tires? The pupil's need for the ability to solve this problem—in which an understanding of the gas laws is required in order for him to indulge in such overt behavior as putting more air in the tires—may serve the teacher as an indicator of science content, materials, and experiences which can be used effectively. The selection of science content based on student needs usually promotes greater learning of science. The teacher aware of the needs of individual students can adapt a syllabus to specific applications

---

[4] Abstract in Francis D. Curtis, *Third Digest of Investigations in the Teaching of Science,* Blakiston Company, 1939, pp. 47–48.

that will increase retention and understanding of scientific principles.

Some educators will interpret needs of the future. Although some pupils do not have bicycles, a teacher may justify the need for this information in terms of the day when the pupils own automobiles and are faced with similar problems. There is a place for selecting science content in terms of present and future pupil needs. Wherever possible, however, selecting and planning science activities according to the present or immediate needs of students should prove more satisfying to them. As a consequence, learning will be in accord with the principle of readiness in learning and will be more effective.

Students need to understand and to be able to use scientific knowledge pertaining to light—for example, that dark-colored objects will absorb more heat from the sun than light-colored objects. A science teacher may approach the teaching of the lesson by presenting a problem: What color clothing should you wear on a very hot summer afternoon if you wish to dress comfortably?

Most secondary school students are consumers of cosmetics, dentifrices, and other advertised personal products. A good understanding of selected science experiences and their applications to pupil consumer needs can help them become more intelligent consumers.

Another category of pupil needs as viewed by adults or teachers concerns the misconceptions, fallacies, and superstitions held about scientific information by large numbers of students. For example, in a health information inventory administered to 250 high school sophomores by Dzenowagis, McPherson, and Irwin, 25 percent subscribed to 111 of 126 harmful health and safety misconceptions.[5] Students should be provided with scientific knowledge to correct their fallacious beliefs.

Students can develop scientific attitudes and give up their superstitions if science experiences are selected and the teacher teaches

[5] Joseph G. Dzenowagis, P. V. McPherson, and L. W. Irwin, "Harmful Health and Safety Misconceptions of a Group of Tenth-Grade Girls," *Journal of School Health,* vol. 24 (November, 1954), pp. 240–245.

directly for this objective. This procedure is advocated on the basis of several investigations.[6] For example, a student in class insists that a rabbit's foot in his pocket brings him good luck. Pupil-teacher planning and activity could test this superstition by having half of the class carry the rabbit's foot for one week. A daily log of what happens to each of the pupils during the week should prove useful when classroom reports and discussions follow. By way of further example, a student needs to know that not all people become ill when they eat ice cream with pickles or whatever the suspect combination of foods may be. The student's original belief may be due to an attitude, misconception, or superstition. The science teacher who promotes a good discussion in class in which pupil experiences and anecdotes are used will help dispel fallacious ideas and poor attitudes.

An out-of-school interest such as membership in the Boy or Girl Scouts or the 4-H Clubs may cause a pupil to need certain kind of information. Merit badges pertaining to nature study, health, and science that are offered by the Scouting program may start as pupil interests and then become needs or vice versa. Woodburn pointed to a vital problem in his study—"determining whether or not the content and the level of experiences offered the students in the ninth-grade science course should be adjusted according to the extent to which these students have participated in other experiences prior to being enrolled in the course."[7] He found that pupils who had previous out-of-school experiences such as are offered by Scouting and other agencies scored higher grades on the Read General Science Test.

In providing for the needs of individual pupils, the general

---

[6] See Glenn M. Blair and Max R. Goodson, "Development of Scientific Thinking Through General Science," *School Review,* vol. 47 (November, 1939), pp. 695–701; Warren F. Geyer, "Functional Chemistry in the Junior High School," *Science Education,* vol. 24 (December, 1940), pp. 264–269; Cyril H. Hancock, "An Evaluation of Certain Popular Science Misconceptions," *Science Education,* vol. 24 (April, 1940), pp. 208–213; Cal McMelly, "An Experiment in the Use of Free Reading in General Science," *Science Education,* vol. 25 (January, 1941), pp. 7–9.

[7] John H. Woodburn, "Relationship Between the Science Information Possessed by Ninth-Grade General Science Students and Certain School and Out-Of-School Science Experiences," *Science Education,* vol. 39 (March, 1955), p. 164.

science teacher should determine their backgrounds in both knowledge and experience and select appropriate materials for science instruction. Otherwise he may discover, for example, that his ninth-grade pupils are finding science extremely dull simply because they are covering science concepts studied in an earlier grade. The science teacher can administer pretests on science information and inventories of previous experiences related to science in order to select stimulating science activity for the students.

A good science teacher will constantly re-examine the basis for selecting, organizing, and teaching specific materials to meet the needs of the class and the individual students. Cohen and Watson write:

> Rather than presenting the exciting adventure that science should be, all too many of our secondary schools tend to teach the student how to solve a limited number of numerical problems, ask him to memorize formulas and definitions, and generally overload his mind with dogmatic assertions—while the great adventure of logical deduction, concept formation, and theory construction never enters the classroom. It is no wonder that so many of our students, their minds offended by rote learning, come to us with open hostility for, and even hatred of, science.[8]

If an evaluation of science content is made regularly as part of instructional procedure, there would be little basis for fear and hysteria as a result of Sputniks.

Needs of the Community and Nation

The newspapers recently gave much publicity to the national shortage of engineers and scientists. On a few occasions, some articles gave the impression that it was almost a bright pupil's duty to become a scientist or an engineer. There were conflicting reports as to the respective quality and quantity of science training in Russia and in the United States. Some educators maintained that the entire science program in the American public schools

---

[8] I. Bernard Cohen and Fletcher G. Watson, *General Education in Science,* Harvard University Press, 1952.

should be overhauled as a result of Sputnik. The need for caution in this regard is noted by Rice in his recent report on trends in curriculum and instruction in science:

Today, during the period of anxiety, we need to be cautious in the bringing about [of] any drastic changes in the secondary school science programs. The future scientists will receive their inspirations and desire to study and develop from their teachers. The manner in which the teachers handle the recent developments in science and the extent to which they are truly interested in their students will bring about the gradual changes which are essential to permanent growth.[9]

Society would not want all people to become engineers or scientists. It is, however, the function of a science teacher to give guidance and counsel to those students who show an interest and ability in becoming scientists. The teacher carries out guidance through group discussions, class activities in which reports on various scientific professions are made, and personal conferences with the students to discuss their vocational plans. Professional scientific organizations make available much free literature outlining the requirements of educational training, the necessary knowledges and skills, the nature of work, and the opportunities for financial and professional advancement in the various scientific professions. Pupil visits and talks with local industrial scientists, physicians, nurses, science professors, and medical technology personnel can provide pupils with many helpful answers. Science teachers can arrange to have summer job opportunities available for some of their science-oriented students in various kinds of scientific industries that would be an integral part of the total guidance program. Through effective guidance and counseling procedures, the science teacher can guide the best future scientists into scientific careers and help meet one of the needs of the community and of the nation.

To meet this basic need, science content and experiences should be selected and well organized both for the junior and senior high

[9] Roy C. Rice, "Trends in Curriculum and in Instruction in the Physical Sciences of the Secondary Schools," *Science Education,* vol. 42 (April, 1958), p. 243.

school levels. A unit of instruction entitled "Careers in Science" might well be offered in the eighth or ninth grades. Pupils could survey occupational information about the various types of scientific careers through reading, reporting, consulting, and visiting. A general collection of such information could be made within a given community. On the senior high school level, a more specific unit of instruction can be prepared covering careers in the field being studied, as, for example, those in biology, chemistry, physics, and earth science respectively. The purpose of this guidance is not to influence all or the majority of the students to select a scientific profession. The aim is to enable students to think of the possible opportunities that may be available to some of them, provided they have the interest, the ability, and the sense of feeling that they would be happy working in the chosen profession. This guidance program should carry through from the junior high school into college. Science teachers can work with the school guidance counselor to conduct periodic follow-up studies to determine the effectiveness of the procedures employed by the teacher and the school.

Communities and the nation are very much concerned with the conservation of natural resources. An excellent reference on this topic was prepared by Kasling for use by junior high school pupils.[10] The study contains helpful suggestions, pupil activities, pictures, illustrations, motion picture sources, and the principles of science and social studies. A conservation unit specifically for seventh-grade teachers was prepared by Brown.[11] Included in this unit are sections on forest, soil, water, and wildlife conservation. Unfortunately, no one approach or method of teaching has been found which guarantees to change the behavior of students so that they will not waste water, food, and other resources. A student can have learned how to conserve a given substance, but fail to

[10] Robert W. Kasling, "Cooperating with Nature; A Reference Book of the Conservation of Natural Resources Prepared for the Junior High School Level," doctoral dissertation, New York University, 1954, 415 pp.

[11] Donald G. Brown, "A Resource Unit on the Conservation of Natural Resources for the Course in Washington State History, Government, Industries, and Resources for the 7th Grade of the Shumway Junior High School," master's thesis, University of Washington, 1954, 374 pp.

practice the actual conservation of the resources. This still remains a challenge to the science and social studies teachers.

Since the nation and the community need to conserve natural resources, the science teacher should select those materials that contribute toward a better realization of the importance of all aspects of conservation. The science teacher can promote pupil activity such as a visit to the local game warden, a study of the requirements of hunting and fishing licenses, an examination and discussion of laws that protect certain animals and fish, an excursion to a nearby farm to learn about erosion and its prevention, an investigation of the community water supply and its treatment. Many schools have recognized the value of selecting for instructional purposes science materials that are centered around community needs and problems. Favorable results were reported in a follow-up study of 225 students when a high school chemistry course offered community problems such as food supply, science in agriculture, and control of the water supply.[12] Banner wrote:

. . . conservation is, in part, a way of looking at Man's relationship to his natural resource environment; that teachers can incorporate conservation education into their school activities with the knowledge they already have, if they desire to do so; and that they will do this if they are interested, if they feel that it is important to do so. It implies that it is easy to start teaching conservation if the proper state of mind exists. If this attitude exists, teachers will transmit interest and awareness in their classroom and community activities.[13]

Another approach that can be employed in identifying, selecting, and evaluating scientific principles for inclusion in the secondary school curriculum was developed by Glidden.[14] Knowing a specific community and national need, such as soil and water conservation, scientific principles can be selected in terms of publications and an evaluation of these printed materials made by specialists. The need for teaching principles of soil and water conservation is stated by Glidden:

---

[12] Warren P. Everote, "Term Problems in Secondary School Science," *Science Education,* vol. 27 (February, 1943), pp. 33–36.

[13] Gilbert Banner, "A Study of Certain Factors Involved in Conservation Education," *Science Education,* vol. 38 (March, 1954), p. 167.

In the past four decades, two World Wars and huge military defense programs have resulted in a tremendous drain on the natural resources of the world and most especially on those of the United States. Concurrent with the defense program following World War II, and the "police" action in Korea, the United States has "enjoyed" an immense business expansion program in an attempt to supply consumer goods for a hungry market and to supply manufactured goods, food, and textile products to war-ravished countries of the world. To meet such needs natural resources in huge quantity are required.[14]

Glidden lists 66 principles of conservation which he suggests should be taught in secondary schools, utilizing carefully selected printed materials, specialists in conservation, education, and science education; the analysis of materials to determine principles; the statistical analysis of evaluations of the principles; and the use of tests and further analysis:

1. Strong nations and high standards of living are possible only if there are ample supplies of water.
2. Soil without water is nonproductive.
3. When soil is conserved, water is likewise saved.
4. In the arid regions the struggle for existence is to a large extent a struggle for water.
5. A well-managed watershed is so developed that the runoff does not carry soil particles with it, but permits snow and rain water to penetrate the soil which acts as a reservoir. This ground water slowly moves through the soil to stream channels, providing a continuous flow of water throughout the year.
6. Most natural watersheds are multiple resource lands; in addition to water they yield crops, forage, recreation, wildlife, and timber. Proper watershed treatment benefits all of the several resources.
7. Water is a resource that is not destroyed by use; the same supply is usable for recreation, propagation of wildlife, development of power, and irrigation of crops.
8. Rain water that runs off the land into creeks and rivers has no value for growing crops locally, although it may be valuable

---

[14] Harley F. Glidden, "The Identification and Evaluation of Principles of Soil and Water Conservation for Inclusion in the Secondary School Curriculum," *Science Education,* vol. 40 (February, 1956), pp. 54.

downstream. It is the water that goes into the ground that grows crops and is available later to tide those crops through a drought.

9. It is wiser and less costly to hold back water at its source through good watershed management, thus reducing or preventing floods, than it is to fight floods and clean up the wreckage.

10. Efficient water conservation practice requires the combination of appropriate watershed management upstream and artificial flood controls downstream.

11. Wet soils can be improved by plowing under green manures and crop residue to make the soil porous so that air can circulate through it, thus providing drainage and drying qualities; dry soils, too, can be improved by plowing under green manures and crop residues; thus adding humus and increasing moisture-holding capacity.

12. Silt carried from abused watersheds makes necessary costly repeated dredging of navigable stream channels and harbors, destroys the habitat of valuable game fish, and shortens the useful life of reservoirs.

13. Great quantities of the best topsoil are loosened by the driving force of raindrops as they strike uncovered soils. The steeper the slope the more serious is the erosive action.

14. Hard rains do great damage to unprotected soil. This means that the farmer must prepare for the worst rains; he must protect uncovered soils by planting grass crops and grassed waterways, by contouring, terracing, and strip cropping if the battle against erosion is to be won.

15. Soil erosion may be reduced or controlled by maintaining vegetative cover and by mechanical practices of land management.

16. Drainage practices have eliminated many natural swamps and lakes which acted as reservoirs for the slow release of water.

17. The practice of water conservation is the best insurance against drought damage in many dry-farming areas.

18. Conservation of irrigated land results in savings in water and labor, prevention of seepage and toxic salt accumulations, better crop yields, and assurance of continued productivity.

19. Farm ponds properly fenced provide a good water supply for fire protection, for garden irrigation, for stock watering, and for refuge for wildlife, as well as providing for recreation such as swimming and fishing.

20. The decay of vegetative litter and animal remains builds soil from the top down.
21. There is an unceasing movement of material between the upper and lower layers of soil. Rainfall or irrigation water passes downward through the porous spaces carrying materials with it, both in solution and in suspension. During drought, the movement is reversed and the moisture rises, either through evaporation or capillary action. Thus the air is alternately drawn in and forced out, causing the soil to breathe.
22. In nature's cycle the plants are returned to the land when they die. Thus the cycle of minerals from the soil to the plant and back to the soil is unbroken and fertility is maintained, provided there is no loss by erosion or fire. When man interrupts nature's cycle by the removal of crops, he then must return the minerals and organic matter as they are depleted.
23. Good soil, the basis for physical existence and a necessity for growing abundant crops, is mineral soil to which has been added the decayed plant and animal matter and the microorganisms referred to as humus or organic matter.
24. The soil on which all life depends lies in a thin surface layer of an average depth of approximately seven or eight inches over the face of the land.
25. Quality and quantity of life depends on the productivity of soil.
26. Healthy soil is necessary to produce healthful food for healthy bodies; if the necessary nutrients are deficient in the soil, they are also lacking in the foods grown on that soil for man's consumption.
27. When erosion is accelerated by human practices so that plant nutrients are eroded away with the topsoil or are leached out faster than they are replaced, the resulting depletion of fertility literally threatens life, including human life, with extinction.
28. The thin layer of the most productive topsoil on insufficiently vegetated sloping land is loosened and part of it lost by every hard rain.
29. Muddy water running off a field is positive evidence of harmful erosion.
30. Erosion is nearly always preceded by the advanced depletion or total loss of the protective layer of vegetation on the surface.

31. Vegetative cover is reduced in plant vigor and density and is eventually removed by overgrazing.
32. When its cover is removed by overgrazing or by unwise cultivation, the soil becomes more compact and soil organisms die. Thus this soil dries out and packs down, losing its porosity and fertility and resisting the entry of water. This is a primary step in the process of erosion.
33. When soil is used for the production of crops, it is progressively robbed of both organic and inorganic materials, thus depleting its fertility. Adequate amounts of manures and chemical fertilizers must be added to replace those materials used by the crops.
34. Contour plowing or other farming operations that follow the contour create numerous small dams and furrows which are level (contour) across the field. These all act to cause the water to stay where it falls.
35. Building terraces or ridges on the contour (level) at right angles to the slope of the ground provides a channel or reservoir for water on their upper side which permits the depositing of washed soil close to its origin.
36. Strip cropping or alternating strips of grass and legumes across the slope of the land helps to stabilize the soil, thus reducing soil movement by wind or water, and aids in adding organic matter to the soil.
37. Terraces properly constructed across a slope following the contour provide a mechanical means to stop runoff water and silt, diverting it into the terrace channel where the water moves slowly. Strips of grass or other close-growing crops between the cultivated crop strips supplement the terraces by helping to slow the water and by catching the silt before it gets into the terrace channel.
38. Generally, steep slopes of hills should be permanently in grass or trees to prevent them from excessive erosion.
39. The most important single factor in preventing erosion by both wind and water is the production and maintenance of as nearly complete vegetative cover for the soil as possible.
40. A complete and permanent retreat to only grass production is impractical unless man is willing to revert to a primitive, animal ex-

istence; so a compromise must be made by keeping protective vegetative cover on the soil as much as possible between growing seasons and by using the land not suitable for cultivated crops for grass and trees only.

41. A good crop rotation aids in keeping the cover on the soil, helps maintain the fertility and organic matter and nitrogen content of the soil through the use of legumes and grasses, and helps control plant diseases.

42. Grasses provide one of the best means for enriching the soil and controlling erosion because of their root and stem structure, resistance to adverse conditions, and their dense growth.

43. Planting belts of trees at right angles to the prevailing wind so that the winds are thrown upward reduces the wind velocity locally and prevents a sweeping surge of air across the soil's surface.

44. Living fences that act as a shelter belt, protecting crops and other vegetation from wind and providing cover for wildlife, might profitably take the place of other types of fences in some areas of the United States.

45. In the control of water erosion, all applied measures have the dual purpose of (1) reducing the amount of runoff to the minimum and (2) controlling the irreducible minimum to such an extent as to cause the least possible soil loss.

46. Both forest and grass land possess enormous value as a regulator of water flow.

47. Natural waterways on a farm should be in permanent grasses and used either for pasture or hay.

48. Gullying can be controlled, if not in an advanced stage, by permanent vegetative cover both in the gully and on the watershed, sometimes needing to be aided at the start by brush dams or other suitable mechanical means to give the appropriate vegetation a chance.

49. Planting adapted forage grasses on badly depleted range land rather than waiting for natural recovery, when properly done, results in much quicker recovery and better yields of forage.

50. Crop waste, when plowed under, feeds helpful bacteria and increases the amount of humus.

51. As long as topsoil remains, plant nutrients can be restored or sup-

plemented through the addition of manure and commercial fertilizer and by growing of grasses and legumes in rotation.

52. Both barnyard and green manures, as well as chemical fertilizers for mineral replenishment, are essential to high crop yields favorable to soil conservation.

53. Incalculable loss of nutritional elements occurs in the method of disposal of sewage and garbage by towns and cities and in the wasteful practices in the handling of farm manures. These wastes contain those elements in the organic forms most readily incorporated in the topsoil and assimilable by most plants.

54. All conservation practices should have as one of their primary aims the maintenance and renewal of organic matter which supplies humus and plant nutrients to the soil.

55. Frontier land or undeveloped land suitable for agricultural purposes no longer exists, so the trend in agriculture must be to make the best use of the land we have through a much wider application of conservation practices and continued improvement of machinery, plant life, livestock, and soil through the efforts of science.

56. The time has come when plant breeding must be widely applied to all crops including trees, for trees permit us to use many of our untillable lands to better advantage than do annual plants or grasses.

57. Conservation and flood control measures must be planned for each field and farm to fit the overall problem of conservation.

58. The conservation of soil and water is not a project that can be completed, but it is a continuous job—a method of farming.

59. Productive industries in the nations of today's world are necessary, but productive agriculture is absolutely essential.

60. Deterioration of soil is the same in effect as a reduction in the amount of land.

61. Each acre of land should be used according to its capabilities and treated according to its needs to protect it from depletion and to secure the greatest returns.

62. Pastures, both permanent and rotation, need good soil the same as other crops and should be treated as needed with fertilizers.

63. Man upsets the natural balance and influences the character of soil through plowing, cultivating, harvesting, deforestation, irrigation, manuring, and farming practices generally.

64. In a given land area, topography, soil composition, and climatic conditions are selective factors in determining suitable crop types.
65. Every farm, no matter where it is located geographically or how its land lies, would benefit from the use of conservation practices.
66. Farm land must not only be preserved, but it must be improved so it can produce the additional food required for the increasing population of the nation and the world.[15]

It is not suggested that all of these principles be taught in all secondary schools throughout the country. To meet the needs of the local community, rural areas may demand that their students understand and practice these principles pertaining to conservation. But in urban localities, students and the community may not have a great need for some of these principles. Bearing in mind the foregoing considerations, the science teacher should carefully study the needs of the community and the nation in order to determine which principles or understandings of science should be taught.

Student Interests and Geographical Factors

Students in the junior high school develop new interests and may expand their existing interests in science. Factors that modify pupil interests in science are: the instruction by the science teacher and his impact upon the pupil, pupil hobbies, reading or not reading scientific literature, clubs, parental encouragement, similar interests maintained by friends, and many varied environmental factors that change with our technology. For example, rockets, missiles, earth satellites, and space travel will influence pupil interest in science.

One of the criteria that is employed by the science teacher in the selection and organization of content is pupil interest. This does not mean that the entire science curriculum is based solely on pupil interest. It is a beginning or an approach to the introduction of a new unit or topic which should lead to the development of other interests. A student may be highly interested in photography. The teacher is aware of this interest and seeks to determine how he can use this interest in developing new inter-

[15] *Ibid.*, pp. 54–78.

ests and extending the present one. The teacher plans to intro-duce the teaching of weather. The science teacher may suggest to this student that he can make a significant contribution to the class if he will bring in several photographs of different types of cloud formations. Another student has been interested in meteor-ology before this unit of instruction is introduced to the class. He has a barometer and a thermometer at home. The teacher can help this student construct other instruments such as a rain gauge to deepen and extend his interests and knowledge in science. One of the students is busily engaged at home with model airplanes. This activity can be guided into a genuine understanding of weather phenomena in relationship to aviation.

There are many ways in which pupil interests in science, if used effectively by the teacher, can serve as springboards to further learning in science. Page reported the following findings concern-ing the factors that influenced 60 high school seniors in becoming interested in science:[16] (1) Although most of the students indi-cated that their interests were initiated in the seventh grade, science interests actually originated from preschool up to and including the senior year; (2) The science teacher first and the general sci-ence course second were the order of importance in causing pupils to develop science interest; few of the students rated the general science course as the best-liked course; (3) When father supplied youngsters with good science books and magazines, interest in science was increased; (4) Hobbies and out-of-school work per-taining to science were significant factors. The students also sug-gested that more laboratory work in biology, chemistry, and physics would improve the course. Some of the significant implications of this study indicate that the teacher of general science plays a vital role in determining whether or not students develop interests in science. More extensive use of science reading materials and lab-oratory work are vital for continued interest in science. Where seventh-grade students enter a general science course without any

[16] Allen D. Page, "A Study to Determine How High School Seniors Become Interested in Science," unpublished doctoral dissertation, University of Wisconsin, 1954.

interest, the teacher can help generate interests by giving pupils the opportunity of carrying out, constructing, and testing scientific ideas.

On the basis of 9689 high school senior questionnaire responses in a 5 percent sample of the public high schools in the United States, Stice, Torgerson and Mollenkopf noted that lack of interest and lack of finances equally contribute to the loss of up to one half of the top 30 percent of the nation's high school seniors to the colleges.[17] About 39 percent of those interested and with financial ability indicated that they wanted to enter scientific careers as follows: engineering—25 percent of the boys; medicine —8 percent; physical scientists—6 percent. Several other studies also indicate the importance of student interest in relation to scientific careers.[18] The science teacher, therefore, has the responsibility of using pupil interests not only in the selection and organization of science content but also in nourishing this continued interest so as to promote the potentiality of capable students as scientists.

Geographical factors are considered by curriculum specialists and science teachers in selecting science problems, topics, or activities. In general science and biology syllabuses constructed for metropolitan or urban areas far removed from agricultural areas, for example, one seldom finds a reference to contour plowing or other farming operations. Within a given locality, the teacher determines the most suitable experiences for the students. As an illustration, the teacher knows that pupils who live in a tenement area are not likely to have an opportunity to cultivate plants on a large scale. Nevertheless, it is possible for a miniature nursery to be cultivated in the science classroom and for students to plant certain seeds in flower boxes at home.

Schools are frequently located near zoos, museums, scientific industries, health stations, radio and television studios, hospitals,

---

[17] Glen Stice, Warren Torgerson, and William Mollenkopf, "A National Study of High School Students and Their Plans," reported in C. C. Cole, Jr., *Encouraging Scientific Talent,* College Entrance Examination Board, 1956, pp. 139–169.

[18] Sylvia S. Neivert, "Identification of Students with Science Potential," unpublished doctoral dissertation, Teachers College, Columbia University, 1955.

and other agencies that offer worthwhile science experiences. These community resources should constitute an important part of the selected learning materials in teaching science.

CRITERIA FOR ORGANIZING MATERIALS

Logical Versus Psychological Approach

The science teacher is always faced with the problem of organizing the content and learning activities which have been selected to develop the objectives. Some general science textbooks begin with the nature of matter because the author or editor believes this is a logical approach to the introduction of science. Some teachers believe this is the best way to organize a beginning science course. Among the reasons given for the so-called logical sequence is that unless students are given a basic understanding of the nature of matter, it becomes difficult to teach subsequent concepts pertaining to energy, chemical changes and more "advanced" ideas. In some biology classes, teachers maintain that the study of the cell is the most logical way to organize instruction. This conviction is based on the assumption that a knowledge of the cell is basic to understanding other principles of biology. In physics and chemistry classes, it is common to observe that the nature of matter and energy usually is introduced at the beginning of the year through a series of definitions. On the other hand, many syllabuses in the sciences approach the organization of science topics or units in quite different ways.

Other topics used to introduce a science course are air, water, how the scientists work, the human machine, and others. Each teacher who organizes the sequence of topics usually can justify through rationalization, for example, that beginning a ninth-grade science course with air is the most logical approach to organizing the syllabus. What is logical in terms of organizing science materials for one teacher may be illogical for another. The important task is to organize instructional materials and use them effectively in accordance with sound, psychological principles of learning. At present, there is no available research which supports the conviction that a particular topic in a given sequential arrangement is superior to other topics in science.

Simple-to-Complex Versus Known-to-Unknown

By definition, the cell is the simplest unit of structure and function in living organisms, and hence, many biology teachers organize a course with this concept as the introduction. Some teachers will carry this meaning further in suggesting it is the simplest way to begin teaching biology. These people maintain that the human organism should appear toward the end of the course because it is more complex. Perhaps the significant question is, For whom is it simple—the teacher or the student? Many students struggle to see a cell through the microscope and may not be in a position to see all that the teacher wishes the student to see.

A few biology teachers prefer to organize the beginning of the course through a study of the biological processes in the human organism. Their conviction is that students are more familiar with the human body than with the cell. Therefore, the selected science materials should be organized on the basis of beginning with what is known to the pupils and continuing with the unknown.

In either case, the teacher can justify the organization of science content through rationalization. The principle underlying the organization of science experiences for students is that effective learning is developed through the use of sound principles of psychology rather than through rationalization. Some of these sound principles of learning based on research are: scientific information should be meaningful and significant; learning materials should be related wherever possible to pupil experiences; audio-visual aids are used for more effective learning; the need for motivation should arise from within the learner; for maximum achievement in science, pupils' social and emotional needs must be taken into account by the teacher.

Nature of Content and Learning Experiences

In addition to organizing the various units or major topics of instruction from the overall point of view in a given sequence, the science teacher is faced with the daily problem of organizing in-structional materials for a daily lesson. Equal attention is focused upon the arrangement of suitable learning experiences within a given unit of instruction which may represent one or more weeks of teaching. The nature of the science content to be taught is an important determinant of the type of organization of instruction. If heredity is to be taught, requiring such understandings as Mendelian inheritance, haploidy and diploidy relationships, sex-linkage, and crossing-over, then the teacher will organize the material in order to teach reproduction, oogenesis, and spermato-genesis first. This organization is based upon the simple-to-complex where pupils need to know that sex cells are formed in order to understand more complex phenomena as genetic changes within the sex cell. On the other hand, if the teacher in a general science class does not demand that pupils understand such ideas as the mechanics of heredity, the organization does not necessarily re-quire that reproduction precede heredity. The important question to be answered by the teacher is: What basic understandings of science must students possess before I can present new scientific concepts?

The organization and selection of science materials for instruc-tional purposes will vary from teacher to teacher, class to class, school to school. In physical science classes a teacher may prefer to begin with atomic energy rather than mechanics. Within a given topic or unit, some teachers may begin by referring to a newspaper item pertaining to atomic blasts or radioactive fall-out as a basis for stimulating learning in this unit. Another teacher may prefer to initiate learning by performing a demonstration such as the de-tection of radioactive materials through the use of a Geiger counter. A different approach will introduce the pupils to a very stimulating motion picture film on atomic energy to be followed by a lively discussion. In a traditional manner, it is typical to find that many teachers use a model of a given atom as a basis for de-veloping the several concepts about atomic energy. A few teachers will use previous pupil readings and experiences such as visits to plants to initiate learning. Basic criteria to be used in selecting and organizing science materials for effective instruction include significant contemporary issues and discoveries in science; pupil needs and interests; the degree of emphasis on specific objectives such as behavioral changes, attitudes, and knowledge; the type of resources available in the community; pupil readiness and motivation to learn; the needs of the community and the nation; the background and experience of the science teacher; the ability to keep abreast with scientific discoveries; and the kind of initiative and resourcefulness employed by the science teacher.

The teacher knows *what* and *how* to teach. Content in science and methodology are inseparable. Hence, school systems will utilize their faculty, supervisors, and consultants in developing a whole sequence in science from kindergarten through the twelfth grades. As an illustration of curriculum development and the kinds of learning activities that are offered in science, reference is made to the recent circular issued by the Portland, Oregon, Public Schools.[19] Since 1950, annual reports presenting a description of progress, plans, evaluation, and committee activity have been made available to all of the staff members in the school system. These reports are invaluable to beginning and experienced science teachers. Some of the materials listed in the circular are: curriculum guides, resource units, elementary principal's file, science books, workshop areas, science kits, supplies and equipment for all schools, objectives and evaluation devices, bulletins, instructional materials department, student opportunities, radio programs, museums, zoos, and the like.

THE UNIT PLAN

The most widely accepted basis for organizing learning materials for a particular science course is called the unit. There may be as few as three or four or as many as fifteen units of instruction in a given science course. Some of the units taught in a general science course are: Health and the Human Body, The Earth and the

---

[19] Portland Public Schools, *Annual Science Progress Report,* Curriculum Publication SC—IR, mimeographed, 1958–1959.

Universe, Obtaining and Improving Our Food Supply, Natural Resources, Matter and Energy, The Atomic World, Transportation and Communication.

The trend has been to teach *units* rather than to emphasize the memorization of isolated or unrelated facts. In teaching a unit, many related facts and experiences are organized around a major topic, central theme, or problem. Some units may be taught in one week; others may require several weeks, depending upon the unit and the kind of learning activities that are planned cooperatively by both pupils and teacher.

Klohr found that in reorganization of the science curriculum resource units are effective aids for improving science instruction.[20] He suggested that scientific data and facts should be included where they contribute toward an understanding of a broad area of experience. The study plan for a broad area of learning is known as a *resource unit*. A resource unit is more comprehensive than a teaching unit in that it contains information and suggested learning materials that may be adapted to different classes and geographical areas. As the name implies, it lists many resources that may be used for teaching purposes in a flexible way. The teaching unit constitutes the actual materials used and taught. The teacher selects the most appropriate learning activities from the resource unit.

In developing the syllabus for a science course, each unit should list an outline of objectives, concepts, principles, applications, questions, pupil and teacher activities, reading materials, and audiovisual aids such as motion picture films and filmstrips. The following sample of a unit on astronomy was employed by the Detroit Public Schools:

GENERALIZATIONS

Space is vast; the universe includes everything in the heavens.

The solar system is a part of the Milky Way Galaxy; there are many galaxies in the universe.

The earth is a very small part of the universe.

[20] Paul Robert Klohr, "A Study of the Role of the Resource Unit in the Curriculum Reorganization of Selected Secondary Schools," *Abstracts of Doctoral Dissertations, 1947–48,* No. 57, Ohio State University, 1949, pp. 111–160.

Gravitation has a great effect upon the movements of bodies in the universe.

Distances in space seem extremely vast when compared with distances on earth.

Units of time are defined by the earth's movements in relation to the sun.

The use of scientific method has made it possible to gain much accurate information about the universe.

The earth's position in relation to the sun and moon is a determining factor of life on earth.

Much knowledge about the universe has been discovered—much remains to be discovered.

I. Introduction

"One of the greatest intellectual achievements of the human race is the understanding of the nature of the stars and planets and their motions."

Carl Leo Stearns, Wesleyan University

II. Goals and Concepts to Be Established

A. Goals

To develop an appreciation of the unity and magnitude of the solar system and man's place in it.

To create a permanent interest in the wonders of the universe.

To develop a respect for the men of science who have given and are supplying man with knowledge about our solar system.

To develop a spirit of scientific acceptance of explanations of physical phenomena rather than a belief in superstitions and unscientific facts.

To gain a knowledge of the kinds and characteristics of the heavenly bodies which make up our universe.

To gain an understanding of the reasons for the apparent motions of the heavenly bodies.

To know the relations of the heavenly bodies to us and their respective effects upon life on earth.

To develop an interest in how modern astronomers study the stars and other heavenly bodies.

To relate the study of astronomy to future developments of space travel.

To develop an enjoyment in watching the stars and planets.

B. Concepts

The universe is vast—it includes everything in the heavens.

Stars are suns, and our sun is a star.

There are millions of stars in space.

Stars vary in size, brightness, and distance from earth.

Astronomers use mathematics to compute star distances.

Astronomers express star distances in terms of light years.

Distances in space seem vast when compared with distances on earth.

Our sun is a mass of extremely hot gases and many times larger than the earth.

Our sun is part of the Milky Way galaxy. There are millions of other galaxies.

Constellations are groups of stars that appear to form patterns in the sky.

The solar system is believed to have originated from the sun when another star came too close.

The evolution of the earth has come as a result of natural forces.

Our solar system includes our sun and all the heavenly bodies that revolve around it.

All the planets revolve in the same direction around the sun but at different speeds and rotations.

The apparent motion of bodies in space is due to the rotation and revolution of the earth.

The earth's position, in relation to the sun and moon, is a determining factor of life on earth.

Our sun is the source of energy for the earth.

Gravitational attraction and centrifugal force keep the earth and other bodies in the solar system in their relative positions.

Gravitational attraction is the force that keeps all heavenly bodies in their relative positions.

Units of time are defined by the earth's movements in relation to the sun.

The earth has seasons because the earth's axis is tilted as it revolves around the sun.

The earth rotates on its axis, causing day and night.

A system of standard time in the United States is based on the earth's rotation on its axis.

Differences in the lengths of days and nights in various parts of the earth occur because the earth's axis is tilted.

Differences in the appearance of the moon are caused by the changing positions of the moon in relation to the earth.

Eclipses of the moon and sun can be explained by the changing position of the moon as it revolves around the earth.

The gravitational attraction of the moon and sun causes the tides on earth.

Early people were interested in stars but knew very little about them.

Superstitions about the heavenly bodies are being overcome by scientific truths established through research.

Scientists advance their studies of the heavenly bodies by studying the light from these bodies with special instruments.

Scientists have in the past, and may in the future, change man's ideas about the universe.

III. Content
   A. The Solar System
      1. The sun
         a. Characteristics
         b. Composition
         c. Relation to earth
         d. Relation to universe
      2. The planets and their satellites
         a. Characteristics and descriptions
         b. Movements
         c. Relation to earth
      3. Characteristics of other bodies in the solar system
         a. Comets
         b. Meteors
         c. Meteorites
         d. Planetoids

4. The earth
   a. Characteristics and description
   b. Position and movements in the solar system
      (1) Seasons
      (2) Day and night
      (3) Gravity and gravitation
      (4) Centrifugal force
5. The moon
   a. Characteristics and description
   b. Movement
   c. Eclipses
   d. Effect on earth
      (1) Tides
B. The Universe
   1. Galaxies
   2. Constellations
   3. Stars
      a. Characteristics
      b. Important ones
      c. Light years
   4. Our own solar system
C. Instruments Used to Study the Heavenly Bodies
   1. Observatories and planetariums
   2. Telescopes
      a. Reflecting
      b. Refracting
   3. Spectroscope and spectrograph
   4. Photography
   5. Radar
   6. Rocket and space explorations
D. Future Development of Space Travel
   1. Jet propulsion
   2. Rocket studies
   3. Recent investigations
   4. Artificial satellite
E. Astronomy vs Astrology
   1. Breakdown of early beliefs and superstitions
   2. Respect for the work of the scientist

IV. Suggested Vocabulary to Be Established
[Definitions of the following terms do appear in the actual unit.]

astrology, astronomy, axis, centrifugal force, constellations, degree, eclipse, ellipse, elliptical, energy, equinox, fact, force, gravitation, gravity, hemisphere, horizon, hypothesis, inertia, light-year, magnitude, meteor, meteorite, nebula, observatory, orbit, perpendicular, phase, planet, planetarium, polar regions, radar, radiation, reflect, revolution, rotation, satellite, seasons, solar system, space, spectroscope, star, sun, sunspot, superstition, telescope, tide, tilt, universe.

V. Required Classroom Materials and Equipment

Balls—various sizes, tennis, ping-pong	Electric light bulb or small lamp
Knitting needles	Protractor
Globe	Corks
Lenses	Large pan or glass dish of water
Prism	Toothpicks or wood splints
Yardstick	Cardboard
String	Bunsen burner
Small cubical box	Sodium chloride
Flashlight	Boric acid
Candle	Copper sulphate
	Potassium nitrate

VI. List of Demonstrations and Experiments
[In the Handbook, all of the demonstrations and experiments listed under VI are treated in detail as—Why is the earth believed to be a sphere?]

Why is the earth believed to be a sphere?

How to demonstrate "turning on an axis"?

How is the earth kept in its orbit?

How do natural forces act opposite to each other to keep the earth revolving around the sun?

Why is the earth flattened at its poles?

How is the earth lighted by the sun?

How does the length of the period of daylight vary?

How can we demonstrate the eclipses of the sun and the moon?

How does the angle of the sun's rays affect the energy which comes to the earth?

Why are summer days longer than winter days?

How does the angle of the sun's rays vary from week to week?

Why does the moon seem to change its shape from time to time?

How to observe the bodies in the sky without a telescope?

What holds the solar system together?

How to draw an ellipse?

How to make the simplest telescope?

How to construct a simple telescope with easily obtained materials?

How is the spectroscope useful in determining the composition of the stars?

VII. Astronomy: *Demonstrations and Experiments*

Why is the earth believed to be a sphere?

What you need:

Globe	Ball or small globe
Tiny boat	Photograph of the earth taken
Light	from out in space

What you do:

1. Show ship coming up over the globe.
2. Show how earth is lighted. Compare to other shapes. Locate a spot on globe and rotate it into light.
3. Make earth's shadow—make the shadow of a box—make the shadow of a boy—make shadows of various sized spheres.
4. Show photo of earth taken from a rocket sent out into space.

VIII. Visual Aids

A. Sound Films

Molecular Theory of Matter

Our Earth

Work of Rivers

What Makes Day and Night

Latitude and Longitude

Life in Hot, Wet Lands

Birth of the Soil

Seeds of Destruction

The Great Lakes: How They Were Formed

B. Filmstrips

Volcanoes in Action

Air Transportation

Story of Time

C. Bulletin Boards

Star map of constellations around the north star

Star map of principal constellations visible during month this unit is studied

Recent eclipses

Photographs taken out in space

Rocket trips into space

Earth's satellite—recent information

Spectroscope and spectrograph

Observatories and planetariums

D. Models and Charts

Spitz planetarium

Star maps—current *Nature Magazine,* school library

IX. Activities

A. Group

1. Perform activities with lamps and globes to demonstrate night and day, seasons, eclipses, etc.

2. Make planetaria showing constellations.

3. Use Spitz planetarium.

4. Perform skits about astronomers and astrologers.

5. Make a bulletin board of constellations.

6. See list of student activities under "Individual."

B. Trips

1. Visit the Cranbrook Institute of Science.

2. Visit the Detroit Astronomical Society meetings.

C. Individual

1. Make a diagram showing the relative sizes of the planets and their distances from the sun.

2. Draw or make a poster to show the relative sizes of the planets.

3. Keep a record of the phases of the moon (from observation).

4. Make a star map of the polar constellations.
5. Make a map showing the location of the large observatories in the United States and the kinds of telescopes used. Use an outline map such as is used in social studies.
6. Make a diagram explaining how a spectroscope is used.
7. Make a diagram or do an experiment explaining how the sun's energy heats and lights the earth.
8. Make a diagram explaining why we could not live on the moon. If we *could* live there, show where and why.
9. Draw a spectrum. Explain how it is formed.
10. Show how gravitation pulls objects to one another.
11. Make posters showing some of the important constellations.
12. Collect clippings of interest.
13. Make a bulletin board on recent news of space travel.
14. Make a short report on how the planets were discovered and who named them.
15. Make a simple telescope. (See Darrow, *Boy's Own Book of Great Inventions.*)
16. Make a planetarium from a round cereal box and a flashlight. Change the constellations by using different covers.
17. Make a report on three star legends and myths.
18. Describe the early astronomers.
19. Make a report on Galileo and the first telescope.
20. Make a report on famous comets.
21. Show how an eclipse helps prove that the world is round. Focus a lantern slide projector on the wall. Pass a ball across a beam of light. Observe the shape of the shadow of the ball.
22. Set up time exhibits. Use several alarm clocks. Set each at a time representing a different time zone. Keep the clocks running for a week.
23. Make a broad map of the world. Divide it into time zones. Make small paper clocks. Paste them along the bottom of the clock. Label the map, "Time Around the World."
24. Make models of the earth, moon, and sun.

25. Make models of various time-telling devices: water clock, candle, sundial.
26. Paint a large globe white. Use this as a celestial sphere. Dot-in constellations and label.
27. Report on the history of celestial navigation and its importance in the discovery of the new world.

X. Additional Reference Materials

Baker, Robert H. *Introducing the Constellations*. New York: Viking Press, 1937.

Baker, Robert H. *When the Stars Come Out*. New York: Viking Press, 1934.

Bernhard, Bennett and Rice. *New Handbook of the Heavens*. New York: Whittlesey House, 1941.

Blough, Glenn O., and Campbell, Marjorie H. *Making and Using Classroom Science Materials in the Elementary Schools*. New York: Dryden Press, 1954.

Branley, Franklin M. *Experiments in the Principles of Space Travel*. New York: Thomas Y. Crowell Company, 1955.

Clarke, A. C. *Going Into Space*. New York: Harper & Brothers, 1954.

Darrow, Floyd Lavern. *Boy's Own Book of Great Inventions*. New York: Macmillan Company, 1941.

Fenton, C. L., and Fenton, M. A. *Worlds in the Sky*. New York: Day, 1950.

Freeman, Mae and Ira. *Fun With Astronomy*. New York: Random House, Inc., 1953.

Frost, Erwin Brent. *Let's Look at the Stars*. Boston: Houghton Mifflin Company, 1955.

Hood, Peter. *Observing the Heavens*. New York: Oxford University Press, 1953.

Meyer, J. S. *Picture Book of Astronomy*. New York: Lothrop, Lee, & Shepard, Inc., 1945.

Parker, Bertha M. *Basic Science Education Series*. Chicago: Row, Peterson & Company, 1941.
   Beyond the Solar System
   Earth's Nearest Neighbor
   The Sky Above Us

Reed, William Maxwell. *America's Treasure*. New York: Harcourt, Brace & Company, 1931.

Reed, William Maxwell. *Stars for Sam.* New York: Harcourt, Brace & Company, 1931.

Spitz, Armond N. *The Pinpoint Planetarium.* New York: Henry Holt & Company, 1940.

Swezey, G. D. *Boy's Book of Astronomy.* New York: E. P. Dutton & Company, 1936.

Wyler, Rose. *Planet Earth.* New York: Schuman, 1952.

Zim, Herbert S., and Baker, Robert H. *Stars.* New York: Morrow, 1951.

Publications:

Sky and Telescope. Sky Publishing Company. Harvard College Observatory, Cambridge 38, Massachusetts.

U.S. Naval Observatory, Washington 25, D.C. Ask for currently available mimeographed material on: Planets Visible, Eclipses and Where Visible, and Phases of the Moon. Free.

U.S. Government Publications, Superintendent of Documents, Washington 25, D.C. Ask for Price List, No. 48, on Weather, Astronomy, and Meteorology.[21]

The above sample of a *resource unit* contains the following headings: Generalizations, Introduction, Goals and Concepts To Be Established, Content, Suggested Vocabulary To Be Established, Required Classroom Materials and Equipment, List of Demonstrations and Experiments, Demonstrations and Experiments, Visual Aids, Activities, and Additional Reference Materials. A *teaching unit* represents the actual use of the selected materials that are organized for effective instructional purposes.

An outline of a teaching unit should contain:

1. An introductory statement which includes age and grade level, length of time needed, the place of this unit in the overall plan
2. A statement of objectives in which specific understandings, skills, and attitudes are to be developed by students
3. An outline of content listing problems to be solved, subject matter headings, and projects to be completed
4. A list of learning activities to be performed by pupils and teacher that are expected to develop the stated objectives and an approxi-

---

[21] The Board of Education of the City of Detroit, *Science, Grades 7, 8, and 9, A Teacher's Handbook,* Publication 400, 1957, pp. 29–53.

mate time assigned to the sequential arrangement of such activities

5. An outline of resources and materials such as printed materials, visits, use of consultants available in the community, and audio-visual aids and an outline of the necessary procedures to facilitate the use of out-of-class resources

6. A list of evaluation procedures to determine student growth and achievement of the specific objectives for the unit

A teaching unit may be developed either for the personal use of the teacher or for the students. In designing teaching units for student use, dates of assignments such as readings, projects, discussions and related student activity are usually included.

When pupils partipicate in planning a teaching unit, more time is usually needed. Klausmeier wrote: "The extent to which students share in planning is dependent upon (1) the nature of the learning involved, (2) the ability of the students to share in the planning, (3) the attitude of the teacher toward student participation, (4) the skill of the teacher in guiding students' planning, and (5) the requirements set up for the particular class by school authorities."[22] Frequently, the science teacher may decide that pupil planning is more appropriate after instruction has been initiated for some units. This may be more pertinent where students have had little experience in such units as microorganisms, atomic energy, or astronomy. A few students may have had considerable previous experience in these areas before the unit is launched. In this event, the teacher may wish to use these students in planning various types of assignments such as pupil projects.

As suggested earlier in the chapter, pupil interests and needs become more evident through the use of pupil planning in developing teaching units. The potential for learning science is increased as a result of greater pupil drive or motivation based upon these interests and needs. In any case the science teacher will be very much concerned with extending these interests and with developing new student interests and ideas.

---

[22] Herbert J. Klausmeier, *Principles and Practices of Secondary School Teaching*, Harper & Brothers, 1953, pp. 176–177.

Planning a Lesson

Although the trend is for school systems to select and organize science materials for a teacher's handbook from Grades 1 through 12, the teacher usually needs a syllabus for a given science course to be taught over a school year. The syllabus consists of several resource units constructed by a group of science teachers. The teaching unit becomes the basic guide actually employed for classroom use. Since the unit represents many hours of work in which it is expected that a class of pupils will learn specific understandings, skills, and other objectives in a limited amount of time, the teacher finds it necessary to be flexible in her organization and selection of science materials on a day-to-day basis. This degree of flexibility is desirable since it may be assumed that not all of the students will learn the same things at the same time.

It therefore becomes necessary for the science teacher to organize and select suitable science materials for daily classroom instruction. Where does the science teacher begin today's lesson with respect to where it was ended the day before? If yesterday's lesson ended with the completion of a demonstration that certain solutions under given conditions will conduct electricity, how does the teacher develop the objectives of the lesson today in which reference to yesterday's demonstration is made? Should the demonstration be repeated at the very beginning of the period? Should pupils be asked to say what they observed? Should the same apparatus of conductivity of solutions be placed on the desk? Does the teacher state the conclusions, or should basic generalizations be elicited from the pupils? What questions should the teacher ask? Does the teacher anticipate the possible incorrect answers she or he may obtain from pupils? Should a diagram of the demonstration be made on the blackboard? Are pupils to copy certain information in their notebooks? What are the applications and uses of this demonstration? How are these applications to be obtained? From reading the text in class? Out of class? From pupil experience or observation? From the teacher's explanation? From a visit to a specific industry? Should a summary be made by the teacher or developed through the responses by pupils? Should students leave the period with more questions to be raised and perhaps unanswered?

There is no one best answer for all of the above questions. But the teacher will give serious thought to such problems in planning the daily lesson in order to arrive at an efficient and economical approach to teaching. The format of the lesson and the actual written material in it are not of great importance. The significant factor is that the planning and thinking through the lesson provide the science teacher with the opportunity of checking which of the above suggested procedures are potentially most effective for developing given aims or objectives of the daily lesson.

Although experienced science teachers may not plan a daily lesson on paper, they do give careful thought to the planning of a lesson in terms of subject matter, materials to be used, or the development of pupil growth in terms of attitudes, reflective thinking, and subject matter. Since scientific advances are responsible for the changes in science content to be taught in the secondary schools, science teachers are compelled to re-examine their plans from year to year. In addition, most supervisors and science teachers will agree that daily lessons plans are vital to both experienced and beginning science teachers for efficient science teaching.

Regardless of the format of the daily lesson, it should contain the following items:

1. A statement of the topic, scientific principle, or the problem to be solved.
2. *Why Teach This Lesson?*—a list of aims or objectives stated in terms of the development of pupil understandings of science, pupil attitudes and behaviors, and possible skills such as problem solving if the lesson lends itself to such activity.
3. *What to Teach in this Lesson?*—an outline of the science content and materials needed for developing the objectives stated in number 2 above.
4. *How to Teach this Lesson?*—a list of methods or procedures to be employed along with the content in order to develop the aims of the lesson.

5. *How Do I Know That I Taught?*—either an evaluation or pupil summary of what was learned; good questions stated by the teacher help in evaluating the degree of learning—this may be a continuous process throughout the lesson and toward the end of the lesson; the kinds of questions asked by pupils and the nature of their activities in the class help the teacher evaluate possible learning.

In the subsequent chapters, specific attention will be given to methods and evaluation of learning science.

In addition to the five items suggested in planning a daily lesson, the science teacher should be conscious of another important question: Why should these students desire to learn the solution to the problem or the scientific principle or understanding? Psychologists often refer to motivation. How does the teacher motivate the students to learn each lesson? At best, the teacher can merely set the stage for learning by presenting an inspiring demonstration, a series of experiments, and questions or problems in which the pupils become involved and perhaps even identify themselves with specific situations. Pupil interests, needs, or experiences can serve as the springboard for introducing the lesson. Some teachers may begin with their own personalized experiences, the showing of a film or filmstrip, conducting a field trip, having a student or a group of students bring in and discuss a science project. These are typical ways in which the science teacher attempts to stimulate learning with the hope that the students will be motivated to learn. Herein is the basis for the need of flexibility in the planning of a daily lesson. Some students may actually assist in the planning of instruction if given the opportunity. The results are likely to cause pupils to become self-motivated and learn the basic ideas of the lesson under the guidance of the science teacher.

Careful lesson planning is not enough to develop the various types of learnings in pupils. The science teacher in the process of executing the daily lesson plan shows a degree of interest or lack of it; his personality and the way he relates to individual pupils —insulting or praising them, encouraging or discouraging them, for example—will also affect pupil attitudes toward science, the teacher, and learning itself. These factors may also determine whether or not the students like or dislike school. A daily lesson plan is essential to the teacher who wishes to be well prepared for effective teaching. The students discover readily if the teacher is prepared and react accordingly.

The science teacher who wishes his pupils to develop scientific attitudes of questioning, examining, open-mindedness, and suspending judgment, and who plans his daily lesson accordingly, cannot himself be rigid in his interaction with individual pupils in the class. To state in the lesson plan that scientific attitudes constitute one of the aims of the lesson would be meaningless and useless if the science teacher presents science as a dogma—a subject of finality rather than one of "Let's discover and continue to question." Scientists approach their problems with a question mark rather than with an exclamation mark.

In the daily lesson plan, the teacher will determine whether or not the objectives will be limited to the development of scientific information alone. The teaching of science for critical thinking should be carefully planned along with the content. Burnett states 16 teaching objectives that are required for the development of critical thinking:

To work with our students in such ways that they increasingly
1. Discover problem situations
2. Delimit problems into workable and procedural proportions
3. Develop critical hypotheses
4. Secure relevant, authoritative reference data expeditiously
5. Secure experimental or observational data critically and expeditiously
6. Recognize the bases of authority
7. Work cooperatively
8. Recognize personal bias and consider it in making judgments
9. Allow ascertainable facts to speak louder than prejudice
10. Communicate effectively and with accuracy
11. Recognize the limitations of both data and conclusions
12. Reopen issues when new data are available
13. Recognize the approximate nature of even scientific truth
14. Recognize the applicability of scientific methods to many non-science problems

15. Recognize the universality of cause-and-effect relations within the framework of probability (the "uncertainty" principle)

16. Recognize the limitations of scientific methods particularly when applied to areas where control is difficult and where contingencies and imponderables are numerous[23]

Not all of these objectives can be developed in the daily lesson; nor can they be attained a the end of a given science course. At the conclusion of a science course, the teacher can expect that progress is being made toward a greater development of these objectives. Hence, the science teacher may find it desirable to select several of the above-listed objectives in planning a daily lesson.

A teacher may, for example, plan one or two lessons for the problem: "How can a navigator of a plane or ship locate his position on the earth while above the clouds or out at sea?" His approach may be one of the following:

Approach I. Teacher explanation (lecture) with pupil recitation: The teacher states the problem of the navigator and writes it on the blackboard. The lesson plan lists primarily "content" objectives in this approach, such as: To solve the problem through the use of the following information and concepts—parallels, latitude, meridians, longitude—a point may be located on a map or globe if one knows the latitude and longitude.

The teacher's explanation—based largely on the assigned reading—may refer to a sextant, a globe, and a map. Definitions are written on the blackboard for each of the terms. The teacher asks pupils to examine, locate, and explain parallels and meridians on a globe. Before the period ends, pupils are asked to copy definitions and concepts in their notebooks. Unless the teacher is dynamic and stimulates interest by engaging in worthwhile pupil-learning activities, this lesson may be taught only for purposes of rote learning. The pupils may feel compelled merely to memorize the definitions and vocabulary without meaning and understanding.

[23] R. Will Burnett, *Teaching Science in the Secondary School,* Rinehart & Company, 1957, pp. 176–177.

Approach II. A developmental lesson in which the major understandings are elicited and formulated by the pupils under the careful guidance or direction of the teacher. Before stating the problem of the navigator, the teacher expects to stimulate pupil interest in this problem to the point that pupils will be motivated to solve the problem and develop understandings which they can then apply in solving other related problems. The teacher may stress other objectives such as scientific methods, critical thinking, attitudes about navigators, pilots, and transportation.

The developmental approach is more adaptable toward the aims of this lesson. The teacher will attempt to determine the pupil interests and previous experiences. Perhaps some pupils may desire to become pilots or navigators, or they may know someone engaged in this work. A brief stimulating discussion initiated by the teacher to arouse the pupil interest in which others' experiences are related to the problem may be one of several ways to launch the lesson. The teacher relates this discussion to the statement of the problem of the navigator. Pupils are asked many questions by the teacher, such as: What are meridians, longitude, parallels, latitude? How can the navigator determine how far north or south he is on the earth's surface? How far east or west? How is time connected with meridians? In the process of eliciting pupil responses to these questions, pupils are examining and working with globes, maps, and sextants. To fulfill one of the major aims of this lesson, pupils are given another problem to solve, if time permits, in the class or at home.

In this lesson, the teacher plans the questions and other learning activities for the pupils with the emphasis on pupil reasoning, thinking, and the ability to formulate the generalization that one can locate a point on the globe or on the map if the latitude and longitude of a given place is known.

Other Approaches. There are probably as many ways of teaching this same lesson as there are teachers. In some communities, a sailor, a navigator, a pilot, or some other appropriate person may be asked to come to class and explain in 10 or 15 minutes a significant experience of how certain knowledge was used to prevent getting lost and to avoid disaster. The teacher will confer with this resource person ahead of scheduled class time to permit effective communication and development of the aims of the lesson. The remainder of the lesson may follow Approach I or II, suggested above, or any combination of these approaches.

If no resource people are available, the science teacher may have a newspaper clipping of a ship or plane lost at sea to use as a means of stimulating interest and discussion. Films or filmstrips on navigation may be used in the lesson. Pupils may create projects such as map making and the construction of globes representing the earth. Some pupils may wish to visit steamship companies or commercial airlines and talk with navigators and pilots to obtain pertinent information before or after coming to class.

Regardless of the approach or method employed in teaching this lesson, a science teacher will use his initiative and resourcefulness in helping pupils to create activity that will promote the best kind of learning situation. The first approach has serious limitations for objectives of the lesson that go beyond the memory of subject matter only. The second approach and any of the creative, well-planned lessons that are modifications of the developmental lesson offer a greater potential for learning science. The effective science teacher will encourage pupil planning of stimulating activities to be performed by the pupils. The science teacher will ask pupils who talked with navigators or pilots to discuss not only scientific information pertaining to the topic but also their impressions that reflect attitudes, interests, and skills.

The teacher plans the daily lesson in science with the view of giving serious thought to the best possible ways of teaching the particular topic or lesson. The daily lesson plan is not used as a "crutch" by the teacher. The format of the lesson plan matters very little. The lesson plan is not looked upon as a rigid contract to be followed; it helps the teacher anticipate various alternate approaches to effective science teaching. It serves the teacher as a guide for thinking through very carefully what materials, resources, ideas, questions and experiments or demonstrations are available in order to promote learning.

SUMMARY

The selection of science materials to be taught should be based upon the objectives, the needs of individual students, and the needs of the community. Student interests and geographical factors should also influence the selection of scientific information. There is no one best system for organizing the sequence of units to be taught. If sound principles of psychology are employed in teaching science, it matters little where or when a topic is placed during the course. The efficient approach in organizing instructional materials is the unit plan. Daily lesson plans can be developed from these units. Careful planning is needed for economical instruction in science.

EXERCISES

1. Prepare a list of criteria to be followed in your community as a guide to selecting and organizing suitable science materials.
2. Discuss at least two different plans for organizing a science course for a given grade level in the secondary schools. Show how the order or sequence of science units varies in both plans.
3. Write a sample teaching unit for a particular science course which contains objectives, outline of content and methods, reading assignments, audio-visual aids, and evaluating procedures.
4. Discuss the factors and their effects on instruction that should be included in a daily lesson plan.
5. Prepare a daily lesson plan, and criticize its structure after following it in the teaching of a science class.
6. How does rigidity on the part of the teacher or the school affect the selection and organization of science materials?

SUGGESTED READINGS

Barnard, J. Darrell (chmn.), *Rethinking Science Education,* Fifty-ninth Yearbook, National Society for the Study of Education, Chicago, University of Chicago press, 1960.

Brandwein, Paul F., Watson, Fletcher G., and Blackwood, Paul E., *Teaching High School Science: A Book of Methods,* New York, Harcourt, Brace & Company, 1958.

Burnett, R. Will, *Teaching Science in the Secondary School,* New York, Rinehart & Company, Inc., 1957.

Cohen, I. Bernard, and Watson, Fletcher G., *General Education in Science,* Cambridge, Mass., Harvard University Press, 1952.

Harris, Chester (ed.), *Encyclopedia of Educational Research,* New York, The Macmillan Company, 1960.

Heiss, Elwood D., and Obourn, Ellsworth S., Hoffman, Charles W., *Modern Science Teaching,* New York, The Macmillan Company, 1950.

Klausmeier, Herbert J., *Principles and Practices of Secondary School Teaching,* New York, Harper & Brothers, 1953.

Rice, Roy C., "Trends in Curriculum and in Instruction in the Physical Sciences of the Secondary Schools," *Science Education,* vol. 42 (April, 1958), pp. 238–243.

Richardson, John S., *Science Teaching in Secondary Schools,* Englewood Cliffs, N.J., Prentice-Hall, Inc., 1957.

Washton, Nathan S., "A Scientific Approach to Curriculum Construction," *School Science and Mathematics,* vol. 52 (April, 1952), pp. 285–290.

5

SPECIAL PROBLEMS OF THE BIOLOGY TEACHER

PRINCIPLES AND PROBLEMS APPROACH

Several significant studies have been published pertaining to the development and teaching of biological principles.[1] These principles are usually located in teaching units, in syllabuses, and in textbooks. The need for teaching biological principles became evident in the last few decades when textbooks and classroom instruction contained a multitude of facts, many of which were isolated from larger understandings in biology. In some cases, students were confused as to what were the essential facts and their relationships to biological principles.

It is important that teachers and students distinguish between a principle and a fact. Martin writes:

For a statement to be a principle:

[1] Refer to the following studies: George J. Bergman, "A Determination of the Principles of Entomology for General Education," *Science Education,* vol. 31 (February, 1947), pp. 23–32, and (April, 1947), pp. 144–157; James McFarland Elliott, "An Evaluation of Certain Courses in Relation to Understanding of Principles in a Biological Science Course," doctoral dissertation, Michigan State College, 1953, and *Science Education,* vol. 39 (March, 1955), pp. 141–156; W. Edgar Martin, "A Determination of the Principles of the Biological Sciences of Importance for General Education," doctoral dissertation, University of Michigan, 1944, published and distributed in microfilm form by University Microfilms, Ann Arbor, Mich.; Margaret Jean McKibben, "An Analysis of Principles and Activities of Importance for General Biology Courses in High Schools," *Science Education,* vol. 39 (April, 1955), pp. 187–196; John H. Owens, "The Ability to Recognize and Apply Scientific Principles in New Situations," *Science Education,* vol. 35 (October, 1951), pp. 207–213; Nathan S. Washton, "A Syllabus in Biology for General Education," *Science Education,* vol. 35 (March, 1951), pp. 84–92, and vol. 36 (October, 1952), pp. 227–237; Nathan S. Washton, "Teaching Biology for General Education," *Science Education,* vol. 36 (October, 1952), pp. 237–240.

1. It must be a comprehensive generalization which summarizes the widest possible range of facts within the domain of facts with which it is directly concerned.
2. It must be scientifically true:
   A. It must be verifiable; i.e., it must be stated so that it suggests, either directly or indirectly, a definite operation of observation or experiment whereby its truth can be tested or verified.
   B. It must be consistent with the body of accepted scientific knowledge and, except for a few limiting or singular exceptions, with all the data (facts) relevant to it.[2]

Heineman defines principle as follows: "A statement of relationships frequently causal in nature between two facts. The principle or generalization is built on the basis of general facts, but once molded, it serves to make meaningful other facts and conditions."[3] Sites maintains: "A principle is a statement of relationship which is significant in its applications."[4] On the other hand, Wise places emphasis on four criteria of a principle of science: (1) It is a comprehensive generalization which describes a fundamental process, a property related to a natural phenomenon, or a constant mode of behavior; (2) Within limitations, it should be true as stated; (3) It can be illustrated; and (4) It should not be a definition.[5]

It is reasonable to assume that it is more efficient for students to learn biological principles than to memorize a vast array of isolated facts. It is not suggested therefore, that facts should not be included. They are significant where they are needed in understanding a principle or a generalization. Likewise, it is not suggested that a given number of biological principles merely be stated by the teacher, for memorization by the students. In develop-

---

[2] W. Edgar Martin, *The Major Principles of the Biological Sciences of Importance for General Education,* Circular No. 308, U.S. Department of Health, Education, and Welfare (June, 1956), p. 2.

[3] A. M. Heineman, "A Study of General Science Textbooks," *General Science Quarterly,* vol. 13 (November, 1928), pp. 11–23.

[4] John T. Sites, Chemical Principles, Concepts, and Technical Terms Used in Science Magazines, master's thesis, University of Chicago, 1930.

[5] Harold E. Wise, A Determination of the Relative Importance of Principles of Physical Science for General Education, doctoral dissertation, University of Michigan, 1941, 767 pp.

mental procedures by the teacher, many varied and stimulating learning activities should be provided to permit students to infer the biological principles. It is also possible that some biological principles will be formulated by students after they are given worthwhile problems to solve.

In a study conducted by the writer, 42 principles of biology were formulated and judged important for general education. Some of these principles may be taught in one lesson; others may require several hours or weeks of instruction; a few may be used in developing a unit plan. The following sample presents 15 of these biological principles:

1. A definite bodily disorder will occur when an endocrine gland ceases to function normally.
2. The cell is the structural and functional unit in most organisms.
3. The processes of a living body occur in the protoplasm; the sum of all of these chemical and physical processes is metabolism.
4. Life is perpetuated through the biological process of reproduction which provides new individuals.
5. Practically all the foods in the world in addition to other substances are produced directly or indirectly through the process of photosynthesis in which carbon dioxide and water in the presence of sunlight and chlorophyll-bearing plants are converted into intermediate substances that ultimately form starch and liberate oxygen.
6. Food, oxygen, certain optimal conditions of temperature, light, and moisture are required for the life of most living organisms.
7. All living things receive and respond to stimuli and attempt to adjust themselves in their environment.
8. Living things alter their types; species that exist today have originated by descent from earlier ones which were derived from still earlier ones, down to the first living forms.
9. Enzymes, vitamins, and hormones are chemical substances that govern the reactions that occur in living things.
10. Although living things are not distributed uniformly or at random over the surface of the earth, they are found in definite zones and in local societies where conditions usually are favorable to their survival.

11. The higher forms of life are more complex in structure and are accompanied by an increase in division of labor.
12. Each organism is composed of specific hereditary characters which are transmitted from one generation to the next through given hereditary factors.
13. New types of living organisms may arise through mutation.
14. Cell division is a fundamental process of reproduction in organisms whose cells possess nuclei; it results in a precise distribution of the chromatin of the nucleus.
15. The modes of reproduction of living things fall into two general categories: asexual and sexual reproduction. Sexual reproduction is the almost universal method and occurs in species of every phylum of plants and animals.[6]

The approach to teaching biology for general education will vary in emphasizing the "content" objectives, "attitudinal" objectives, or other kinds of objectives such as overt behavioral changes in pupils. There should be flexibility in content, materials and methods of teaching to meet the needs of individual students, the community, and the teacher. It is interesting to note the response by 25 teachers of biology, most of whom are members of the National Association for Research in Science Teaching, to a questionnaire submitted by the writer. The majority of these teachers indicated the following:

1. Teach biological principles pertaining to behavior, reproduction, heredity, and evolution so that students may be provided with the necessary knowledge, skills, and attitudes to (a) attain an emotionally stable personality and make a worthy social adjustment; (b) be better fit for successful family and marital relationships.

2. Teach the principles pertaining to heredity and evolution so that students (a) understand the social, economic, and spiritual forces at work in society and develop a sense of social responsibility; (b) participate more effectively in solving problems of

[6] Nathan S. Washton, "The Preparation of a Syllabus Based upon a Determination of the Relative Importance of Biological Principles Judged in Terms of Criteria of General Education," doctoral dissertation, New York University, October, 1949. (On microfilm from University of Michigan, Ann Arbor, Mich.)

contemporary society; (c) recognize the interdependence of the different peoples of the world.

3. Teach the principles of nutrition so that students (a) understand the place of the consumer in society and learn to become intelligent consumers of goods, services, and time; (b) participate more effectively in solving problems of contemporary society.

4. All of the principles of biology should be emphasized to students in terms of the following objectives of general education: (a) to gain a better understanding of the meaning and purpose of life and a truer sense of values; (b) to maintain and improve their health and share in the responsibility for protecting the health of the community; (c) to use a scientific approach in solving problems dealing with society and human welfare.

Each instructor may wish to organize the principles of biology in terms of the needs of a given geographical area or other criteria based upon psychological principles of learning. Some instructors may wish to consolidate or integrate several principles into another form of generalization. Most of the biological principles may be grouped into one of the following categories or units of instruction: protoplasm and the cell, energy and life, ecology—plant and animal relationships, nutrition, behavior, reproduction and development, heredity, evolution, and applied biology.

The philosophy of teaching biology is usually expressed by the teacher through his organization of the course. Some biology teachers begin with a systematic study and start with protoplasm and the cell; others begin with applied biology; a few begin with everyday problems of living. Each teacher can justify his organization of the course in terms of his rationalization but it should be based on psychological principles of learning.

The approach to teaching biology for general education is very significant. Martin writes, "All of the principles lend themselves to the understanding and use of the scientific approach if the teacher uses the problem approach and the inductive method for developing an understanding of the principles and the deductive method for applying the principle to everyday familiar happenings."[7] Some biology teachers may wish to restate the principles as problems, employing the problem-solving method of teaching.

Bless states: "It would be best and more in keeping with our problems of education if we omitted many topics, concentrating our attention on the important ones, and spent some time in showing the relation and application of these principles to our everyday life and to the development of our ideas."[8] Although the following statement was prepared more than a decade ago, it is as pertinent today as it was years ago:

Science is today on a plane of high significance and importance. It is no longer, if indeed it ever was, a mysterious and occult hocus pocus to be known only to a select few. It touches, influences, and molds the lives of every living thing. Science teachers have a great opportunity and responsibility to make a large contribution to the welfare and advancement of humanity. The intellectual aspects of this responsibility are at least coequal in importance with the material. Science is a great social force as well as a method of investigation. The understanding and acceptance of these facts and this point of view and their implementation in practice will more than anything else make science teaching what it can and should be.[9]

Principles of biology should be taught in terms of developing the objectives of general education. Questions should be encouraged from students that would stimulate their thinking about the implications and applications of biology to everyday living. The art of formulating questions is a major task of the teacher. The outline on the following page is an illustration of how to organize the teaching of one biological principle pertaining to heredity.

This same outline suggests that biological principles may be developed in a teaching situation with implications for sociology, psychology, anthropology, and economics. It is also possible to

[7] W. Edgar Martin, in a letter addressed to the writer dated January 17, 1949.
[8] Arthur A. Bless, "Aims of a College Course in Science," *Journal of Chemical Education,* vol. 9 (May, 1932), p. 659.
[9] National Society for the Study of Education, *Science Education in the American Schools,* Forty-sixth Yearbook, Part I, University of Chicago Press, 1947, p. 39.

Heredity Provides an Organism with Its Native Capacities Whereas Environment Determines to a Large Extent How Fully These Potentialities Will Be Developed.

OBJECTIVES—GENERAL EDUCATION

1. Understand the world of nature, physical and biological, and be able to interpret natural phenomena.
2. Participate more effectively in solving problems of contemporary society.
3. Gain a better understanding of the meaning and purpose of life and a truer sense of values.
4. Have some appreciation of the background of the civilization which is our heritage.
5. Understand the social, economic, and spiritual forces at work in society, and develop a sense of social responsibility.
6. Maintain and improve one's health, and share in the responsibility for protecting the health of the community.
7. Attain an emotionally stable personality, and make a worthy social adjustment.
8. Utilize a scientific approach in solving problems dealing with society and human welfare.
9. Be better fit for successful family and marital relationships.
10. Develop a code of behavior which is based on ethical principles consistent with democratic ideals.
11. Recognize the interdependence of the different peoples of the world.
12. Discover own abilities, aptitudes, and interests, and choose a vocation.

LEARNING ACTIVITIES

I. Student-teacher discussion of:
  A. Heredity and environment
    1. Environmental conditions affecting development and transforming adult features of an organism
      a. Plant response to environmental changes
        (1) Chinese primula (temperature–color)
        (2) Maize (sunlight–color)
      b. Animal response to environmental changes

  (1) Green parrots of South America (diet–plumage)
  (2) Axolott vs. Amblystoma (water–gills)
  (3) common sea minnow (Fundulus)
   (chemicals–number of eyes)
 2. Mental differences in humans
  a. The effects of heredity, environment, and educational opportunity
  b. Attitudes influenced by
   (1) Religion
   (2) Economic theories
   (3) Race prejudice
  c. Environmental effects
   (1) Twins of unlike sex vs. identical and fraternal twins of same sex
   (2) Twins reared in same home vs. twins reared in different homes
   (3) Normal child vs. imbecile (effects of iodine and thyroid gland)
B. Eugenics
 1. Marriage
 2. Segregation and sterilization
 3. Education
 4. Immigration
 5. Dangers and difficulties
  a. Inbreeding
  b. War
C. Euthenics
 1. Sociological factors
 2. Economic factors
 3. Political factors

II. *Visual aids*—opaque projection of:
A. Three photographs of the same child suffering from thyroid deficiency, on page 114, S. J. Holmes' *Human Genetics and Its Social Import*. New York: McGraw-Hill Book Company, 1936.
B. Photograph of Japanese twins (identical but of unequal development), on page 122, Holmes' *Human Genetics and Its Social Import*.

III. *Individual student activity:*
   Determine the noticeable differences and similarities in several traits such as stature, color of eyes, hair, intelligence, character, and temperament among the members of your family. How can you account for these differences and similarities as a result of heredity and environment?

IV. *Questions:*
   1. How do heredity and environment influence the personality of an individual? What is the relationship of one's personality to social adjustment?
   2. How can scientific thinking be applied to minimize or eliminate prejudice pertaining to heredity and environment? To what extent do economic theories, religion, and race prejudice influence these attitudes?
   3. What knowledge is available from the study of heredity and environment that may be applied to successful family and marital adjustments?
   4. What are the advantages, disadvantages, and limitations of a eugenics program in America? Of a euthenics program?

relate the teaching of biological principles to solving real problems.

Problems of living are common to all mankind, regardless of acquired interests, aptitudes, abilities, or vocational choice. All people have social, personal, family, and vocational problems. Every individual is concerned with such problems as: How can I get along with my friends and neighbors? How shall I select my mate? What job or profession shall I prepare for? How can I use my income for better security and live an enriched life? How can I maintain and improve good health? What problems shall I be prepared for in marriage and in rearing a family?

No one course or subject will give the answers to all of these problems. Good instruction that emphasizes relationships and implications as well as applications from biology, sociology, economics, psychology, and other areas can help in the development of a good program of general education. Problem solving and other methods of integrating instruction will vary among teachers as well as schools. A major function of general education is to help students solve their problems and to advance the welfare of the individual student and the public. With this goal in mind, teachers of biology can make a worthwhile contribution.

An effective approach in organizing and teaching a high school biology course was proposed by the Harford County Board of Education in Bel Air, Maryland. This approach suggests organizing the units of instruction in terms of major problems and subproblems. To solve these problems and subproblems, many varied learning activities are introduced with the result that concepts, generalizations, or biological principles are formulated. The units and subproblems suggested are:

Unit I: How will the study of biology help me?
    Problems: 1. What specific branches of science are included in the field of biology?
              2. How can we understand and apply the principles of biology?
              3. How does the study of biology help us to control more effectively and even to improve our environment?
              4. In what ways does biology help us in our personal and social lives?
              5. What vocational and avocational opportunities and interests are suggested to us by our study of biology?

Unit II: What are the characteristics and problems of the living things around us?
    Problems: 1. What are living things?
              2. What can living things do that nonliving things cannot do?
              3. In what ways are plants and animals alike?
              4. What factors are necessary in the environments of living things to insure their survival?
              5. How do plants and animals depend upon each other?
              6. How are plants and animals adapted for self-protection?

7. Why and how are living things grouped (classified) and named?

Unit III: In what ways do we depend upon plants for food, clothing, shelter, and recreation?

Problems: 1. In what ways are our lives affected by the simplest plants such as algae, bacteria, molds, yeasts, mosses, ferns, and their relatives?

2. Why are green plants able to make their own food while we cannot do this?

3. What are the important characteristics of the four great groups of plants?

4. What structures do green plants have that enable them to carry out the manufacture and storage of food, as well as reproduce their kind?

5. In what ways do we make use of plants and plant products?

Unit IV: What groups of life make up the animal kingdom of which we are a part?

Problems: 1. What interesting groups of animals that lack backbones will we find in our environment, and how are they important to us?

2. What interesting facts can we learn about the five large classes of animals that have backbones, and in what ways is each group important to us?

Unit V: How does your body do its work?

Problems: 1. How is the human body built?

2. What does the body need from the food we eat?

3. How does the body prepare its food for the use that must be made of it?

4. Why is it important for the blood to circulate in the body?

5. How does the human circulatory system operate?

6. How does the body get rid of its wastes?

7. How does the human brain control our behavior?

8. What are the special senses, and how does each one function?

9. How do the endocrine glands control the kind of person you are?

Unit VI: What progress has been made in the scientific control of disease?

Problems: 1. What superstitions about diseases and their control have been eliminated by science?
2. What kinds of organisms cause infectious diseases?
3. How are noninfectious diseases caused?
4. How does your body guard against attacks of disease germs?
5. What can you do to keep your body able to resist the attacks of disease germs?
6. What progress has been made in providing medical aid against attacking microbes?
7. How can we develop and maintain good mental health?
8. How can we safeguard and improve community health?
9. What effect does the use of alcohol, tobacco, and narcotics have on our physical and mental health?

Unit VII: How may our knowledge of reproduction and heredity be used in improving living things?

Problems: 1. How can plants reproduce without seeds?
2. How do flowering plants reproduce?
3. How do the various classes of vertebrates reproduce?
4. To what extent are traits inherited?
5. What factors influence acquired traits?
6. What are the aims of plant and animal breeders?
7. How are new types of plants and animals developed?
8. What new and improved plants and animals have been obtained by breeders?

Unit VIII: Why is conservation of our natural resources of vital importance to you and your family?

Problems: 1. What is meant by the "balance of nature," and what efforts are made to preserve this balance?

2. How can we save our soil?
3. Why and how should we practice forest conservation?
4. How can we practice the necessary conservation of our wildlife?
5. How can we use our water resources more wisely?
6. What agencies are working to improve and increase effective conservation practices?[10]

The biology teacher may wish to refer to the following check list of learning activities to promote the development of concepts and biological principles. It is not suggested that all of these activities be performed by pupils or teachers for all units. Furthermore, the teacher and the pupils should exercise initiative and resourcefulness in creating other ways and means of discovering biological knowledge.

A Check List of Learning Activities

To solve problems and develop biological principles, *do your students:*

1. Design and perform individual and group laboratory experiments?
2. Create individual scientific projects of biological import?
3. Prepare posters, charts, and graphs that depict biological information for display on bulletin boards?
4. Observe, report, and discuss current films and television programs pertaining to biology?
5. Consult experts in the biological sciences who are in private practice, industry, or governmental agencies?
6. View television and listen to radio programs pertaining to science and make use of this acquired knowledge both in and out of the classroom?
7. Lead discussions on contemporary issues or problems of biology such as conservation, radioactive fall-out?
8. Explore career opportunities in the biological sciences through readings and visits to relevant industries?

[10] Harford County Board of Education, Bel Air, Maryland. *Science—A Curriculum Guide, Grades 1–12*, 1957, pp. 76–79.

9. Go on field trips to observe flora and fauna and study their ecological relationships?
10. Bring to class hobbies that are related to the study of biology?
11. Construct and interpret graphs to show the decline in incidence and mortality rates as a result of biological progress made in conquering disease?
12. Photograph plants and animals in their natural habitat and place them on exhibit in school?
13. Prepare biological exhibits and/or research projects for the science fair and school assembly program?
14. Survey the community in determining the various kinds of facilities available for maintenance of good health?
15. Collect and use articles in newspapers and magazines that pertain to biology and its import?
16. Collect and prepare biological specimens for the school museum?
17. Read supplementary books in biology in addition to required readings?
18. Use microscopes and prepare slides?

Martin reported that of a total of 783 high schools surveyed, 599 based the organization of the general biology course on principles following a basic text; 98 on specialized treatment of botany, zoology, and physiology; only 86 on problems of daily living.[11] Many variations in following a text, a state course of study, or a local course of study were also reported. However, it should not be assumed that principles of biology can be taught best by merely stating them and supplying the necessary facts to prove them. Some biology teachers who teach biology in terms of everyday problems are able to develop an understanding of the principles of biology more effectively as one of the outcomes of solving biological problems or of organizing the course around daily problems.

In the survey conducted by Martin, the average number of days of instructional time devoted to each of the following topics were:[12]

[11] W. Edgar Martin, *The Teaching of General Biology,* Bulletin 1952, No. 9, Federal Security Agency, Office of Education, 1952, p. 21.
[12] *Ibid.*

Kinds of living things	49.75
Health, disease, and nutrition	34.16
Heredity, genetics, and eugenics	18.06
Conservation	18.98
Organization of living things	35.92
Protoplasm, cells and life processes	33.33
Modification of species	13.08
Energy, matter, and life	17.95
Ecological relationships	19.22
Paleontology	11.25
Embryonic development	16.88
Geographical distribution of living things	11.25
Miscellaneous	22.94

For the talented student in biology, many high schools offer an advanced biology course similar to the introductory college course. Jerome Metzner of the Bronx High School of Science in New York reports:

A curriculum for the talented student in biology provides a variety of environments and learning experiences through which the student may explore his interest and be stimulated to capitalize on his native abilities. It includes guidance and inspiration by well-trained enthusiastic teachers; orientation to all major fields of science; a minimum of one year of high school chemistry and physics; development of the realization that modern biology is closely interrelated with chemistry and physics; a rich co- and extracurriculum where his special interests may be pursued through readings, visits to scientific institutions and laboratories, science projects and possibly science research; ready access to a library of up-to-date scientific books and journals; a course in college biology enabling the student to enter college with advanced standing; laboratory experiences that challenge his ability to perceive and formulate scientific problems and to devise procedures for solving them; opportunity to serve as an apprentice to a practicing biologist; opportunity to study or work at a biological laboratory during the summer; availability of school space and equipment for working on biology projects; career guidance so that he may plan intelligently for the realization of his professional aspirations; opportunity to advance in the study of science according to his ability and not in accordance with prescribed steps; opportunity for the study of living things and their ecological relationships in the laboratories of the out-of-doors.[13]

EQUIPMENT AND SUPPLIES

To teach biology for the development of basic laboratory skills and an understanding of the biological principles, it is necessary that minimum apparatus and supplies become available. The required or suggested laboratory furniture and fixtures will be discussed in Chapter 11.

Fig. 5.1. A well-equipped biology classroom has microscopes for individual pupils in addition to standard equipment. (Courtesy of Ralph Sonen, Northport High School, Northport, N.Y.)

In June, 1958, it was estimated that the approximate costs of high school laboratory apparatus and supplies for the biology laboratory was $3,235 for the small school, $5,685 for the average- or medium-size school, $8,240 for the large school.[14] Minimum requirements of apparatus and supplies for the biology laboratory

[13] In a paper delivered at the Thirty-first Annual Meeting of the National Association for Research in Science Teaching, Chicago, 1958.

[14] *A Guide for Evaluating Your Science Facilities,* published by the Laboratory Equipment Section, Scientific Apparatus Makers Association, 20 N. Wacker Drive, Chicago 6, Ill., 1958, p. 12.

are: a microprojector, microscopes, microtome, slides, cover slips, chemical reagents including biological stains, chemical glassware (beakers, evaporating dishes, bottles, stoppers, corks, bell jars), triangular files, glass and rubber tubing, burners, ringstand and clamps, balances, cages for living specimens, flower pots or boxes, Riker mounts, insect-killing bottles, jars, fish food, dissecting trays, pins, and kits, nets, and models and charts of organs, systems, and life histories of selected flora and fauna. Living and preserved specimens of representative phyla in the plant and animal kingdoms for laboratory study are strongly recommended.

Many of the biological and scientific supply companies will gladly furnish lists of suggested equipment and supplies. The biology teacher should request catalogues and other pertinent information describing the material to be purchased. Where the budget is extremely limited, the teacher may wish to order one microprojector in place of several microscopes. The most desirable laboratory should have both a microprojector and a number of individual microscopes for the students. The individual microscopes are essential for the development of skill in using the microscope as well as individual study of specimens. The microprojector is employed by the biology teacher to illustrate, explain, and emphasize what to observe and study during individual work. Both types of equipment are needed to reinforce the learning of biological principles, functional information, and laboratory skills.

The following directory of biological and other scientific supply companies is divided according to geographical areas.

EAST

Allied Chemical & Dye Corp., 40 Rector St., New York 6, N.Y.
American Hospital Supply Corp., 40–05 168th St., Flushing, N.Y.
American Optical Co., Buffalo 15, N.Y.
American Type Culture Collection, 2029 M St. NW, Washington 6, D.C. (bacteria cultures)
Bausch & Lomb Optical Co., 635 St. Paul St., Rochester, N.Y.
Biddle & Company, 1316 Arch St., Philadelphia 7, Pa.
Cambosco Scientific Co., 37 Antwerp St., Brighton 35, Mass.
Carolina Biological Supply Co., Elon College, N.C.

Certified Blood Donor Service, 146–16 Hillside Ave., Jamaica 35, N.Y.

Clay-Adams Co., 141 E. 25th St., New York 10, N.Y.

Corning Glass Works, Corning, N.Y.

Eastman Kodak Co., 343 State St., Rochester 4, N.Y.

Eimer and Amend, Greenwich and Morton Sts., New York 14, N.Y.

Fisher Scientific Supply Co., 139 Fisher Bldg., Pittsburgh 19, Pa.

Kelly-Koett Manufacturing Co., 24 E. 6th St., Covington, Ky.

Knickerbocker Blood Donor Service, 300 W. 43rd St., New York, N.Y.

Lederle Laboratories, Div. American Cyanamid Co., Midtown Rd., Pearl River, N.Y.

Leitz, Inc., 468 4th Ave., New York 16, N.Y.

Marine Biological Laboratory, Woods Hole, Mass.

Merck & Co., Rahway, N.J.

New York Scientific Supply Co., 28 W. 30th St., New York, N.Y.

Polaroid Corp., Cambridge 39, Mass.

Charles Pfizer & Co., 11 Bartlett St., Brooklyn, N. Y.

Standard Scientific Corp., 34 W. 4th St., New York, N.Y.

United Scientific Co., 204 Milk St., Boston 9, Mass.

Ward's Natural Science Establishment, 3000 Ridge Rd. E., Rochester 9, N.Y.

MIDWEST

Aloe Scientific Division of A. S. Aloe Co., 5655 Kingsbury St., St. Louis 12, Mo.

Biological Research Products Co., 243 W. Root St., Chicago, Ill.

Central Scientific Co., 1700 N. Irving Park Rd., Chicago 13, Ill.

Chicago Apparatus Co., 1735 N. Ashland Ave., Chicago 22, Ill.

Denoyer-Geppert Co., 5235 N. Ravenswood Ave., Chicago 40, Ill.

Difco Laboratories, Inc., Detroit 1, Mich.

Dow Chemical Co., Midland, Mich.

General Biochemicals, Inc., 677 Laboratory Park, Chagrin Falls, Ohio

General Biological Supply House, Inc., 8200 S. Hoyne Ave., Chicago 20, Ill. (Turtox)

Gradwohl Laboratories, 3514 Lucas Ave., St. Louis 3, Mo.

Graf-Apsco Co., 5868 N. Broadway, Chicago 40, Ill.

Harshaw Scientific Division, Harshaw Chemical Co., 1945 E. 97th St., Cleveland 6, Ohio

Kimble Glass, P.O. Box 1035, Toledo, Ohio

Monsanto Chemical Co., 1700 S. 2nd St., St. Louis 4, Ill.

Nutritional Biochemicals Corp., 21010 Miles Ave., Cleveland 2, Ohio

Nystrom & Co., 3333 N. Elston Ave., Chicago 18, Ill.

Sheldon Equipment Co., 149 Thomas St., Muskegon, Mich.

Sprague-Dawley, Inc., P.O. Box 2071, Madison 5, Wis. (laboratory rats)

Welch Manufacturing Co., 1515 N. Sedgwick St., Chicago 10, Ill.

Western Laboratories, 826 Q St., Lincoln, Nebr.

Windsor Biology Gardens, Moore's Creek Rd., Bloomington, Ind.

WEST

Ainsworth & Sons, Inc., 2151 Lawrence St., Denver 5, Colo.

California Biological Service, 1612 W. Glenoaks Blvd., Glendale, Calif.

California Botanical Materials Co., 861 E. Columbia Ave., Pomona, Calif.

Erb & Gray Co., 854 S. Figueroa St., Los Angeles 14, Calif.

Los Angeles Biological Laboratories, 2977 W. 14 St., Los Angeles 6, Calif.

Oregon Biological Supply Co., 1806 SE. Holgate Blvd., Portland, Ore.

Pacific Laboratory Apparatus Co., 3555 Whittier Blvd., Los Angeles 23, Calif.

Product Design Co., 2796 Middlefield Rd., Redwood City, Calif. (conservation and water purification kits)

Testa Manufacturing Co., 418 S. Pecan St., Los Angeles 33, Calif.

CANADA AND UNITED KINGDOM

Beaconing Optical and Precision Materials Co., Ltd., 455 Craig W., Montreal, Canada

Canadian Laboratory Supplies, Ltd., 403 St. Paul W., Montreal, Canada

C. Hearson and Co., Ltd., 68 Willow Walk, Bermondsey, London SE. 1, England

Fine Chemicals of Canada, Ltd., Toronto, Canada

General Optical Co., Ltd., Montreal, Canada

Laboratory Glassware Manufacturers, 200 Ravenscroft Rd., Beckenham, Kent, England

Richards Glass Co., Ltd., Toronto, Canada

Scientific Instrument Manufacturers' Association of Great Britain, Ltd., 17 Princess Gate, London SW. 7, England

United Scientific Instruments, Ltd., 62 Sherland Rd., Maida Vale, London W9, England

IMPROVISING FOR LACK OF EQUIPMENT

If the budget for the biology laboratory is extremely limited, the teacher can use initiative and resourcefulness in creating some basic equipment. For example, a microprojector can be assembled from one microscope and an ordinary slide projector which is used as a source of light. By tilting the microscope so that the viewing cylinder or barrel is parallel with the surface of the table, the image can be projected on a screen placed in front of the ocular. It is necessary that the mirrors and light box be removed and that the source of light (slide projector) be directed close to the stage of the microscope to permit the light to enter the objective and leave through the eyepiece onto the screen. The size of the projected image on the screen can be controlled by varying the distance between the screen and the eyepiece of the microscope. Ruth Frank suggests that a microscope can be used with a home-made slide projector which students can construct.[15] The materials needed are a coffee can, convex condenser lens, and a spotlight. Pupil construction activities in the laboratory can serve as an excellent means of stimulating further interest in science.

Some of these construction activities by pupils should be encouraged even if there is a sufficient budget to purchase many of the required laboratory supplies. Even though excellent Riker mounts in which hard-to-find insects are displayed should be purchased from biological or other scientific supply companies, students of biology should also be encouraged to make their own displays. Obtain cardboard boxes from $1/2$ to 1 inch in height. Fill the box to its capacity with inexpensive, nonsterile absorbent cotton. Place the insects with labels in appropriate places on top of

[15] Ruth Frank, "Microprojection Method," *The Science Teacher,* vol. 25 (November, 1958), p. 402.

Fig. 5.2. Improvising equipment, as in pupil construction of models and preparation of museum jars, is an important learning activity in biology. (Courtesy of Ralph Sonen, Northport High School, Northport, N.Y.)

the cotton. Cover the box with a piece of plate glass, strong transparent plastic, or saran. Cut out the cover of the cardboard box so that it serves as a frame with about a one inch border, and place it on top of the glass or substitute. Seal the cardboard cover frame tightly with scotch tape or a substitute around the edges of the box to make it airtight. To decorate the homemade Riker mount, a coat of paint can be applied to the edges of the box and the top frame. These mounts may be displayed in the classroom, the laboratory, the museum, or in the home.

Schmitt boxes may also be prepared by pupils and teachers. Discarded cigar boxes, a few corks, glue, labels, straight pins, and insects comprise the necessary materials. Slice 6 to 12 pieces of cork into cross sections about $\frac{1}{4}$ inch thick. Glue these cork sections to the bottom inside the cigar box. Place a straight pin through the thorax (center) of the insect and into the section of the cork which is mounted in the cigar box. Care should be exercised in moving the insect close to the head of the pin so the legs of the insect remain undisturbed and suspended above the cork. A label containing information such as name (genus and species), date collected, and locality or habitat should be pasted under each specimen. For display purposes, a glass plate or saran can replace the regular cigar box cover. The cover should be well sealed by using scotch tape or a similar substance. The Schmitt box is suitable for insects that do not have prominent wings or too-fleshy bodies. Moths and butterflies should be mounted in the Riker display described in the previous paragraph. It is desirable to use a pair of forceps to put the pin through the insect or when spreading wings of other insects.

Many other kinds of equipment can be constructed by both students and teachers. Animal cages, terraria, aquaria, herbaria, and flower boxes will provide adequate housing for many interesting species of flora and fauna. A living laboratory consisting of white rats or mice, guinea pigs, hamsters, snakes, turtles, frogs, birds, flies (Drosophila melanogaster), earthworms, snails, and fish can provide students with worthwhile experiences in the care and feeding of animals. Biological principles can be taught effectively through the use of living as well as preserved specimens. Mesh wire from the hardware store, sheet metal or tin plates, coffee cans, discarded glass jars and bowls, plate glass, and a few wooden crates are the basic materials for making homes for representative plant and animal life. The industrial arts teacher in the school may contribute materials and advice in the construction of animal cages.

Fig. 5.3. Projects in biology can integrate knowledge and skills in other sciences: electricity, psychology, physiology. (Courtesy of Board of Education, Long Beach Public Schools, Long Beach, N.Y.)

Museum jars for display and study purposes are invaluable as teaching aids in biology. Empty pickle, fruit, coffee, and large olive jars can serve as museum jars to house preserved biological specimens. Many insects can be preserved in glass jars that are filled with 70 percent alcohol. Aquatic snails, clams, lampreys, fish, mammals, and grassfrog eggs can be preserved in jars containing 8 percent formalin. Worms, frogs, and salamanders can be preserved in 5 percent solutions of formalin.

Many flying insects can be obtained in the fields with the aid of a collecting net. Most insects can be picked by hand. Under dead leaves, rocks, and in moss, many species of insects and arthropods can readily be acquired. "Killing" jars for insects may be purchased from most scientific supply companies. These jars usually contain sodium or potassium cyanide, the fumes and crystals of which are very poisonous.

Another useful aid in teaching biology may be purchased for less than one dollar.[16] Venus-flytrap and other insectivorous and carnivorous bulbs and plants are very interesting to study in the classroom and are helpful in teaching principles of nutrition, plant-animal food relations, enzymes and extracellular digestion, electrical charges versus tropisms in plant life and "nerve" reactions. The Venus-flytrap bulb (Dionaea muscipula) usually sprouts within a few weeks. A mature plant containing between 5 and 12 traps will develop in 8 to 10 weeks. Students will enjoy catching insects and observing how the lobes of the plant close to trap an insect.

Students who possess their own individual microscopes should be encouraged to bring them to the biology laboratory. Some microscopes that offer magnification power up to 300x may be purchased for as little as $15.00.[17] These are not substitutes for regular laboratory equipment; but they can be used to provide individual students with microscopes if the budget prevents purchase of regular laboratory microscopes.

[16] Armstrong Associates, Inc., 15 Ash Street, Basking Ridge, N.J., specializes in insect-eating plants.
[17] Refer to catalogue from Edmund Optics, Barrington, N.J.

LEARNING ACTIVITIES

In addition to demonstrations, individual and group laboratory work, projects, there are unique learning activities in biology: through the use of community resources, field trips, and special equipment such as the microprojector and dissecting equipment. The extent to which these materials and methods can be employed to promote the learning of biology will vary from school to school and from one geographical area to another. Wherever it is possible to make use of them, satisfying results may be anticipated.

Community resources include professional scientists who work or reside in the school community, science professors from nearby colleges, health officers in local agencies, pharmaceutical or biological industries, nearby research centers, museums, zoological gardens, out-of-school science clubs, and photography clubs. Many of the scientists who either reside or work in the community are very pleased to speak to science classes, school assembly programs, science fairs, and science clubs. They may be used to give stimulating demonstrations and talks followed by discussion or to discuss scientific opportunities and careers.

Biological field trips constitute an important part of learning biological principles and relationships. A trip, with basic equipment and the instructor, to local marshes, woodlands, forests, parks, ponds, lakes, or rural areas can be a most satisfying learning experience. Basic equipment such as collecting nets for insects, fish, eggs, amphibia; identifying and keying

Fig. 5.4. The greenhouse is an important part of laboratory work in teaching biology. (Courtesy of Board of Education, City of New York)

manuals of local flora and fauna; collecting jars and boxes; envelopes; and scrapbooks should be available on the field trip.

Specific instructions should be given to students, and careful plans should be developed before going on a field trip. Students should know beforehand exactly what they should look for and study. Plant-animal communities should be discussed in class along with the understanding of ecological relationships. It is recommended that the instructor survey the area before inviting the class on a field trip. This will enable the science teacher to introduce the "what" and "how" to look for the living species. For example, in an area where there are decaying tree limbs or trunks, one can discover sow bugs, centipedes, millipedes, and toadstools. Many of the specimens can be collected and brought to the school laboratory for further study. These specimens should be preserved according to the procedures recommended in the previous section.

The use of the microprojector is not only helpful in learning biological information, it also reinforces the ability to observe what should be observed. For example, in the biological laboratory, it may be difficult for the teacher to determine whether or not the students actually see the cilia in a paramecium. The teacher may draw a diagram on the blackboard, refer to a picture in a textbook, or have the pupils prepare a drawing of the paramecium. The microprojector is a very valuable visual aid which enables the teacher to point out on the screen the cilia or other microscopic structures to be observed by the students.

When living organisms are subjected to microprojection, the condenser should contain a dilute solution of copper sulfate. This will reduce the intensity of the heat from the source of light. Avoid the evaporation of the culture liquid on the slide. A ring of Vaseline around the cover slip will reduce evaporation. A depression slide is useful for projecting living organisms since they will have a liquid medium for their locomotion.

Temporary wet mounts may be stained to depict more accurately specific parts of a cell. The nucleus and granules of cytoplasm will stain effectively through the use of methylene blue (1 to

10,000 parts of distilled water. Congo red (1:1000) or neutral red (1:4000) may also be used in place of methylene blue. Although Lugol's iodine solution is frequently employed, the cells die rapidly. To avoid crushing an organism such as hydra, a small bristle should be inserted under the cover slip. The nematocysts in hydra can be released if a small drop of the stain safranin is placed on the wet mount. If a mixed group of protozoa such as blepharisma, stentors, and paramecia are to be used for microprojection, either a bristle under the cover slip or a depression slide should be used. Frequently beginning students in biology experience difficulty in observing some of the structures such as the nucleus in a paramecium. To slow down the rapid locomotion of the paramecium and other protozoa, allow the water to evaporate slowly and with the aid of a dark field; the nucleus and contractile vacuole can then be observed without difficulty. When evaporation is completed, the protozoa will disintegrate.

The students of biology and the instructor may wish to prepare their own cultures for microprojection. Many techniques that may be accomplished in the laboratory or in the classroom have been described by Brandwein and by Needham.[18]

The biology teacher should have a file covering various learning activities such as the development of skills in the use of the microscope and microprojector; the showing of suitable films and filmstrips; the dissection of organisms; the maintaining of a herbarium, terrarium, and aquarium; the preparation and maintenance of living cultures; the sectioning and preserving of materials for slides; possible field trips to be made with the respective kinds of learning activities; and the use of community resources. This file should be made available to students who show interest and ability in developing newer skills and knowledge in the biological sciences. It is also possible that a student may show the first signs of

[18] P. F. Brandwein, "Culture Methods for Protozoa," *American Naturalist,* vol. 69 (1935), p. 628; J. Needham (ed.), *Culture Methods for Invertebrate Animals,* Comstock, 1937.

interest in the biological sciences as a result of his or her encouragement in the use of some of the materials that are located in this file.

SUMMARY

The teaching of biological principles as a result of many worthwhile learning activities can establish a good relationship between the need for facts and generalizations. It is also possible to teach biology through solving problems that stress important skills, attitudes, and knowledge. Although much equipment is needed to teach biology efficiently, science teachers and their students frequently improvise, and the results can be a productive learning experience. Field trips pertaining to ecology, the use of community resources (such as personnel, places, and equipment), and the use of special aids such as the microprojector are vital for effective teaching of biology. Greater use of industries and museums should be made in the teaching of biology.

EXERCISES

1. Prepare a list of significant biological principles that you would teach in a biology course, and compare with the materials suggested in the adopted textbook.
2. List 10 homemade or classroom projects that can be used in a school museum.
3. What community agencies are available to augment classroom instruction in biology?
4. Compare the conditions under which you would use the microprojector and individual microscopes for your students.
5. Discuss in detail the preliminary preparations that are needed before a biology class goes on a field trip.
6. How are field trips in biology related to laboratory and other classroom activities?

SUGGESTED READINGS

Burnett, R. Will, *Teaching Science in the Secondary School,* New York, Rinehart & Company, Inc., 1957.

Heiss, E. D., Obourn, E. S., and Hoffman, C. W., *Modern Science Teaching*, New York, The Macmillan Company, 1950.

McKibben, Margaret J., "An Analysis of Principles and Activities of Importance for General Biology Courses in High Schools," *Science Education*, vol. 39 (April, 1955), pp. 187–196.

Martin, W. Edgar, *Facilities and Equipment for Science and Mathematics*, Washington, D.C., U.S. Department of Health, Education, and Welfare, 1960.

Martin, W. Edgar, "The Major Principles of the Biological Sciences of Importance for General Education," Circular No. 308, U.S. Department of Health, Education, and Welfare (reprinted June, 1956).

Morholt, E., Brandwein, P. F., and Joseph, A., *A Sourcebook for the Biological Sciences*, New York, Harcourt, Brace & Company, 1958.

Obourn, Ellsworth S., *et al.*, "General Facilities and Equipment," *Science and Mathematics in Public High Schools, 1958, Part 1*, Washington, D.C., U.S. Department of Health, Education, and Welfare, 1960.

Richardson, John S., *Science Teaching in Secondary Schools*, Englewood Cliffs, N.J., Prentice-Hall, Inc., 1957.

Van Deventer, William C., "The Teaching of Basic Premises as an Approach to Science in General Education," *Science Education*, vol. 39 (December, 1955), pp. 389–398.

Van Deventer, William C., "Teaching Science in Relation to Man's Thinking," *Science Education*, vol. 35 (March, 1951), pp. 104–106.

Washton, Nathan S., "A Syllabus in Biology for General Education," *Science Education*, vol. 35 (March, 1951), pp. 84–92, and vol. 36 (October, 1952), pp. 227–237.

Washton, Nathan S., "Teaching Biology for General Education," *Science Education*, vol. 36 (October, 1952), pp. 237–240.

6

SPECIAL PROBLEMS OF THE PHYSICAL SCIENCE TEACHER

PRINCIPLES AND PROBLEMS APPROACH

As in the biological sciences, several studies pertaining to the teaching of the physical sciences by means of the *principles approach* have appeared in the literature. A study by Wise, for example, has significance for general education in that it integrates principles from physics, chemistry, and geology, as shown in the following samples:

The free surface of a liquid contracts to the smallest possible area due to surface tension.

The distance a body travels, starting from rest with a constant acceleration, is one-half the acceleration times the square of the time.

Dark, rough, or unpolished surfaces absorb or radiate energy more effectively than light, smooth, or polished surfaces.

Atoms may be broken down by bombarding the nucleus with high-speed particles such as protons, alpha particles, and neutrons.

The earth's surface may be elevated or lowered by interior forces.[1]

The 270 principles stated by Wise can be restated to meet the needs of individual classes in physics, chemistry, earth science, or physical science.

The danger in the direct use of the principle approach is that each principle may be presented in consecutive order with the feeling that pupils must memorize each of them. Modern concepts in the psychology of learning stress the need for providing suitable

---

[1] Harold E. Wise, "A Determination of the Relative Importance of Principles of Physical Science for General Education," *Science Education,* vol. 25 (December, 1941), pp. 371–379; vol. 26 (January, 1942), pp. 8–12; vol. 27 (February, 1943), pp. 36–40; and vol. 28 (September–October, 1943), pp. 67–76.

learning experiences such as demonstrations, experiments, science projects, and other related activities that ultimately lead the learner to the ability to formulate the principle or generalization. Frequently, the science teacher may have to direct or guide pupils in developing their ability to formulate generalizations. He may suggest to the students what they should look for and proceed to elicit from them the nature of the response that resembles the basic principles of physical science. The art of questioning plays a vital role in eliciting the desired responses. The skilled teacher will help students to develop the principles or understandings without depriving them of inductive and analytical reasoning.

The New York State Department of Education suggests:

The objectives of courses in physics and chemistry should extend far beyond a minimal comprehension of the basic facts and principles outlined in these syllabuses. The appreciation of the scientific method, the ability and willingness to change beliefs and opinions after careful weighing of new evidence, and the development of the habit of critical thinking are the intangible but most important outcomes of the study of these sciences. These methods of thought and action will remain long after many specific details of subject matter are forgotten.[2]

In teaching physics or chemistry, the teacher is indeed concerned with the formation of student attitudes and the ability to modify opinions in the light of new evidence. How can a science teacher help a student see the degree of self-rigidity which is a hindrance to critical thinking? He can help students perform self-evaluations while they perform experiments and can indicate whether or not they reveal signs of prejudice in interpreting data. Constructive attitudinal and behavioral changes should be goals in the science classroom along with the scientific understandings or principles.

Several research studies show how to identify, select, evaluate, recognize, and apply the principles of the physical sciences.[3] Basi-

[2] New York State Education Department, Bureau of Secondary Curriculum Development, *Chemistry and Physics,* 1957, p. 7.

[3] See Milton Babitz and Noel Keys, "An Experiment in Teaching Pupils to Apply Scientific Principles," *Science Education,* vol. 23 (December, 1939) pp. 367–370; Vaden W. Miles, "A Determination of Principles and Experiments for an

cally, the data is obtained from a careful examination and analysis of newspapers, magazine articles, books, judgments by experts, syllabuses, references indicating use of scientific information, surveys, and questionnaires.

In "An outline of the scope of content and related understandings of the Courses of Study," the New York State Education Department recommends the following areas in a high school physics course:[4]

Areas	*Number of weeks*	*Percentage of time*
Mechanics	8	27
Heat	5	17
Transfer of energy by wave motion	5	17
Electricity	7	23
Alternating current and electronics	3	10
Nuclear energy	2	7

It is suggested that 30 weeks of the school year consist of teaching the above topics; optional topics can be taught during the remaining 8 weeks. The selection of the optional topics should be made in terms of pupil interests and needs.

The following extract from the New York State Education Department's teaching outline lists the major understandings or principles of physics for each of the recommended areas:

1. MECHANICS

TOPICS	UNDERSTANDINGS
Forces in equilibrium	An object is in equilibrium and is at rest or moving with constant velocity when there are no unbalanced forces or moments acting on it.

Integrated Course of Physical Science for High School," *Science Education,* vol. 33 (March, 1949), pp. 147–152, and (April, 1949), pp. 198–205; John H. Owens, "The Ability to Recognize and Apply Scientific Principles in New Situations," *Science Education,* vol. 35 (October, 1951), pp. 207–213.

4 New York State Education Department, *op. cit.,* pp. 46–72.

Forces and motion   The change in motion of an object is determined by the forces acting on it and their points of application.

Work and energy   Energy is needed to do work.

Machines   Machines are used to change the magnitude or direction of a force, or the speed and distance through which it acts.

Fig. 6.1. Group and individual laboratory work can be effective in teaching physics, especially some topics in mechanics. (Courtesy of Uniondale High School, Uniondale, N.Y.)

2. HEAT

TOPICS   UNDERSTANDINGS

Heat, a form of energy   Heat is a form of energy that flows between two bodies which are at different temperatures. (Note—Heat is now distinguished from the internal energy of a body and is thought of as energy in transit. Work done on or by a system and heat transferred to or from a system are methods whereby the internal energy of a system is changed. The addition of heat energy to a body either increases the kinetic energy of the random translatory motion of its molecules or increases their potential energy of position, as when melting or evaporation occurs.)

Expansion

Most forms of matter expand when heated by an amount which is proportional to the original size and the temperature change, and which depends on the nature of the material.

Calorimetry

When two objects at different temperatures are together, heat passes from the hot object to the cold object, the heat lost by the hot object equaling the heat gained by the cold one.

Change of state

When a substance undergoes a change of state, energy is either absorbed or liberated. This heat is used to separate and free the molecules from adjacent ones and does not produce a temperature change.

Heat and work

When work is done on a thermally insulated gas by compressing it, its temperature rises; when it does work by expanding, its temperature decreases.

3. Transfer of Energy by Wave Motion

TOPICS	UNDERSTANDINGS
General characteristics of waves	A wave is a vibratory disturbance which travels through a medium.
Sound	Longitudinal waves in matter transmit sound. Sound originates in vibrating bodies.
Electromagnetic radiation	Energy may be transmitted by radiation waves which are electromagnetic in nature and origin.
Visible light	When a ray of light is reflected, the angle of reflection equals the angle of incidence.

4. Electricity

TOPICS	UNDERSTANDINGS
Static electricity	When different substances are brought into close contact by rubbing, they become oppositely charged.
The electric current	A flow of electric charge is an electric current. In metallic conductors, the moving charges are electrons.
Magnetism	A magnet attracts magnetic materials.
Induced electromotive force	An e.m.f. is induced in a circuit whenever there is a change in the total strength of the magnetic field passing through it.

5. Alternating Current and Electronics

TOPICS	UNDERSTANDINGS
Alternating-current circuits	Alternating current makes possible the use of devices and phenomena quite different from those encountered with steady direct current.
Vacuum tubes	Electronics owes its present state of development to the vacuum tube.
Radio	Radio transmission uses a long wave portion of the radiation spectrum.
Television	Television uses AM for picture transmission and FM for the sound.

6. Nuclear Energy

TOPICS	UNDERSTANDINGS
Structure of the nucleus	Two of the fundamental particles which compose the nuclei of atoms are protons and neutrons.
Radioactivity	Radioactive substances emit particles or radiation from the nucleus.
Fission	Fission is brought about by the capture of a neutron by the nucleus. Fission results in the liberation of energy. The mass of the fission products is less than the original mass.

| Thermonuclear reactions | The fusion of light elements to form elements of intermediate mass releases energy. Fusion products are not generally radioactive. |
| Peacetime uses of nuclear energy | Release of nuclear energy has many uses and future possibilities.[5] |

The above understandings are major generalizations that should be formulated by students in physics classes as a result of demonstrations, experiments, and discussions. The New York State Handbook of Physics suggests a series of demonstrations that can be performed by the science teacher. The demonstration method places the emphasis on the development of the understandings or principles of physics. It is more desirable to use the developmental approach in which the students formulate the principle or understanding as a result of observing a demonstration or performing an experiment than merely to offer the principle of physics at the beginning of the demonstration. The science teacher should avoid as much as possible the mechanical, rote learning of the principles.

The teaching of principles of physics can also be accomplished by the problem approach. For example, a physics teacher poses the following situation: A student discovers one dollar protruding out from under a 250-pound rock in the backyard.

After presenting the above-stated situation, the teacher proceeds to elicit the statement or formulation of the problem from the students. Usually, after two or three attempts by students, the teacher guides the pupils into the statement of the problem: To find a good way to lift the rock to obtain the dollar without hurting oneself.

With the identification or statement of the problem, the teacher asks pupils for their ideas (hypotheses). The teacher elicits a few hypotheses, as, for example, use a pulley, a crowbar, or an inclined plane. A brief discussion may occur at this point since it is important for students to learn how to suggest and screen hypotheses.

The next step should encourage pupils to test each of these hypotheses by designing experiments. The process of experimenta-

[5] *Ibid.*

tion enables the students to reject, modify, or accept a hypothesis. The self-rejection or self-acceptance of a hypothesis appears to be more effective for greater retention and learning. A student is most willing to give up the idea of the inclined plane from his own experience or experimentation. Another student uses the crowbar and discovers that he can push the rock to get the dollar.

A significant part of the problem-solving approach is the evaluation of the experiments. The observations made during the experiments and the evaluation of data in a critical fashion constitute a major step before the students are able to formulate a generalization or a conclusion.

This problem does not necessarily demand that the class adjourn to the student's backyard. A replica of the situation can be established in the class. Through the use of weights and measuring instruments, the forces required to obtain the dollar from under the rock or stone can be calculated in the class through proportional methods. Perhaps the actual problem can be designed in terms of the classroom rather than the backyard.

Through the problem approach the pupil acquires not only a skill in solving problems but also the ability to develop a scientific understanding or principle based upon problem-solving activity or experimentation. The teaching of principles of physics, chemistry, or physical science will afford science teachers numerous opportunities to use the problem-solving approach or the principle approach in developing an understanding of the basic principles.

Miles developed a number of principles and experiments for courses of integrated physical science. The functional understanding of these scientific principles constitutes an important objective of science teaching. The following is a sample of a principle to be established and understood as a result of a series of experiments:

Diffusible substances tend to scatter from the point of greatest concentration until all points are at equal concentration.

EXPERIMENTS

If concentrated sulfuric acid is carefully released from a pipette at the bottom of a tall glass cylinder containing a solution of blue litmus, what is observed over a period of time? . . .

Will ammonia gas from an open bottle move to all parts of a room that is, do gases diffuse through gases?

Will a crystal of copper sulfate or potassium permanganate diffuse upward throughout still water in a tall cylinder, that is, do molecules move from solids into liquids and diffuse through liquids? . . .

If a bottle of ink with a flat glass cover is set under water in a large beaker and the cover is carefully pushed aside, what is observed over a period of time?

If moth balls are placed in a large jar, smelled, then closed, and again smelled the next day, is there any evidence that molecules move from solids into gases and diffuse through gases? . . .

If a gas jet is barely open, can the odor of gas soon be detected at a considerable distance from the jet? . . .

Will ammonia vapor diffuse from the bottom of a bottle upward through filter paper into a chimney on top of the bottle? . . .

If two drops of ammonia water and hydrochloric acid are placed in separate warm glass bottles covered with glass plates, what is observed after the bottle of ammonia is inverted on top of the other bottle and the glass plates are removed? . . .

Does a rubber balloon inflated with hydrogen or gasoline vapor remain inflated or collapse in a short time? . . .

Does hydrogen diffuse readily from an upper bottle of hydrogen to a lower bottle of air placed mouth to mouth? . . .

Do molecules of carbon disulfide move from the bottom of a bottle into a deflated balloon over the mouth of the bottle? . . .[6]

These experiments proposed by Miles place much emphasis on the development of principles of physical science rather than on problem-solving ability. The science teacher will discover that not all of the scientific principles lend themselves to the problem-solving approach as the most effective method of teaching science. Hence, simple experiments designed by either the teacher or the pupil can be used in the classroom to help students arrive at principles or scientific conclusions via inductive reasoning as well as deductive reasoning. In the problem-solving method, the experiments are usually designed cooperatively by the science teacher

[6] Vaden W. Miles, *Principles and Experiments for Courses of Integrated Physical Science,* Detroit, Wayne State University, published by author, 1950.

and the pupils. It is always advisable for the science teacher to evaluate whether or not the students have arrived at the correct scientific principle rather than to assume that the deduction or the induction has been made correctly. Likewise, students should be encouraged to make applications of the scientific principles for a better understanding and use of them.

EQUIPMENT AND SUPPLIES

A storage or preparation room should house the following equipment and supplies for teaching general and physical science.

1 air pump, compression and vacuum
2 air-thermometer bulbs
1 alpha-ray tip
8 ammeters, D.C. 0–5
1 ammeter, A.C. 0–5
1 anatomical model (human head and torso)
1 aneroid barometer
1 ant observation chamber
2 aquariums, with glass covers
1 doz. asbestos squares
1 atomizer
1 audio-amplifier
1 audio-generator
1 balance, trip or beam
24 balances, spring, 250 gm.
1 package balloons
1 doz. balls, steel, $\frac{1}{2}$ inch diam.
1 doz. balls, steel, $\frac{3}{4}$ inch diam.
2 doz. balls, steel, 1 inch diam.
2 doz. balls, steel, $1\frac{1}{2}$ inch diam.
2 doz. balls, steel, 2 inch diam.
1 ball and ring expansion apparatus

1 barometer, mercury
2 battery jars, 6 x 8 in.
6 sets of beakers, Pyrex glass, 100, 150, 250, 400 ml.
2 beakers, Pyrex, 1000 ml.
24 beads, wood, $\frac{1}{2}$ inch.
2 bells, electric
1 bell jar
1 doz. bottles, 12 oz., wide-mouth
1 brake horsepower apparatus
1 Brownian movement apparatus
2 brushes, test tube and bottle
2 Bunsen burners
1 capacitor (condenser) 100–200 mf.
4 clamps, burette, adjustable
3 clamps, pinch
2 clamps, screw compressor
2 calcite crystals, clear (Iceland spar)
2 calorimeters (nickel-plated brass)
1 centrifuge rotator accessory
1 Charles' Law tube
8 sets coils, laws of resistance
3 compasses, magnetic

1 crane boom
1 crystal, fixed germanium diode, IN34
1 cum-bak
1 deflagrating spoon
1 drying tube, 200 ml.
1 earphone, high impedance
1 electric iron
1 electric whirl and stand
1 earphone, high impedance
1 electromagnet, demonstration
1 electrophorus
1 electroscope
2 evaporating dishes (porcelain)
1 ea. filters—red, green, blue, infrared
1 feeding ring (fish)
1 fire syringe
1 first aid kit
6 flasks, Erlenmeyer, 250 ml.
6 flasks, Florence, 250, 500, and 1000 ml.
1 set fluorescent minerals
1 set fluorescent paints
1 foot-candle meter
12 forceps, 5 inch
1 friction pad, fur
1 friction pad, silk
1 galvanometer (lecture table)
12 galvanometers (student type)
1 gas mantle thorium
1 Geiger counter
24 glass plates (index of refraction)
1 generator A.C., D.C.
1 generator, 6-volt
1 graduated cylinder, 100 ml.
1 graduated cylinder, 1000 ml.
1 guinea and feather tube

12 Hall's car
6 hand lenses
1 hot water bottle
1 hydraulic press, glass model
12 inclined planes
1 induction coil
12 inductors, 20–30 henry, 200 ohm
1 inertia ball with hooks
1 jug, gallon
1 kilowatt-hour meter
12 knife-edge clamps, lever
2 lenses, double convex, mounted 3/4 inch diam., 10–12 inch focal length
2 lenses, achromatic, 2–3 inch diam., focal length 8–10 in.
12 lenses, double convex, 50 mm. diam., 15 cm. focal length
12 lenses, double convex, 50 mm., diam., 10 cm. focal length
2 lenses, double concave, 50 mm. diam., 15 cm. focal length
2 lens holders, adjustable
12 lens supports to fit meter stick
4 line cords
12 linear expansion apparatus, each with 2 different test rods
1 liter measure
2 loudspeakers, 4 inch, permanent magnet
1 lucite rod, coiled
24 magnets, bar, 15 cm. long
12 magnets, U-shaped

1 magnet, horseshoe
2 magnets, cylindrical, alnico
1 magnet, magnetron
24 meter sticks
1 metronome
1 microphone
1 microscope with microprojector attachment
12 milliammeters, D.C., 0–10
1 milliammeter, D.C., 0–1
24 mirrors, small
1 motor, water
1 motor and generator demonstrator
12 motors, St. Louis, with commutator, sliprings and electromagnetic field
1 motor, ¼ horsepower
24 mouse traps
1 ohmmeter
1 optical disk and accessories
1 oscilloscope, cathode-ray, 5 inch
12 pendulum balls, wood
12 pendulum balls, steel
12 pendulum clamps
1 periodic chart
2 doz. ping-pong balls
12 photometers, Bunsen
1 doz. pith balls
2 polaroid disks
1 power supply, 0–300 v., D.C., at 60 ma., with taps at 75 v.
12 prisms, 2.5 x 5 cm.
12 protractors
2 pulleys, mounted on rod
1 pulley, large ball-bearing
24 pulleys, single sheave
12 pulleys, double sheave

12 pulleys, triple sheave
1 quart measure
1 radio receiver
1 radiometer
1 radium button
1 refraction tank
12 resistors, 2 ohm, 5 watt
12 resistors, 3 ohm, 5 watt
12 resistors, 5 ohm, 5 watt
1 resistor, 1200 ohm, 1 watt
1 resistor, 5000 ohm, 1 watt
1 resistor, 10,000 ohm, 1 watt
1 resistor, 25,000 ohm, 5 watt
2 resistors, 0.1 megohm, 1 watt
1 resistor, 0.2 megohms, 1 watt
1 resistor, 0.5 megohm, 1 watt
2 resistors, 1.0 megohm, 1 watt
2 resonance bars
2 resonance tubes 1½ x 36 in.
1 resonance tube 1½ x 18 in.
1 revolution counter
12 rheostats, 5 ohm, 25 watt
1 rheostat, 5 ohm, 25 watt
1 ea. rheostats, 25, 200, 500 ohm, 50 watt
1 ea. rheostat-potentiometer, 100, 1000, 2000, 10,000 ohm, 4 watt
12 ringstand supports
12 rings, 4 inch diam.
1 rod, hard rubber
1 rod, glass
8 rods, soft iron from magnet cores
1 rotator
24 rulers, metric and English, 1 foot
12 salt shakers (iron filings)
1 screen, translucent
1 screen, opaque projection

12 screen supports (for meter stick)
1 signal generator, rf
1 siren disk
12 sockets, octal
1 socket, four-prong
12 sockets, standard, screw base
12 sockets, miniature screw base
1 socket, drop cord
1 spectrum chart
1 spectrum tube, neon
1 spectrum tube, helium
1 spinthariscope
1 spotlight
1 spring, coiled, 1.5 cm. diam., 20 cm. long
1 spring, coiled, 1.5 cm. diam., 200 cm. long
12 steam generators, with caps, stacks, and tripods
12 stop watches
1 stop clock, electric
2 switches, single-pole, double throw
12 switches, single-pole, single throw
4 switches, double-pole, double throw
2 switches, double-pole, single throw
12 switches, push-button
2 support rods and bases, height 100 cm.
12 pr. supports for meter sticks —optical bench

12 test tubes, Pyrex, length 150 mm.
12 thermometers, —20° C to 110° C
1 thermostat, bimetallic
1 transformer, variable toy train
2 transformers, radio output
1 transformer, bell-ringing
1 triangle support, wire
1 tripod, three concentric rings
12 tubing clamps, spring
5 tuning forks, 128, 256, 320, 384, 512 v.p.s.
1 vacuum pump, motor driven, with pump plate
12 vacuum tubes, type 6H6
6 vacuum tubes, type 6J5
1 vacuum tube voltmeter
12 voltmeters, D.C. 0–10
1 voltmeter, D.C., 0–100
1 voltmeter, D.C. 0–300
12 voltmeters, A.C., 0–10
1 voltmeter, A.C., 0–150
3 watch glasses, Pyrex, 75 mm. diam.
1 set weights for balance (1 gram–1000 grams)
3 sets hooked weights, 10 gm.– 1000 grams
12 sets slotted weights and hangers, 1 gm.–500 gms.
1 Wimshurst static machine
1 wingtop attachment for Bunsen burner
12 wire gauze squares

In addition to basic equipment, varying quantities of chemicals and other supplies are needed for the teaching of general and physical science. The ordering of supplies from year to year will be influenced by the number of students, the number of demonstrations and experiments, and the kind of laboratory manual or open-end type of experiments. It is recommended that each science teacher examine all of the demonstrations and experiments planned for chemistry, physics, and physical or general science during the year and prepare a list of supplies needed for each class. It is reasonable to assume that such items as methyl alcohol, absorbent cotton, ammonia, aluminum foil, balloons, candles, glass and rubber tubing, corks, stoppers, lamps, and wire are basic supplies. It is also desirable that an inventory of all equipment, supplies, and tools be made in early Spring in order to permit delivery of needed materials in early Fall.

IMPROVISING FOR LACK OF EQUIPMENT

Where a school budget does not permit the purchase of scientific equipment to be used for instructional purposes, the teacher may wish to solicit the aid of the industrial arts department and students in creating such equipment. For example, a bimetallic thermostat can be made in the shop, using a copper and iron strip. Calorimeters can be improvised with the help of several "tin" cans. Christmas tree electric lights and wiring can be employed in teaching series and parallel circuits. Principles of light can be taught with the help of ordinary face mirrors found in the home. Cigar boxes may be converted to printing boxes for photographic purposes. Students will be glad to bring simple machines from the home: nut crackers, screws, hammers, and other tools.

Equipment that is needed to demonstrate ionization or electrolytic dissociation can be assembled easily by utilizing a strip of copper and zinc, an electric socket, wire, acids, bases, salts, a glass jar, and an electric bulb. If there is no gas outlet, a hot plate may be a good source of heat. Some teachers have used "canned heat" like Sterno in the absence of an electric outlet and gas. Although running water and a sink are essential in teaching science, a few teachers were compelled to use buckets for bringing in water and as a means of disposing of it.

It is also possible that improvising equipment will lead to an application or translation of a scientific idea. For example, the discovery of the cyclotron extended man's knowledge of the atom. The application is the production and utilization of atomic energy. The development of scientific instruments (such as the cyclotron) is needed for more critical measurement and is also vital to uncovering new information.

Ideally, students would be called on to improvise scientific equipment only when such improvising is primarily for the transfer of an idea into an instrument, with the ultimate goal of gaining additional knowledge. This would constitute a method of instruction which would emphasize the creative talents of students. But the real solution to the problem is to provide, along with the opportunity for improvising, an adequate school budget to purchase essential equipment and supplies.

UNIQUE SKILLS IN CHEMISTRY

The teaching of chemistry in the senior high school can make a worthy contribution toward general education as well as preprofessional or vocational education. Most of the students who elect chemistry are very much interested in the subject and/or plan to specialize in some area in science. For the future scientist, basic skills unique to the field of chemistry are taught in the laboratory. It isn't enough to know how to use a Bunsen burner, bend a piece of glass tubing, heat a test tube, and other laboratory skills. Students should be able to perform these and other laboratory operations as a result of mastering these skills through satisfactory laboratory practice and supervision. These necessary skills are taught more effectively through the laboratory period of instruction than through demonstrations. In the case of acquiring chemical knowledge, however, as contrasted with acquiring basic skills, most of the research studies indicate that there is little significant difference in the effect on student achievement between laboratory instruction and demonstration.

The Manufacturing Chemists' Association in cooperation with

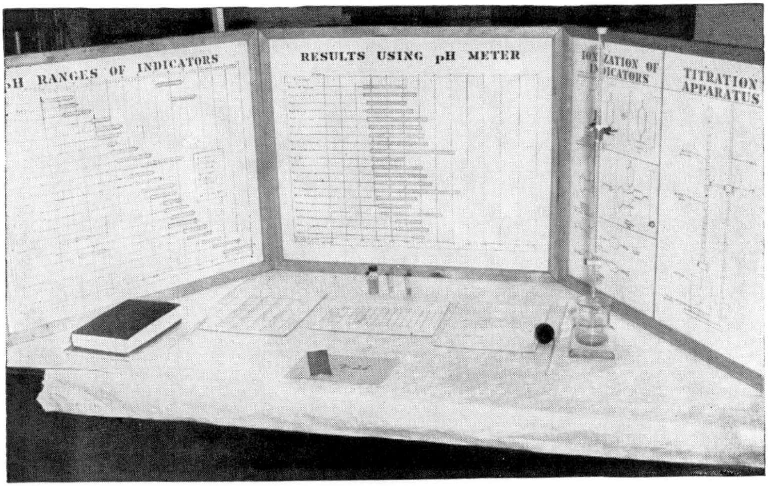

Fig. 6.2.   Much chemical information and skill as well are required to perform projects that determine pH and ranges of indicators. (Courtesy of Uniondale High School, Uniondale, N.Y.)

a planning committee recently developed a group of "Scientific Chemistry Experiments" for individual students in the high school laboratory.[7] The experiments were developed for several specific objectives—to apply chemical principles to industry, agriculture, everyday living; to provide highly interesting and challenging experiences in the high school chemistry laboratory; to develop greater enthusiasm of able students for careers in science; and to "foster intellectual activity by posing questions to be answered through laboratory experiences." Titles of the experiments include: Heating Metallic Oxides, Reactions Between Oxides and Water, Effect of Weight of Catalyst on Reaction Rate, Neutralizing Phosphoric Acid, Effect of Concentration on Rate of Reaction, Making a Solubility Curve, Concentration of Hydrogen Peroxide and Its Decomposition Rate, and Use of Bunsen Burner.

[7] The Manufacturing Chemists' Association, 1625 Eye Street NW, Washington 6, D.C., will supply open-ended chemical experiments. The background and planning committee consisted of: Keith Johnson, Morris Meister, Elbert C. Weaver, and Elwood J. Winters.

These open-ended experiments differ from the conventional laboratory manuals in that they do not give as much information (cookbook, recipe style) and demand more planning and thinking on the part of the student in performing the experiment. This program does not ask the student to supply a missing word or phrase. The student writes a report in his own manner on the experiment and states the evidence for his conclusions. The answers to the questions cannot be anticipated at the start of the experiments. Students are asked to make predictions and to verify them on the basis of their laboratory work. Real-life situations are used wherever possible, and applications are emphasized throughout the laboratory experiments. The teacher is provided with information sheets to help guide and direct the pupil laboratory experience.

In some chemistry classes, teachers have encouraged their students to help design completely or partially the chemistry exercises to be performed in the classroom laboratory. Student-designed activity often falls in the area of qualitative and quantitative analysis, for example, offering much opportunity to search for the unknown. Activity of this kind is really an experiment and not an exercise to verify knowledge that can be obtained from the text. It differs from the demonstration in that the student-designed experiment in qualitative or quantitative analysis under the guidance and direction of the chemistry instructor is an activity to explore or discover an idea that is unknown to the student and not an activity to prove or demonstrate an idea which is known.

Chemistry can be taught for developing skills in problem solving. A group of chemistry teachers can search for appropriate materials from their past experiences as well as from periodicals. In the past, most of the laboratory manuals and workbooks placed the emphasis on developing the ability to follow directions as well as on developing laboratory skills such as bending glass tubing. Most of the laboratory exercises stressed the confirmation and illustration of the basic principles found in the textbook. Horton's study showed that there are at least 55 laboratory techniques to be mastered by pupil experiments in the chemistry laboratory which can be done about as effectively as the teacher demonstrations during the year.[8] Schlesinger suggested that a problem-solving approach can be achieved by changing directions in the laboratory work.[9] Problem-solving activity in the chemistry laboratory can be based on consumer chemistry that involves problems such as a determination of the percentage of acid in orange juice and the pH of bicarbonate of soda; and the analysis of dentifrices, cosmetics, and various soaps.

Testing hypotheses constitutes the real work of an experiment. "Inflexible following of detailed instructions for laboratory work stands in the way of a true experiment," writes Richardson.[10] He suggests the following precautions for the teacher when students test hypotheses in the laboratory:

1. The hypothesis—suggestions should not be presented to the students as a laboratory experiment to be done. If there is a hypothesis, it must exist in the student's consciousness; it must be a result of his own thinking and doing.
2. The suggestion is for the teacher to use judiciously with the student; it is presented only if needed and to the degree needed.
3. Each suggestion could be accompanied by others; but students should be encouraged to find other ways of testing the hypotheses.
4. The teacher may need to help the student determine precise quantities in some instances. The initiative should not be taken from the students, however.
5. In many instances controls are needed. The teachers may raise the question of the need for a control, and of ways of providing the control.
6. The adequacy of the test of the hypothesis is an appropriate concern to be raised with each experiment.[11]

Two sample hypotheses that lead to the design of experiments and testing of hypotheses are : (1) The speed of a chemical reaction

[8] Ralph E. Horton, *Measurable Outcomes of Individual Laboratory Work in High School Chemistry,* Teachers College Contribution to Education, No. 303, Teachers College, Columbia University, 1928.

[9] H. I. Schlesinger, "The Contributions of Laboratory Work to General Education," *Journal of Chemical Education,* vol. 11 (November, 1935), pp. 524–528.

[10] John S. Richardson, *Science Teaching in Secondary Schools,* Englewood Cliffs, N.J., Prentice-Hall, 1957, pp. 365–366.

[11] *Ibid.*

varies as the ionic concentration of the reactants; (2) Under ideal conditions, the volume of a gas varies inversely with the pressure, assuming that the temperature remains constant.

Open-end experiments, problem-solving activities, and testing of hypotheses emphasize inductive thinking. Colyer and Anderson compared two methods of teaching formula writing in chemistry: the traditional method (matching radicals mechanically) and the sequence method (diagramming the empirical formula).[12] Four classes were taught by each method. The same books were used in three-fourths of the cases. An analysis of covariance showed a significant difference in favor of the experimental group which used the sequence method. On the basis of this study, it appears justifiable to spend the additional time required to teach formula writing by an inductive approach.

Boeck conducted an experimental study to compare the learning of students who were taught by the inductive-deductive approach with that of students taught by the more conventional deductive-descriptive method in high school chemistry.[13] Classes were selected at random from schools in Minnesota, and experimental and control groups were set up to compare the two instructional procedures. Comparisons were made on the basis of the following four objectives: (1) knowledge of facts and principles of chemistry; (2) applications of the chemical principles to new situations; (3) knowledge of and the ability to use the scientific method with accompanying scientific attitude; and (4) ability to perform in the laboratory. For all the objectives, differences were observed in favor of the inductive-deductive class; statistically significant differences were revealed in knowledge of and ability to use the scientific method and attitude and in ability to identify proper laboratory procedures.

The variances arising from two approaches to the learning of

[12] Luther M. Colyer and Kenneth E. Anderson, "A Comparison of Two Methods of Teaching Formula Writing in High School Chemistry," *School Science and Mathematics,* vol. 52 (January, 1952) pp. 50–59.

[13] Clarence H. Boeck, "Teaching Chemistry for Scientific Method and Attitude Development," *Science Education,* vol. 37 (March, 1953), pp. 81–84.

high school chemistry were investigated by Lucow.[14] The two approaches were described as textbook centered and laboratory centered, with the distinction being one of emphasis rather than abstraction. These teaching approaches were prevalent in the Manitoba high schools where this experiment was conducted. The experiment was conducted individually for each of two groups: the "accelerated" (college preparatory) students and the "nonaccelerated" students who were not interested in university admission. The students were given an examination which was divided equally among three objectives: (1) recall of basic concepts, (2) application of concepts and principles, and (3) comprehension and interpretation. Pretests and posttests were employed, and increases in variances compared. The findings showed that: (1) "Accelerated" students increased in variance as a group regardless of approach, textbook, or laboratory; and (2) The "nonaccelerated" students profited more from the laboratory approach insofar as increase in variance of the group was concerned. Lucow recommended that the laboratory approach be used for all students; his suggestion was based on the educational philosophy that great variation in classroom achievement is typical of accommodation to individual differences among students during the learning process.

UNIQUE SKILLS IN PHYSICS

Brainerd attempted to determine to what extent individual elements of the scientific method were to be found in physics laboratory workbooks and manuals for students in the introductory high school physics course.[15] The experiments in 12 high school physics workbooks and manuals were listed in question form and checked by a specialist in science teaching for accuracy and suitability. In-

[14] William H. Lucow, "Estimating Components of Variation in an Experimental Study of Learning," *Journal of Experimental Education*, vol. 22 (March, 1954), pp. 265–71.

[15] Arthur B. Brainerd, *A Determination of the Extent to Which Individual Elements of the Scientific Method Are Found in High School Physics Laboratory Workbooks and Manuals*, master's thesis, Boston University, 1952, 97 pp.

dividual steps in the scientific method were checked for each of the experiments in the workbooks considered. The author's findings were: (1) Most of the individual steps of the scientific method applicable in high school physics experiments were included in the manuals, but not necessarily all steps in any one experiment; (2) The most serious omission was the need for repeating an experiment; and (3) The manuals neglected to include a discussion of the scientific method and to point out clearly each step of the method as it occurred in the experiments. The scientific method or problem-solving approach should include the need for repeating experiments.

The unique skills in the physics laboratory can be developed through manipulation of apparatus, design of experiments, measurement and/or observation, application of mathematical skills, and writing technical reports. Finch made a study of simple projects which could be carried on in a high school physics laboratory.[16] He sent questionnaires to 400 physics teachers in New York State, received 200 replies, and reported the following findings: (1) In general, New York schools offering courses in physics allotted at least one period a week for laboratory work; 48 percent of those replying devoted two periods a week to laboratory work; (2) There was a considerable difference of opinion as to which experiments were important; (3) Measurements of volume and density appeared to be most widely used; (4) Very few schools required students to perform exercises dealing with the tensile strength of solids.

Although an intensive skill in mathematics is not needed by the high school student in order to perform measurements of volume and density, Curtis found that an understanding of certain mathematical terms is needed to make possible an understanding of the principles of physics.[17] She listed the mathematical terms which appeared in five textbooks in high school physics and those

[16] Raymond C. Finch, *A Study of the Methods of Conducting Physics Laboratory Work in Secondary Schools with Some Suggestions for Improvement by Means of Simple Research Projects,* master's thesis, Cornell University, 1952, 92 pp.
[17] Charlotte Curtis, *A Determination of Mathematical Terms in Secondary School Physics Textbooks,* master's thesis. Boston, 1953.

principles of physics which appeared in at least three of the five books. The study suggested that students were required to have a knowledge of arithmetic, simple algebra, geometry, and the fundamentals of trigonometry in order to understand high school physics textbooks. The greatest amount of mathematics was needed in the study of mechanics; the least, in the study of atomic energy. Curtis recommended that mechanics be taught during the latter part of the course rather than at the beginning.

Several studies have shown that the effective use of visual aids and the discussion method of teaching physics, especially mechanics, can contribute to pupil growth in scientific thinking and to the measurement of such growth. Such studies were conducted by Thelen, Read, Goehring, and Abrahamson.[18] Goehring constructed a film slide test which is designed to measure pupil ability to apply "a scientific method of thinking to the solution of practical problems in the area of mechanics in high school physics." The reliability and validity of this test were established as a result of sampling 1173 pupils.

Abrahamson compared two methods of teaching elementary mechanics. Traditional teaching was employed in the control group, and experimental teaching through discussion and use of visual aids was employed with a group of less able students of low socioeconomic status. Pretests and posttests were administered to both groups. The control group had been significantly better at the beginning, but no reliable difference between the groups was noted on the posttest or on a recall test given two months after the conclusion of the study. Significant gains were reported for the experimental group, and it appeared that the visual method was successful, especially with the less able students.

---

[18] H. A. Thelen, "Testing by Means of Film Slides with Synchronized Recorded Sound," *Educational and Psychological Measurement,* vol. 5 (Spring, 1945), pp. 33–48; John G. Read, "Evaluation of High School Science Instruction," *Bulletin,* National Association of Secondary School Principals, vol. 37 (January, 1953), pp. 169–177; Harvey J. Goehring, Jr., A Film Slide Test to Measure Ability to Apply Scientific Method in the Area of Mechanics in High School Physics, doctoral dissertation, University of Pittsburgh, 1956; Bernard Abrahamson, "A Comparison of Two Methods of Teaching Mechanics in High School," *Science Education,* vol. 36 (March, 1952), pp. 96–106.

The science teacher must distinguish between specific skills—mathematical, manipulative, reporting, observing, and writing—and must teach each one directly to the students in the laboratory. Students do not necessarily learn how to make a coil by turning wire, for example, from a teacher's demonstration alone. The students should learn the technique by turning the wire themselves under the direction of the teacher. This type of "skill" learning is different from "knowledge" learning such as the number of turns of wire required for a particular coil. Visual aids and a discussion of them in developing specific skills in physics are important.

Similarly, students must be taught mathematical skills for solving problems in physics. It cannot be assumed that a student who has studied trigonometry and algebra can automatically master all of the skills and knowledge required to solve physics problems. Students should be trained to transfer mathematical skills and knowledge to solving problems in physics.

UNIQUE SKILLS IN PHYSICAL SCIENCE

Within the past few years an integrated physical science course has become part of the science curriculum in the tenth grade and has become increasingly popular. This basic course usually emphasizes the application of student experience to physical science concepts. Although most of the work is centered around physics and chemistry, principles from astronomy, geology, and meteorology are also taught. The depth to which each branch of physical science is taught in any given school is usually determined by pupil interest, ability, and needs as well as the interests and specialization of the teacher.

The success of a physical science course is very much dependent upon the staff. When staff members are selected to teach this course, the following criteria may be helpful: a genuine interest in all aspects of science with an excellent background in the physical sciences, a flexibility in point of view and an adaptability in different situations, a cooperative attitude toward other staff members, and ingenuity in teaching the program. In addition to selected faculty, pupil ability and the criteria used in grouping pupils for special science classes will determine the success of an integrated physical science course.

Dean Nelson L. Lowry of Arlington High School, Arlington Heights, Illinois, in his experiences with a physical science course at the tenth-grade level reports:

Ability grouping of students is used in most subject areas in the school. In physical science various criteria have been used for the placement of students in ability groups. There has been dissatisfaction with all the methods tried. Recommendations by the biology teachers seem to be about as good as any found in placing students in physical science ability groups. Students having an interest in one subject area in science usually exhibit some of that same interest and ability in other science areas.

This past fall one of the science teachers and a student teacher from the University of Illinois became interested in proper placement of students in ability groupings. In this study all available test scores were used: grades in mathematics courses, grades in other subjects, biology grades, and achievement scores. They found that the highest correlation existed between grades in physical science and those grades received in biology. It was thought that there would be a high correlation between the ability that students showed in mathematics and science, but this does not seem to be true as far as physical science scores are concerned.[19]

Based on a study of the 1957 graduating class of 316 students, Lowry offered the following conclusions: Following the ninth-grade biology, physical science is widely accepted as a tenth-grade course. It is pursued by both terminal science students and those who use physical science as an introduction to courses in chemistry and physics. The success of this program is very much dependent upon ability placement and guidance.

It is interesting to note that Lowry reported no increase in

[19] Nelson L. Lowry, "Experiences with a Physical Science Course at the Tenth Grade," paper presented at the annual meeting of the National Association for Research, Chicago, 1958.

enrollment in chemistry or physics courses. Hence, in reality, the physical science course becomes the terminal science course for most students if the course is offered.

For the talented or above-average student in science there appears to be a need of physical science textbooks. Most of the present physical science textbooks are satisfactory for the slow or average learner.

The status of integrated physical science courses in senior high schools was investigated by Ray who queried 100 secondary schools in cities of 5000 or more population in 24 states.[20] Of the 70 schools responding, 40 offered a physical science course, chiefly in Grades 11 and 12, which integrated physics, chemistry, geology, meteorology, and astronomy. Findings showed an increase in such courses and in enrollments in them. These courses were usually substituted for the traditional chemistry or physics courses by students not planning to go to college.

Mudge undertook a similar study although it was less extensive.[21] He concluded that the senior science survey course was widespread and that attempts were made to gear the subject to the community and its youth. Consumer education was frequently emphasized; some courses appeared to be designed to occupy the uninterested student's time. The courses were comparatively new. Flannigan's findings were much the same.[22]

Since Sputnik several school systems have decided to alter the science program by offering biology in the ninth grade and physical science in the tenth grade. Students who elect to specialize in the sciences continue in the eleventh year with chemistry and/or in the twelfth year with physics. Some science teachers hesitated to design a physical science course because of problems in the laboratory. The study by Miles indicates how individual laboratory

[20] Sister M. Amadeus Ray, *Nationwide Status of Integrated Courses in Physical Sciences,* master's thesis, Boston University, 1953, 34 pp.

[21] John E. Mudge, *The Feasibility in Present Usage of the Senior Advanced General Science Course in High School,* master's thesis, Cornell University, 1952, 84 pp.

[22] Norman A. Flannigan, "A Study of High School Science Courses in Grades 9–12 Designed for General Education," *Dissertation Abstracts,* vol. 15, no. 1 (1955), pp. 62–63.

experiences can be made suitable for the development of the understanding of basic principles of the physical sciences.[23] A large number of principles of physics, chemistry, and geology were found to be feasible objectives for courses in physical sciences; and many experiments already in use in high school science courses were deemed adaptable for use in physical science courses.

The skills and knowledges to be obtained from a course in physical science are different from the traditional courses in that few, if any, of the students in these courses need the highly specialized manipulative skills in the laboratory. These students are primarily concerned with studying science for general education. Consumer education, science and its social impact, the functional use of science in the home, and understanding science for better living are the real concerns of science teachers who teach physical science courses.

SUMMARY

The teaching of principles from the physical sciences are selected frequently according to the need for interpreting natural phenomena and the applications of such principles. Physics, chemistry, and other physical sciences also offer excellent opportunities to teach students the skills in solving problems. There are also unique skills such as manipulating special laboratory equipment, designing laboratory equipment, skill in observing and evaluating experiments, balancing chemical equations, applying mathematical skills, and writing technical reports. The science teacher needs to distinguish each skill if he is to teach these skills to his students. These various skills can also be taught in physical science courses that integrate several sciences. In this course, the functional approach is stressed, and science and its impact upon the individual are studied.

EXERCISES

1. Describe the conditions that determine whether specific courses in physics, chemistry, and geology should be offered rather than

[23] Miles, *op. cit.*

an integrated physical science course in a senior high school. Under what conditions should a school offer both kinds of courses, that is, the general and specific?

2. What instructional procedures should a science teacher employ in teaching manipulation of laboratory equipment such as skill in bending glass tubing, use of a Bunsen burner, or measuring the angle of reflection?

3. List six basic principles that are common to teaching physics and chemistry, and for each one suggest an application for everyday use.

4. Discuss a physical science principle that can be taught by means of a specific laboratory experiment in comparison with a demonstration by the teacher.

5. Suggest 10 pupil projects representing each of the following sciences: chemistry, geology, meteorology, and physics.

SUGGESTED READINGS

Bowlby, Walter D., "A Philosophical Critique of Chemistry Teaching," *The Science Teacher,* vol. 25 (May, 1958), pp. 190–191 ff.

Brandwein, Paul F., Watson, Fletcher G., and Blackwood, Paul E., *Teaching High School Science: A Book of Methods,* New York, Harcourt, Brace & Company, 1958, chaps. 13, 14, 16.

Goehring, Jr., Harvey J., "A Film Slide Test to Measure Ability to Apply Scientific Method in the Area of Mechanics in High School Physics," doctoral dissertation, University of Pittsburgh, 1956.

Kruglak, Haym, "Experimental Outcomes of Laboratory Instruction in Elementary College Physics," *American Journal of Physics,* vol. 20 (March, 1952), pp. 136–141.

Lucow, William H., "Estimating Components of Variation in an Experimental Study of Learning," *Journal of Experimental Education,* vol. 22 (March, 1954), pp. 265–271.

Martin, W. Edgar, *Facilities and Equipment for Science and Mathematics,* Washington, D.C., U.S. Department of Health, Education, and Welfare, 1960.

Obourn, Ellsworth S., *et al.,* "General Facilities and Equipment," *Science and Mathematics in Public High Schools, 1958, Part 1,* Washington, D.C., U.S. Department of Health, Education, and Welfare, 1960.

Smith, Herbert A., and Washton, Nathan S., "Science in the Secondary Schools," *Review of Educational Research,* vol. 27 (October, 1957), pp. 343–355.

Washton, Nathan S., "Applying Biological Principles to Physical Sciences," *Science Education,* vol. 38 (March, 1954), pp. 136–139.

Wise, Harold E., *A Comparison of the Effectiveness of Courses at Three Levels of Instruction in Developing Understandings of Selected Principles of Physics,* a study published by the University of Nebraska, 1956, 13 pp.

7

EFFECTIVE USE OF METHODS
OF TEACHING SCIENCE

Educational research does not indicate that any particular method of teaching should be abandoned. The science teacher should have at his command both the knowledge and skills of a variety of teaching methods. One teacher may consider a particular method to be superior for a given science class, but another teacher may find the same method inadequate for a different class. It is also possible for a science teacher to find that demonstrations which are most appealing to a seventh-grade science class are not satisfactory for a particular ninth-grade class. Hence, the science teacher should be capable of using several methods of teaching science and of applying them where they are most effective.

Some methods are more effective for developing skills than scientific knowledge. The laboratory method, for example, is efficient in teaching students how to perform specific tasks in an experiment such as bending glass tubing. The student will not be able to master the skill of bending glass tubing merely from hearing a lecture on the subject. He must be given an opportunity to develop his skill in the laboratory.

Many science teachers will argue the use of the lecture demonstration method as compared with the individual laboratory method in terms of superiority. Cunningham analyzed 13 articles, 6 doctoral theses and 8 master's theses pertaining to the problem of lecture demonstration versus individual laboratory methods of teaching science.[1] The report indicated that the data did not con-

[1] Harry A Cunningham, "Lecture Demonstration versus Individual Laboratory Method in Science Teaching—A Summary," *Science Education,* vol. 30 (March, 1946), pp. 70–82.

clusively favor one of the two methods. The method selected for a given course is determined by the conditions under which the course is taught and by the objectives of the course. In comparing the effectiveness of a lecture method with a small-group discussion method of teaching high school biology, Taylor wrote: "Since there doesn't seem to be any 'best' method of teaching, as evidenced by this and other studies, teachers should for the present use that method which is most convenient and satisfying."[2]

DEVELOPMENTAL AND PROBLEM-SOLVING METHODS

The developmental method of teaching science is dependent upon inductive and deductive reasoning. When an array of facts or a series of informational material leads to the development of a generalization, the process is inductive. When applications of a generalization are made in terms of testing the power to predict, the process is deductive. Stated differently, induction is a process of building from small bits of information toward a major idea, principle, or generalization. Deduction is a process of moving from the generalization to the particular. Hunter writes:

By means of the developmental approach, an experiment or indeed any kind of science problem is made to take on a new aspect. Interest is obtained by constant interaction between the mind of the teacher on the one hand and that of the students on the other. Close oral questioning which leads definitely to the formulation of the problem and the fact that the pupils have an oral as well as a visual approach to the work in hand make for greater activity and interest. A clever teacher will so manipulate this means of leadership that not only will it be used in the formulation of the discussed problem, but it is also applicable in the laboratory for oral discussion of a given problem. After discussion, pupils may be given a period for writing up their observations with the results of their discussion. Also this developmental method if used in the laboratory results in the ultimate saving

[2] Harold O. Taylor, "A Comparison of the Effectiveness of a Lecture Method and a Small-Group Discussion Method of Teaching High School Biology," *Science Education,* vol. 43 (December, 1959), pp. 442–446; Taylor refers here to Lindley J. Stiles, *et al.,* "Methods of Teaching," *Encyclopedia of Educational Research,* rev. ed., p. 748.

of time because, by means of the discussion group, the laboratory findings may be corrected in class, and thus a bugbear for the teacher removed.[3]

The developmental approach can be used in the classroom or in the laboratory. The essential feature is that it becomes a problem-solving experience. Because of the continuous interaction between the thinking of the teacher and the students, a high interest level is usually maintained. Careful questioning on the part of the teacher is important. Trial-and-error activity should be regarded as a major step in the problem-solving method. Since Paul Ehrlich required 605 errors in his experimental procedures before he obtained 606 (Salvarsan), the correct formula, the science teacher should understand that students may suggest incorrect hypotheses or designs of experiments. The basic philosophy in the problem-solving method is a "let's find out" approach.

Ven Deventer describes the problem-solving method as follows:

An individual is confronted with a new situation, or with a modification of an existing situation, such that a problem or challenge is presented. The nature of the situation demands that the problem be either solved or avoided. Possibly if it can be avoided there is no problem, or at least the solving of it can be indefinitely deferred. Probably most of us avoid such problem situations when we can. However, if the problem must be met, it must. The individual, if he is proceeding in a practical way, surveys the situation as well as he can. He draws on his own past experience and the experience of others for whatever may bear upon the problem. Then he sets up one or more tentative solutions to the problem and tries these out, one at a time. If the first attempt succeeds, he goes on his way, the problem solved. If it does not succeed he adds the results of the unsuccessful attempt to his experience. On this basis he builds a new or modified solution, or tries another of his first possibilities. He repeats this procedure again and again, until he either finds a workable solution or comes to the conclusion that a workable solution cannot be worked out, in which case he "tables" the problem as unsolved and perhaps as unsolvable, and lives around it as best he can. . . . Once a solution is reached

[3] George W. Hunter, *Science Teaching,* American Book Company, 1934, p. 187.

it is used again and again, whenever the same or a similar problem arises. Affinities between related types of problems are recognized, and established solutions are used and modified as necessary.[4]

The following sequence of activities usually makes up the problem-solving behavior displayed by students:

1. Students are asked to identify, state, or formulate the problem.
2. Students are encouraged to propose or screen hypotheses.
3. A few students design and perform experiments to verify one or two of the hypotheses.
4. Students evaluate the observations, deductions, and data obtained from the experiments performed.
5. Ultimately the students are guided into formulating a conclusion based on experimental evidence.

To perform a problem-solving activity in the classroom, the science teacher should be guided by the following considerations:

1. The teacher should state an anecdote or briefly describe a situation which lends itself to the formulation and statement of a problem by the students.
2. The teacher should display a variety of laboratory equipment to serve indirectly as a guide to pupils who will design experiments to test hypotheses.
3. The teacher should understand the conclusion to be formulated by the pupils as a result of the problem-solving activity.

Science teachers report very effective results when the problem situation is written on the blackboard or distributed in mimeographed form. The problem should be related to real living experiences and should be described in about 50 words. For example, a ninth-grade general science teacher wishes to have his pupils develop the following conclusion as a result of a problem-solving activity: As part of digestion, certain chemicals in the mouth help to change starch to sugar.

The teacher begins by relating the following anecdote: John wanted to eat sweet cake with his milk, but there was no cake in

---

[4] William C. Van Deventer, "A Simplified Approach to the Problem of Scientific Methodology," *School Science and Mathematics,* vol. 58 (February, 1958), p. 99.

Fig. 7.1A. Different students test several hypotheses while other students observe the laboratory session. (Courtesy of British Information Services)

Fig. 7.1B. Student demonstrations in chemistry also serve as laboratory experiments for the performers. (Courtesy of Board of Education, Manhasset Public Schools, Manhasset, N.Y.)

Fig. 7.1C. Examining blood smears constitutes an important laboratory procedure. (Courtesy of British Information Services)

Fig. 7.1D. The proper use of the microscope is an important laboratory skill in biology. (Courtesy of Ralph Sonen, Northport High School, Northport, N.Y.)

the house. John's mother said, "Chew the unsweetened crackers we have, and as you continue to chew slowly, they will become sweet." John questioned this statement, but he did as his mother suggested. To his surprise, after a while the cracker did taste sweet.

The following equipment is then displayed: sugar-free soda crackers, Lugol's solution, Benedict's solution, test tubes, clamp, Bunsen burner and gas outlet. (Earlier in the course, the students had been taught the tests for starch and sugar.) The problem is then formulated by the pupils and several hypotheses were proposed. Finally, the teacher guides the students into chewing several crackers (in the front of the mouth), and samples of the chewed crackers are tested respectively for starch and for sugar. After a discussion in which evaluations are made of these experiments, students conclude, "Digestive juices in the mouth help to change starch to sugar."

Another science teacher presents the following situation: "Jack's project for the science fair is the effect of specific antibiotics on bacteria. He has a sufficient supply of the antibiotics but no bacteria. One of the rules of the science fair is that the students must prepare their own materials." The teacher elicits from the students that Jack's problem is, How can I grow bacteria? The problem for the class is not only to learn the technique of growing a culture but to develop this understanding: Bacteria will grow best under optimum conditions of moisture, food, and moderate temperature.

It is not suggested that the problem-solving method is superior to other methods or that it should be used more extensively than other methods. But if we are interested in helping our students to learn how to solve science problems and to develop worthy scientific attitudes, then we should provide them with appropriate opportunities to develop the skill of solving problems. From the learning point of view, students will reject their own incorrect hypothesis more readily during the attempt to solve a problem than ideas that may originate with the teacher. For this reason it is important to encourage students to propose at least two or three of their own hypotheses and to give them the experience of working out experiments to disprove their own hypotheses. We do learn from our own experience or mistakes. We also find it easier to give up our own misconceptions than to have others like the teacher tell us that we are wrong. This learning through trial and error is a most useful feature of the problem-solving method.

GROUP WORK METHOD

The science teacher may often find it desirable to organize the class into several small groups of students in order that each group may perform a different type of experiment and present its findings to the entire class. The problem-solving method, the project method, the field trip, the case study, and in some instances the laboratory may permit effective learning experiences through group work. Science activities should, of course, encourage students to participate as individuals as well as in groups; but in learning scientific information, attitudes, and skills, the students should learn how to work with fellow students in seeking solutions to common problems.

If group work is to be incorporated in the problem-solving method, the science class can be divided for example, into three groups to perform the experiments related to the growth of bacteria. One group can culture one of the cocci bacteria on petri dishes; another group can grow one of the bacilli bacteria; the third group can prepare and grow one of the spirilli cultures. As a result of these cultures, students can prepare and stain slides for projection on the screen via a microprojector. Through the use of the microprojector, the entire class can see all of the cultures and then discuss similarities, differences, and the effects of different types of bacteria.

Group work in science may have great significance for the future scientist. Research in science is more often team research than individual research. Frequently, scientists with related specialties and skills are brought together to form a team in attacking a given problem. This is another reason for encouraging the forma-

Fig. 7.2. Group work in the chemistry laboratory provides students with valuable cooperative experiences and also promotes individual observations and thinking. (Courtesy of Board of Education, Manhasset Public Schools, Manhasset, N.Y.)

tion of pupil committees to perform group activities in various methods and problems to be used.

The science teacher should be aware that there are certain dangers in the group approach and that it should be used with caution. The effect of a group's social influence and social power on individual oral response was investigated by Asch.[5] He observed that many of the students gave incorrect judgments in order to give conforming responses to those of the group and thus avoid ridicule. Raven writes ". . . a student should function better if he is informed not only of his immediate assignment but also of how it contributes to a long-range goal. If he is involved in team activity, he must be aware of how his part links with that

[5] Refer to Solomon E. Asch, "Studies of Independence and Conformity," *Psychological Monographs,* vol. 70, no. 9, whole no. 416 (1956), 70 pp.; and M. Deutsch and H. B. Gerard, "A Study of Normative and Informational Social Influences upon Individual Judgment," *Journal of Abnormal and Social Psychology,* vol. 51 (November, 1955), pp. 629–636.

Fig. 7.3.   Group work in a physics laboratory is sometimes required by the nature of the experiment. (Courtesy of Board of Education, Manhasset Public Schools, Manhasset, N.Y.)

of others to contribute to the ultimate aim."[6] Recent social-psychological research provides us with an abundance of information as to how we can improve classroom learning situations as well as human relations.[7]

PROJECT AND RESEARCH METHODS

Although individual and group research activities constitute projects, not all projects are of a research nature. The project method is employed by the science teacher to provide for the needs of individuals or for small groups of students. It may be used, for example, with much success with the intellectually gifted or highly interested science student.

Projects are usually elected, but occasionally they may be assigned. The project method is more effective for a good learning situation in science when the undertaking is conceived and ulti-

[6] Bertram H. Raven, "The Dynamics of Groups," *Review of Educational Research,* vol. 29 (October, 1959), p. 334.
[7] See W. W. Charters, Jr. (chmn.), "Human Relations in Education," *Review of Educational Research,* vol. 29 (October, 1959), pp. 313–390.

Fig. 7.4. Gifted and interested students will spend much time after class in doing group work such as nutrition experiments on white rats. (Courtesy of Board of Education, Philadelphia Public Schools, Philadelphia, Pa.)

mately carried through to its final stages by the student. The science teacher may inspire the birth of the idea or project and may encourage as well as nourish all of the learning activities that are associated with the final development of the project.

The science teacher helps students decide whether or not a project will be selected. He should display enthusiasm and pass some of it on to the students. This can be done by showing students a variety of projects developed by students in previous years. Suggestions for improving these projects should be solicited from the students. Parental influences and personal hobbies should enter into the selection of a given project with many pupils.

Dr. Francis St. Lawrence gives the following helpful advice on science projects:

1. The teacher must invite continual, genuine interest in the stu-

dent's undertaking. Boys and girls frequently need assistance and assurance in overcoming the many obstacles which are certain to be encountered all along the way.

2. Most projects require many, many hours of freedom from other distractions for concentrated attack on the science problem. Good working climate, including space, light, equipment, and the like are essential. Often money is an important limiting factor. Hence, it is sometimes necessary to confer with parents. Parental approval and understanding should be obtained.

3. The superior student needs frequent opportunities to share with his fellow classmates unusual problems arising from his own peculiar method of approach. These problems are submitted to the class orally. In the free (give and take) of these buzz sessions, criticisms flow freely. Not only the student himself benefits, but his peers profit also.

4. It is advisable to establish a working calendar for the project construction. Ordinarily, each student proceeds at his own rate of speed, conditioned by the amount of time he has available. A progress report is required about the first of November. This may be submitted to the teacher in written form if the work is proceeding smoothly. If not, it may be presented orally to the class for the reasons noted earlier. A second report, including sketches and plans, is due about the first of December. These are later arranged in the school display cases. It is hoped in this way to kindle the interest of the entire student body in the activities of the science students. A third report consists of the project itself. This takes place the first week of January. Each student is provided with an opportunity to demonstrate his handicraft to the class. Suggestions are made at this time for final improvement.

Fig. 7.5. High school student shows astrophotographs taken through his homemade telescope. Uniondale High School Science Fair, 1960. (Courtesy of Uniondale High School, Uniondale, N.Y.)

. . . One question that often derives from a discussion of the project method is this: "How does a science teacher especially a neophyte, get started on the project method?" This question stems from the fact that many teachers probably assume that they must be very conversant with a veritable host of projects in order to succeed with this method. This, however, is not necessarily the case. Though experience breeds confidence, the beginner may start without too many misgivings. Those interested in utilizing projects in their science teaching will find it helpful to review the literature with reference to the following titles. These projects are suitable for either junior or senior high school students. The list of course, is by no means exhaustive.

Suggested sources for additional projects: *Popular Science, Popular Mechanics, Science Teacher, Scientific American, Scientific Monthly,* and commercial literature such as that provided by the NSTA packets.[8]

Science projects become more popular when a science fair is announced, and this heightened interest causes a greater number of students to participate. The science fair also gives all students an opportunity to view the results of the student projects. Care should be exercised that students are not creating projects merely to obtain some extra credit. Creativity should be stressed rather than simply copying a model from the textbook. However, some students may develop a genuine interest in science as a result of developing a science project, even though it may be a menial task. Projects and science fairs not only provide for the needs and talents of individual students but also enable them to gain recognition and achievement which may serve as a "spark" in promoting a scientific career.

Often working as a limitation of science projects and science fairs is the requirement on the part of a few schools or some science teachers that all students must submit a project for the science fair. More rewarding use of projects in science fairs may well come instead from intelligent guidance on the part of the science teacher, the student's feeling of freedom in electing in-

[8] Francis St. Lawrence, "Science Projects for Superior Students," Gold Medallion Winner Entry, 1958 STAR Program, National Science Teachers Association pamphlet.

Fig. 7.6. Biology student explains effects of radiation on plants. Uniondale High School Science Fair, 1960. (Courtesy of Uniondale High School, Uniondale, N.Y.)

dividual science projects, a natural enthusiasm, suggested project titles, and a good social climate in the classroom.

The many project titles that have appeared in science fairs include: computing machines, anemometers, ant colonies, atom models, blood circulation demonstrations, models of a cell and mitosis, cloud chamber, constellation viewers, radio receiver and crystal sets, electric motors, heaters and electronic devices, gas turbine, Geiger counter, rocket models and fuels, steam engine, volcano, weather station, and various devices that illustrate scientific principles and their applications. The Science Clubs of America sells an illustrated booklet which lists many projects.[9] In comparing the conventional method of teaching a college general

[9] "Thousands of Science Projects" available at 25¢ a copy from The Science Clubs of America, 1719 N Street NW., Washington, D.C. (10 copies for $1.00).

Fig. 7.7. Although the model of a villus is not a dramatic type of project, it requires a considerable amount of reading and research. (Courtesy of Ralph Sonen, Northport High School, Northport, N.Y.)

botany course with the project-centered method, Novak reports: ". . . the project-centered method provided better for individual differences with achievement under this method proportional to level of ability."[10]

Within the past few years, the research project has been employed in a number of senior high schools. In several instances a given sum of money has been made available to a high school biology, chemistry, or physics teacher for carrying out a specific research project. The science teacher's students have become involved in the research, and as a result many of these pupils have become exceedingly interested in the sciences.

[10] Joseph D. Novak, "An Experimental Comparison of a Conventional and a Project-centered Method of Teaching a College General Botany Course," *Journal of Experimental Education,* vol. 26 (March, 1958), p. 229.

Fig. 7.8. The preparation of a science fair should stimulate much pupil interest in projects and research. (Courtesy of Board of Education, Philadelphia Public Schools, Philadelphia, Pa.)

In Cleveland, Ohio, a research project is being undertaken for the purpose of studying nitrogenous compounds in the blood, especially the guanidine compounds in nonprotein filtrates.[11] Since it is known that in normal blood these compounds are present in low concentration, the teacher and the students hope to find that in cases of uremia, some compounds may be present in a concentration elevated to the point where their importance is greater. In such cases they may make up a portion of the "rest" nitrogen of the blood.

The five guanidine compounds being studied are: creatine, creatinine, guanidinoacetic acid, arginine, and methylguanidine. Under the supervision of the science instructor at the high school,

[11] Based on a grant given to Mrs. Ethelreda Laughlin of Cleveland Heights City School District by the National Science Teachers Association.

each of the compounds is being studied by a student. In addition to making up required solutions, the students determine reference curves relating concentration of the material in the sample to percent transmission of light by the Klett Colorimeter. Upon completion of the graphs, the results will be checked with data in the literature for concentration of the compounds in normal blood; these procedures will then be applied to the study of these compounds in human patients and dogs with kidney disease and damage.

The research project undertaken in this case is slow moving because of the need of basic information and skills. The students have had to learn the anatomy and physiology of the kidney and some facts about the intermediate metabolism of proteins. It has also been necessary for them to learn the skills in using an analytical balance, pipettes, centrifuge, and colorimeter. Each of the techniques has been taught as the need occurred. The five students have been starting their work on the research project during the last period of the school day and have continued for many hours after school. The science teacher, Mrs. Laughlin, reports that all of the chemistry students have been extremely interested in this type of project and that at times the enthusiasm of outsiders has presented a problem to the five students who are busily engaged in this research.

The trend in recent years has been to encourage more projects of the research type in high school science classes. In this way, students learn the attitudes and problems of scientists in the process of solving problems pertaining to the research project. Talented and interested students in science should benefit greatly from this kind of experience.

SUPERVISED STUDY AND RESEARCH METHODS

The research project may also fall within the domain of supervised study under similar conditions. The use of the library and its resources may constitute a vital part of the supervised study period. Pupils should be able to use references, prepare bibliog-

Fig. 7.9. Supervised study in science need not be confined to study halls. This type of individual supervised study requires much effort on the part of both teacher and student. (Courtesy of Board of Education, Long Beach Public Schools, Long Beach, N.Y.)

raphies, and evaluate the relative importance of printed materials during a supervised study period.

Perhaps the most significant aspect of supervised study is that the student must know exactly what he or she is to do with respect to working on a specific assignment, whether it is a project, a research study, an individual or a group activity. The student should be motivated to seek additional knowledge in the process of solving the problem or fulfilling the assignment. Frequently, many reference books and supplementary readings are available in the science classroom to facilitate supervised study. Although not all of the library materials are immediately accessible in the science classroom, there is an advantage in providing the pupils with the opportunity of checking supplementary references with actual science materials in the classroom or in the laboratory. On the other hand, there will be many advantages in permitting students to have supervised study in the library when immediate reference to scientific materials is unnecessary—such as looking at a dissection of an animal when reading a book about the animal.

Science teachers may wish to assist their pupils in learning how to study. The following suggestions may be helpful.

1. Does the student have a definite goal? Does he know exactly how much is to be accomplished in the course of the study period? The student should not be interrupted unnecessarily, and he should be cautioned to avoid daydreaming. For example, if his science text refers to Oak Ridge in connection with atomic energy, he may suddenly begin daydreaming if he contemplates making a trip to Oak Ridge during the summer. At the end of the study period, the student should be asked to consider very carefully whether or not he has accomplished what he intended. If he has not, the teacher may suggest ways that he may modify his study habits and his goals.

2. Does each study period begin with a brief review of the previous lesson or work accomplished in the last study period? Continuous review will reinforce the retention of learned materials.

3. Do the students force themselves to read faster during a study period? This can be encouraged along with an increase in comprehension as well as rate of reading.

4. Do the students take notes of the reading during the study period? Notes that reflect important ideas from each of the paragraphs in a given chapter should be recorded in a suitable notebook. These notes may be used for review purposes at a later study period.

5. Do the students evaluate reasons and evidence that may be offered to substantiate a given theory in the text? Encourage students to understand the reasons for generalizations and not to accept the printed page without question.

6. Are the students aware of clues that appear in the text? The following are illustrations of clues to important information or

ideas appearing on the printed page: The *causes* for—the *results* of—the *important reasons* for—first. . . . and second . . . or (1) . . . (2) . . . —italicized or underlined words—reference to experiments or famous scientists—the use of tables, statistical information or graphs.

DEMONSTRATION METHOD

One of the most widely used methods of teaching science in the secondary schools is the demonstration. It is accepted by most educators as an effective and economical means of helping pupils visualize, memorize, and understand specific kinds of scientific information. The demonstration can be used in ways that vary from the one extreme of imposing knowledge, ready-made, on the student to the other extreme of eliciting solutions from the student and thereby developing his knowledge.

The one extreme use of the demonstration is a method of showing, proving, or illustrating a scientific idea which is imposed upon the student. The teacher expects the students to accept the idea because the demonstration is proving it or because it is in the textbook. This is a common use of the demonstration method and is a visual way of getting students to accept an idea because the teacher said so.

The other extreme application of the demonstration method in teaching science occurs when it is used in a way that approaches the problem-solving method. Scientific thinking and some of the elements that comprise problem solving—such as the ability

Fig. 7.10. The preparation of gases requires scientific knowledge, attitudes, and skills as shown in this demonstration. (Courtesy of Board of Education, Philadelphia Public Schools, Philadelphia, Pa.)

to formulate hypotheses, the ability to evaluate data, the ability to formulate a generalization or suspend judgment—can be developed through careful employment of a modified demonstration lesson. The important factor is for the teacher to elicit from the pupils their ideas and arguments that are based on observations and analysis of the demonstration. Careful questioning by the teacher is necessary to provoke pupil thinking. The teacher should avoid as much as possible the giving of too much information in the modified demonstration which stresses several elements of scientific thinking and problem solving.

Actually, the demonstration method, like any other method of teaching science, is used along with other methods of teaching such as discussion or recitation in the course of a given period. There is artistry in teaching when the teacher learns how to blend one or more methods of teaching science into another (wholly or partially) in such a way that students can make progress toward the goals or aims of instruction. The teacher should therefore always be cognizant of the objectives of teaching science, as discussed in Chapter 2, and of how each of the methods can contribute most effectively toward the development of those objectives.

The following outline of the modified demonstration method was employed successfully in teaching a ninth-grade general science class. It is a typical illustration of how a science teacher combines several methods such as discussion, demonstration, and problem solving to make a teaching situation more interesting and effective.

THE GEIGER COUNTER

1. Discuss the reasons for the development of a device which determines the presence of radioactivity. The nature and implications of fall-out should also be discussed.
2. Demonstrate the Geiger counter in operation through the use of different types of radioactive substances such as colored ceramics which can be brought into class by students. Observe the different readings when various materials such as radium watches are used. Aluminum, lead, paper, and wood may be employed to serve as shields.

3. Lead a discussion on how the Geiger counter operates. A diagram will be helpful in teacher and pupil explanations.

A science teacher modified a problem-solving method to a demonstration method by stating the problem arising from the following situation: "When Harry came down to breakfast on the morning of his fourteenth birthday he noticed a guitar beside his chair which he wanted as his present. Harry was not deaf, and yet he did not hear the sounds from the guitar when he plucked the strings." The teacher designed a demonstration to determine an explanation for the range of audibility of sound for humans.

A series of demonstrations such as the following can be performed by either the pupils or the science teacher: Hold a ruler over the edge of the table or desk. Vibrate the extended part over the edge of the table by striking it. Repeat this procedure by moving the ruler so that different lengths of the ruler are extending over the edge of the table or desk. Note differences in audible sounds compared with frequency and variations in length of ruler. Another useful demonstration can be done by a student who plays the violin. Demonstrate bowing when strings are very loose. Note difference when strings are tightened. A discussion may follow as to how dogs are able to hear sounds that the human cannot hear. Much information on ultrasonic high-frequency sounds above 20,000 v.p.s. should be elicited from students.

In performing any of the demonstrations in a science class, it is suggested that the science teacher try out the demonstration before coming to class. Even if a demonstration is to be done by a pupil, it is recommended that a teacher perform the same before having it done in class before the students. The teacher will be in a better position to guide the pupils if some problems develop that do not permit a successful demonstration. This procedure will insure the availability of the required equipment and supplies to conduct the demonstration. Incorrect techniques such as bending glass tubing without gradually heating the tubing for a well-rounded bend can be avoided when actually performed before the science class. There are many possibilities for errors in any given demonstration, and hence it is wise to detect them before class performance. Common pitfalls are inaccurate amounts of chemicals or substances, the need for airtight systems such as corks and stoppers, heating too rapidy or too slowly, improper substitutes for chemicals or other items, insufficient timing, poor timing of the lesson as well as the demonstration.

Other criteria to be used in planning good demonstrations are: Is the purpose of the demonstration clear to the science teacher and to the pupils either at the beginning or during the demonstration? Can everyone in the classroom observe all parts of the demonstration without any difficulty? Is the equipment simple so that it does not obscure the real function of the demonstration? Are the demonstrations and their related methods such as discussion pertinent to the objectives of the lesson?

Another important aspect of the demonstration is whether or not it should be performed by the student or by the teacher. If the purpose of the demonstration is to show or verify or illustrate a clear-cut scientific principle, the teacher should perform the demonstration. As Burnett writes:

[The teacher] has a mature understanding of the principle or phenomenon, whereas the student is at the learning stage where there are many hazy aspects. The teacher is experienced in handling the equipment and in interpreting and explaining it to others, whereas the student tends to be inept and confused about the best means of clarifying for others points of difficulty or ambiguity. It is for these reasons that every science class should have the opportunity of observing many clean-cut, clear demonstrations by the teacher.[12]

On the other hand, science objectives in terms of scientific thinking, scientific attitudes, and problem solving will cause the science teacher to modify the demonstration so as to elicit much work on the part of the pupils. It may be desirable to have some demonstrations performed by the pupils to encourage interest and stimulate further learning in science through experimentation and additional study. The science teacher will know under what conditions he desires to perform a demonstration himself or to have

[12] R. Will Burnett, *Teaching Science in the Secondary School*, Rinehart & Company, 1957, p. 200.

Fig. 7.11. The demonstration of the dissection of a fish can teach basic physiological functions. (Courtesy of British Information Services)

it performed by a group of students.

For over 30 years many investigators have tried to determine whether the demonstration method is superior to the laboratory method in teaching science. As stated earlier, Cunningham analyzed 27 studies pertaining to this problem and found that the data does not favor one method over the other.[13] It seems that the objectives and the conditions under which a science course is being taught should determine the suitability of the method to be employed by the science teacher. In the teaching of general science in the junior high school, the demonstration is an economical and effective method of teaching science when compared to individual laboratory work.

LABORATORY EXPERIENCES

There should be no conflict between the use of the demonstration method and the individual laboratory method. There is a need for the demonstration method in the teaching of science in the junior and senior high schools. There is also a need for students to learn basic skills through the manipulation of apparatus. This type of learning activity lends itself more appropriately to the individual laboratory exercise. Manipulation or study of objects contributes more efficiently to an understanding of scientific ideas than a teacher's lecture according to the study by Carpenter.[14] He found that in the process of concept formation meaningful learning as opposed to rote learning makes for a greater retention of the fact and an

[13] Cunningham, *op. cit.*
[14] Finley Carpenter, "The Effect of Different Learning Methods on Concept Formation," *Science Education,* vol. 40 (October, 1956), pp. 282–285.

Fig. 7.12. Laboratory experiments require pupils to make careful measurements and observations. (Courtesy of British Information Services)

Fig. 7.13. Calorimetry is a basic laboratory experiment in France and throughout the world. (Courtesy of French Embassy and Institut National Pédagogique)

understanding of the concept. Learning can be made more meaningful by the manipulation of objects such as are in the laboratory and through the use of pupil experiences and interests.

It should not be assumed that the individual laboratory is a desirable method only for the teaching of scientific skills. Open-ended chemistry experiments, research projects, problem-solving exercises that avoid the cookbook type of laboratory manual can do much in the development of scientific concepts as well as skills if sound practices of the psychology of learning are observed. Scientific data become important to the learner when facts are related to a science concept or generalization. Johnson lists the following 5 ideas as trends in studies on concept formation:

1. Learning that is meaningful is more effective than learning that lacks significance.
2. Learning takes place somewhat in proportion to the involvement of the learner in learning activities.
3. The role of the teacher as a guide or participant in pupil-teacher planning stimulates learning.

4. Manipulation and sensory learning continue to demonstrate superiority over verbal learning.

5. The goal acceptance by the learner appears to be involved in the learning situation.[15]

Principles 2, 3, and 4 should serve as the basis for the development of a good individual student laboratory program in science. As science teachers, we can involve our students in helping design the nature of the laboratory problem or exercise. The student should do some planning of the experiment which will lead to thinking and analytical reasoning. The experiments to be performed by the student should be checked by the teacher. As a result of manipulation of equipment and materials related to concept formation, economical learning should occur if other factors are satisfactory.

An illustration that involves pupil planning and analytical reasoning in the laboratory is given by Mallinson and Buck:

We've more or less had an introduction to the study of oxygen. However, we haven't discussed all of its characteristics. Perhaps it's about time we found out some more facts about it. You may recall that oxygen is a gas that is only slightly soluble in water and a little heavier than air. One makes it by mixing two solids and then heating them. Try to set up an apparatus that can be used to prepare and collect it. *Don't start it working until I have a chance to examine it.*[16]

This inductive approach will demand more thinking than the conventional laboratory manual which indicates precisely how the student is to set up the apparatus. Mallinson also reports that the trend of the concept of laboratory work in the sciences is to emphasize the investigative approach rather than the illustrative exercise.[17] The cookbook approach in the laboratory manual, rapidly

[15] Donovan A. Johnson, "Implications of Research in the Psychology of Learning for Science and Mathematics Teaching," *Review of Educational Research*, vol. 27 (October, 1957), p. 402.

[16] George G. Mallinson and Jacqueline V. Buck, "The Inductive Method in the Chemistry Laboratory," *Journal of Chemical Education*, vol. 31 (December, 1954), p. 635.

[17] George G. Mallinson, "Promising Practices in Science Teacher Education: A Report from the Midwest Regional State College Conference on Science and Mathematics Teacher Education," *School Science and Mathematics*, vol. 58 (January, 1958), pp. 13–25.

becoming obsolete, appears to stress the student's ability to follow directions and to master the basic manipulative skills such as bending glass tubing and so forth.

A new approach to teaching chemistry to college freshmen was used by the late Professor Harold A. Fales of Columbia University. Perhaps the basic idea can be employed with much success in high school chemistry classes. Instead of running typical titration and neutralization exercises with standard solutions and ultimately teaching the students how to determine a pH of a given solution, he invited students to bring in their favorite detergents, fruit juices, tooth pastes, cosmetics, and other useful substances. The students not only enjoyed taking the pH of these substances but also learned the significance as well as the concept of a pH determination. As part of a creative chemical laboratory experience, students in a chemistry laboratory class were asked to submit experiments of their own design to study the properties and behavior of liquids, solids, and gases. These experiments were not to be obtained from existing laboratory manuals. The instructor evaluated each of the proposals with the individual students. The results indicate that much creativity as well as learning skills and knowledge resulted from this procedure.

Another approach is to propose stimulating problems as part of the laboratory method. "The value of problem solving through laboratory work in the school lies not in the factual knowledge that may result from it but in the attitudes and habits of reflective thinking it encourages and in the understanding it gives of how the knowledge of science gained by the student from description was attained in the first place."[18] The problem-solving procedure is part of the *inductive-deductive* approach to teaching in the laboratory. Methods of science and accompanying scientific attitudes are likewise involved.

Boeck conducted an experiment in high school chemistry laboratory classes by comparing the inductive-deductive to the deductive-

[18] Progressive Education Association, *Science in General Education,* Report of the Committee on the Function of Science in General Education, Appleton-Century-Crofts, 1938, p. 317.

descriptive approach.[19] The inductive-deductive method in the laboratory utilized data related to a real problem of significance to the students. Under the guidance of the teacher, the pupil played a vital role in planning the procedure to be followed when a principle of chemistry was introduced in the process of solving a problem. Boeck states: "Teaching progressed from the particular to the general. The pupils were encouraged to recognize the value of controlled experiments, the assumptions which were basic to the laboratory plans, the desirability of clear and easy-to-use records, the necessity for using good laboratory techniques and careful observations, and the limitations of the data collected for drawing conclusions."[20]

On the other hand, the deductive-descriptive approach was based on the laboratory exercises from a typical published laboratory manual. This method did not provide students with opportunities to plan or to solve real problems or to develop generalizations inductively. On the basis of the findings, Boeck made the following significant conclusion and recommendation:

Because of the fact that the inductive-deductive class did as well or better than the deductive-descriptive class in the attainment of the general outcomes of a high school course in chemistry but was significantly superior with respect to the crucial problem of attaining knowledge of and ability in the use of the methods of science with an accompanying scientific attitude, the acceptance of the inductive-deductive method for use with future classes in chemistry at University High School was justified and this method of instruction is now in operation.[21]

FIELD TRIPS

Field trips may be considered a special kind of laboratory situation. On some field trips, the student becomes actively engaged in collecting, observing, evaluating, and manipulating; in this case the field trip actually is a laboratory situation. On other trips, the student has an opportunity to observe and gain specific informa-

---

[19] Clarence H. Boeck, "The Inductive-Deductive Compared to the Deductive-Descriptive Approach to Laboratory Instruction in High School Chemistry," *Journal of Experimental Education,* vol. 19 (March, 1951), pp. 247–253.

[20] *Ibid.*

[21] *Ibid.*

tion, as on trips to industries that are dependent upon the biological and physical sciences. This type of field trip may be used to stimulate the learning of a specific topic—for example, when endocrine glands and hormones are being studied, students can learn a great deal from visiting a pharmaceutical plant that manufactures hormones. An industrial plant that manufactures sulphuric acid or other chemicals may also stimulate interest in learning and at the same time serve to introduce the students to various kinds of careers in science.

A field trip to engineering plants can offer students an excellent opportunity to determine the various types of engineering opportunities, the requirements for training, and the advantages and disadvantages of the profession. If science careers are of vital interest to the class, perhaps the industry to be visited should be carefully selected in terms of the wide range of scientific personnel who are employed.

In planning field trips such as visits to industries and museums, the science teacher should discuss and plan with the class what to look for and how to obtain the information in terms of the purposes of the visit. Unless pupil-teacher planning is done before the visit, some pupils may merely be "going along" without developing any of the objectives of the field trip. It is also important for the science teacher to contact the appropriate official at the industry or museum to make the arrangements beforehand and at the same time to agree as to how the objectives of the field trip can best be developed.

The day following the field trip, it is good practice to discuss with the class what the students obtained from the visit. The science teacher should evaluate whether or not the purposes or the objectives of the trip were developed. A discussion of this type becomes more meaningful if all of the students in the class observe the same things and places. For this reason it is desirable to keep the class together rather than to separate into smaller groups.

In teaching biology, field trips can play a most vital role. The study of ecology—plant-animal relationships to each other and to the environment—may constitute a good portion of the laboratory work. The purposes are to help students learn to understand

Fig. 7.14.   Field trips in biology are effective methods for teaching ecology. Careful preparation is needed by the teacher and the students. (Courtesy of Board of Education, Philadelphia Public Schools, Philadelphia, Pa.)

and interpret natural phenomena in the environment; to understand basic principles of ecology and their applications for better living and conservation; and to develop skills such as collecting, identifying, and studying specimens.

Before the biology or science teacher plans a field trip, he or she should become familiar with the area and be able to identify most of the living organisms in the area. The teacher should make a number of keys (outlines) available and help the students learn how to use them in order to identify the various species of flora and fauna. It may be desirable to have the class prepare a local key for the specific area to be studied. This could become a fine project for the class or for a smaller group.

Before actually going on the trip, the science teacher should ask the pupils to bring along some or all of the following materials for an ecological study as needed: various sizes of collecting bottles, plastic bags, camera, clip boards, thermometers, nets for collecting insects or aquatic specimens, magnifying lenses, field glasses, penknife, preservatives, and a first aid kit. A traveling library should be encouraged to permit identification of some specimens from a handbook or manual when a key is not available. Some teachers may prefer to do this in the laboratory at school, but many biology teachers report effective results as students learn to identify and study various species on the spot. Students find it helpful to learn the basic fundamentals in the use of a key before going on a field trip. This type of planning and activity can provide for various needs of individual students. Special assignments or tasks can be delegated to interested students and to some students who may develop interest in ecology.

With proper pupil-teacher planning for a field trip in studying ecology, it is possible that some students who never cared for biology may suddenly become highly motivated. Outdoor education may have a popular appeal to some students who may not be too fond of the typical laboratory or vice versa. The skill with which the teacher makes pupil assignments may determine the nature of motivation in pupils.

In developing a technique for organizing and planning an ecological field trip in a biology course, the teacher may wish to consider the following questions: Am I selecting an area rich in the number of species of flora and fauna which show important ecological principles? Am I considering the nature of the canopy, the sky, and the terrain? Do I know exactly what I want my students to observe in order that they may learn certain scientific or ecological principles? Do I help them to avoid overgeneralizations? Do I assist the students in learning to differentiate between interpretative and experimental biology? Will this field trip serve as a stimulant to encourage students to make their own field trips in their communities or neighboring areas?

CASE STUDY METHOD

Although the case study method of teaching has been employed for many years on the college and university level, it was only recently introduced in the high schools. The case study should not be confused with historical information which may be introduced in various lessons. The case study as an approach to teaching science is dependent on (1) the selection of specific scientific ideas or principles, and (2) the use of a historical treatment to show how a major scientific idea or generalization evolved as a result of the work of many scientists or investigators.

The Harvard Case Studies provide excellent illustrations of specific scientific ideas that might be applied to the secondary school level.[22] For example, a detailed study of any of the following ideas will result in a thorough background in the basic sciences: The Overthrow of the Phlogiston Theory, The Atomic-molecular Theory, Plants and the Atmosphere, Pasteur's Study of Fermentation, Pasteur's and Tyndall's Study of Spontaneous Generation, The Development of the Concept of Electric Charge, Boyle's Experiments in Pneumatics, and others.

The concept of cause and effect and scientific method can be traced historically through a systematic study on what causes disease. In the days of Hippocrates many diseases were thought to be caused by gods, demons, or supernatural beings. But if one reads Hippocrates' "On the Sacred Disease," it becomes obvious that scientific method and thinking were employed as early as 400 B.C. The book states: "The fact is that this invoking of the gods to explain diseases and other natural events is all nonsense." Yet, many students of science believe that scientific method or thinking is modern. The case study method of teaching science should appeal to both the scientist and the historian. Some students will enjoy the detective type of work in tracking down the origin of certain beliefs, misconceptions, or origins of scientific ideas.

The origin of several basic scientific principles including electricity is developed in a case study approach by Cohen.[23] This reading and discussion are suitable for a general science class in the junior high school. The science teacher may wish to introduce the

---

[22] James Bryant Conant (ed.), *Harvard Case Histories in Experimental Science,* Harvard University Press, 1957, vols. 1, 2.

[23] I. Bernard Cohen, *Science, Servant of Man,* Boston, Little, Brown, & Co., 1948.

case study approach by relating some of the following information and suggesting to some interested students that they continue specific reading assignments. At a future date, these students may report orally on their readings or by preparing written reports and pictures.

The electric current was discovered in 1780 by an Italian doctor, Luigi Galvani. He noticed that the leg of a dissected frog would twitch under certain conditions. The story of this discovery is that one of Galvani's assistants happened to touch a nerve of the dissected frog with the point of his scalpel. Immediately, a violent twitch in the frog's muscle (leg) was observed. Careful experiments to follow up this "kick" in the frog's leg were performed. It was very unusual to observe this "kick" of the leg which was separated from the body. Two different metals were joined together in a chain through the moist muscles and nerve of the frog. The investigators thought that electric current passed through this "chain" or closed circuit. Galvani believed that the twitching was due to the circulation of an "animal electricity." However, Alexander Volta had a different idea.

An investigation by reading about Volta's experiments, the electroscope, the first battery, the work of Swammerdam and Sulzer, the experiments on the "Leyden jar" by Benjamin Franklin, the lightning rod, and related historical materials will enable the reader to appreciate the case study method.

The historical development of events and activities that lead to the formulation of a basic scientific idea is emphasized by the case study method, rather than an application such as the invention of a motor, the electric iron, or the toaster. The information that is usually obtained from readings in a case study approach is of an esoteric nature. Since different ideas are postulated as a result of other experiments, some of the earlier information reported in the literature may be incorrect. Therefore, careful guidance in the use of the case study method is suggested. Perhaps some teachers may wish the students to evaluate older ideas in comparison with recent experiments.

There are some very basic scientific attitudes that can be taught via the case study approach. One important attitude is the search for knowledge as an intellectual and worthy endeavor even though no application or money-making gadget is made. The point of emphasis is that there could be no toasters, radios, TV sets, and all of the other electrical appliances if the basic principles of electricity had not been discovered. Other attitudes such as perseverance or stick-to-it-iveness may also be reflected as one reads the great discoveries in science.

The case study method like the other methods of teaching science is used at different levels, in different classes, for different topics, at various intervals. No one method is suggested as the best method. The artistry of teaching science is dependent on how skillfully the teacher blends several of the methods into a unified teaching lesson. The nature of the lesson, the personality and goals of the teacher, the climate of the class, and the interests and needs of the students will determine the ultimate selection and utilization of appropriate teaching methods in science.

SUMMARY

There is no one method of teaching science which is the best method. For some objectives such as the ability to solve problems, the problem-solving method is very effective. Instruction in science should be varied, using methods of group work, projects, supervised study and research, demonstrations, laboratory experiences, field trips, case studies, discussions, and recitations. Some topics or problems may be taught more economically through the use of one method than another. Each science teacher should explore the use of each of these methods for different topics in different classes. Through teaching experience, the science teacher will learn which methods are most productive in promoting the learning of science in various classes.

EXERCISES

1. Plan a lesson for teaching a science topic, and illustrate how three different methods may be used in teaching the same topic.
2. Discuss the characteristics of a developmental lesson, and compare it with a traditional lecture.

3. List the steps involved when students are engaged in problem solving.
4. Write three different situations, and for each one explain how the problem-solving method of teaching could be used.
5. How can the demonstration and the laboratory methods of teaching be modified to stress inductive reasoning?
6. Explain how the science teacher can use the project method for both classroom teaching and preparing students for the science fair.
7. What philosophy should you adopt with respect to the use of different methods of teaching science?

SUGGESTED READINGS

Barnard, J. Darrell (chmn.), *Rethinking Science Education,* Fifty-ninth Yearbook, National Society for the Study of Education, Chicago, University of Chicago Press, 1960.

Boeck, Clarence H., "The Inductive-Deductive Compared to the Deductive-Descriptive Approach to Laboratory Instruction in High School Chemistry," *Journal of Experimental Education,* vol. 19 (March, 1951), pp. 247–253.

Brandwein, P. F., Watson, F. G., and Blackwood, P .E., *Teaching High School Science: A Book of Methods,* New York, Harcourt, Brace & Company, 1958.

Burnett, R. Will, *Teaching Science in the Secondary Schools,* New York, Rinehart & Company, Inc., 1957.

Cole, William E., *The Teaching of Biology,* New York, D. Appleton-Century Company, 1934.

Davis, Warren M., "Factors of Effectiveness in Science Teaching and Their Application to the Teaching of Science in Ohio's Public Secondary Schools," *Science Education,* vol. 38 (March, 1954), pp. 150–159.

Harris, Chester (ed.), *Encyclopedia of Educational Research,* New York, The Macmillan Company, 1960.

Heiss, E. D., Obourn, E. S., and Hoffman, C. W., *Modern Science Teaching,* New York, The Macmillan Company, 1950.

Hunter, George W., *Science Teaching,* New York, American Book Company, 1934.

Jacobson, Willard, "Helping Young People to Deal With Their

Problems," *The Educational Forum*, vol. 17 (January, 1953), pp. 219–225.

Jacobson, Willard, "Science Education and the Development of Abilities to Cope with Problematic Life Situations," *Science Education*, vol. 37 (April, 1953), pp. 172–182.

Mallinson, George G., "Practices in Science Teacher Education: A Report from the Midwest Regional State Colleges Conference on Science and Mathematics Teacher Education," *School Science and Mathematics*, vol. 58 (January, 1958), pp. 13–25.

Mallinson, George G., and Buck, Jacqueline V., "The Inductive Method in the Chemistry Laboratory," *Journal of Chemical Education*, vol. 31 (December, 1954), pp. 634–636.

National Education Association, American Educational Research Association, *Review of Educational Research* (October, 1948; October, 1951; October, 1957).

Novak, Joseph D., "An Experimental Comparison of a Conventional and a Project-centered Method of Teaching a College General Botany Course," *Journal of Experimental Education*, vol. 26 (March, 1958), pp. 217–230.

Preston, Carleton E., *The High School Science Teacher and His Work*, New York, McGraw-Hill Book Company, Inc., 1936.

Richardson, John S., *Science Teaching in the Secondary Schools*, Englewood Cliffs, N.J., Prentice-Hall, Inc., 1957.

Van Deventer, William C., "A Simplified Approach to the Problem of Scientific Methodology," *School Science and Mathematics*, vol. 58 (February, 1958), pp. 97–107.

Washton, Nathan S., "Changes in Teaching from the Use of Research in Science Education," *Science Education*, vol. 40 (December, 1956), pp. 383–387.

8

USE OF AUDIO-VISUAL AIDS
IN SCIENCE TEACHING

CHALKBOARD

Although much criticism has been launched against using the "chalk-talk" method to the exclusion of other methods of teaching science, the use of the chalkboard is essential and very helpful. Whenever a diagram or illustration or chemical equation is written on the chalkboard, it reinforces learning. Imagine the following statement given orally and not placed on the board: "see oh two plus ach two oh yields see six ach twelve oh six plus oh two." If students only hear this equation and do not see it on the board, they will find it extremely difficult to perceive the reaction. The shorthand version or chemical equation is: $CO_2 + H_2O = C_6H_{12}O_6 + O_2$. The symbolic abstraction has meaning after the student learns the translation of symbols and the meaning of atoms, molecules, and formulas. The use of the chalkboard is very important, therefore, for developing meanings of abstractions such as equations and formulas and for making concepts concrete by way of illustrations.

The size of the letters in writing on the chalkboard should be large enough to be seen from all parts of the room without causing any eyestrain. Yet, the letters should not be so oversized that little information can be recorded at any given time. The space of the board should be used judiciously. The unknown or new words or ideas may be written on the board. A word, idea, or picture already known may be produced on the board to give it special emphasis or relate it to a new idea. The essential feature in organizing the writing on the board is to make it resemble an intelligent outline of the lesson.

A number of other suggestions may be recommended as helpful

in the use of the chalkboard. Avoid crowding too much information on the board. Erase material on the board when it confuses or distracts from the development of the lesson. Plan the chalkboard from simple to complex words and ideas. Some quizzes may be placed on the board before the class arrives; under such conditions, the board should be covered with a wall map or similar substitute to permit all students to begin the quiz at the same time.

In physics and chemistry classes where consideration is given to problems such as gas laws, calorimetry, and other topics that require the use of mathematics, it is effective teaching to call on the students to solve problems by writing on the chalkboard. This procedure enables the teacher to evaluate the learning of a sample of a class by having perhaps five or six pupils work at the board. It also permits the teacher to make a rapid diagnosis of what specific part or parts of the problem may cause undue difficulty in the learning situation. While the pupils are working at the board, the remaining members of the class should be working at their desks. It is likely that student errors on the board may also appear at the desks of other students. Thus, the science teacher can use the board work by some students as a basis for correction to help all students understand the way of solving the problem.

Although there are stencils of flasks, beakers, and other typical scientific equipment that can be employed in making diagrams of laboratory apparatus on the chalkboard, the science teacher can easily learn how to sketch many of these illustrations. The diagram from the film "Chalkboard Utilization" illustrates how simple it is for anyone to learn how to make sketches.[1]

Chalkboard sketches are important not only in the teaching of the physical sciences but in the teaching of biology. Although there are many excellent charts of biological specimens and systems, a teacher may wish to draw an enlarged version of a portion of a given tissue on the board. The chart may show the alimentary tract, for example, but fail to show a cross section of the four layers of tissue found in the intestine. If the teacher wishes to emphasize this, a diagram on the board is most helpful.

[1] Young America Films, McGraw-Hill.

The utilization of colored chalk will frequently be employed for clarity, emphasis, and contrast. Red chalk for the arterial system in contrast with blue chalk for the venous system may facilitate the learning of the pathway of blood in the circulatory system. If a picture of an animal or plant is dissected in terms of the various systems, the use of a different color chalk for each system would be helpful.

CHARTS, MAPS, AND POSTERS

The chalkboard technique is suitable when the material to be presented is not to be used on a permanent basis. When certain topics or concepts are to be taught regularly and pictures or illustrations of these concepts are desirable, scientific charts are economical and stimulating. Charts such as the Periodic Table, the various systems of common plants and animals that are studied in a science or biology class, the microscopic world of molds, the bacteria that cause disease, simple machines, and many others are available from commercial sources. Since charts are used for many years, it is wise to obtain the well-designed and well-constructed commercial charts that will serve most usefully in the classroom.

Scientific charts are available for purchase from the following companies:

Cambosco Scientific Co., 37 Antwerp St., Brighton 35, Mass.
Central Scientific Co., 1700 W. Irving Park Rd., Chicago 13, Ill.
Chicago Apparatus Co., 1735 N. Ashland Ave., Chicago 22, Ill.
Clay-Adams Co., 141 E. 25th St., New York 10, N.Y.
Denoyer-Geppert Co., 5235 N. Ravenswood Ave., Chicago 40, Ill.
Fisher Scientific Supply Co., 717 Forbes St., Pittsburgh 19, Pa.
General Biological Supply House (Turtox), 761–63 E. 69th Pl., Chicago 37, Ill.
Nystrom & Co., 3333 N. Elston Ave., Chicago 18, Ill.
Pacific Laboratory Apparatus Co., 3555 Whittier Blvd., Los Angeles 23, Calif.
Ward's Natural Science Establishment, 3000 Ridge Rd., East, Rochester 9, N.Y.
Welch Scientific Supply Co., 1515 N. Sedgwick St., Chicago 10, Ill.

Making maps and posters can become individual student projects. If a science topic such as malnutrition and the distribution of population in various parts of the world is to be studied in conjunction with social studies, some students may enjoy preparing maps. A poster showing how an arm works was designed by a student in Los Angeles. These maps and posters should attract the eye and cause readers to note the caption which should present a clear understanding of a scientific concept. The poster should be a pictorial design which communicates a major scientific principle or idea. The message should be understood in a few seconds. The research work involved in the preparation of a map or a poster constitutes a worthwhile project that may be worthy of display in the class or at a science fair. The following are the titles of posters prepared by high school science students: The Human Digestive System, Circulation of Blood, The Nervous System in a Frog, The Life History of the Grasshopper, The Electromotive Series, The Alkaline Earth Metals, Radioactive Decay, Ionization of Salts, The Electromagnetic Spectrum, How Machines Work, Photosynthesis, Food for the World, Purification of Water, Making a Radio Receiver, Principles of Direct Current, and Applications of the Electromagnet.

MOTION PICTURE FILMS, FILMSTRIPS, AND SLIDES

Motion picture films are available in almost all scientific subjects. Two guides should be consulted in selecting a scientific film since complete annotated lists of educational films appear in them.[2] The *Educational Film Guide* lists the title of the film, the date of production, black and white or color, sound or silent, the producer, the running time, and the grade level for which the film is suitable. It is best for the teacher to preview the film before the decision is made to select it. The preview is important for evaluation as well as for becoming familiar with the film content in the event it is to be used in the classroom.

[2] See current issues of *Educational Film Guide,* H. W. Wilson Company, New York, N.Y.; and *Educator's Guide to Free Films,* Educator's Progress Service, Randolph, Wis.

What are the criteria to be employed in selecting a particular science film? If the film merely shows a series of diagrams, the kind usually found in the textbook, it may not be suitable for classroom use. The major criterion should be: What does this film offer in presentation of content, illustrations, and explanations that go beyond what is possible for the science teacher to do in a given period? For example, the biology teacher cannot show in a 45-minute period how changes occur in a seedling over a period of three months. This can be shown very effectively by a motion picture film within a few minutes. The chemistry teacher may wish to demonstrate the formation of crystals of a particular salt. The physics teacher may wish to have animated pictures of nuclear fission. The earth science teacher is concerned with portraying significant changes in the "face" of the earth. How can a volcano or an earthquake be demonstrated as effectively as with actual motion picture films? How can the science teacher portray a falling meteor, a solar eclipse, and other natural phenomena as well as they are depicted in good educational motion picture films? These should be the major criteria for the selection of a particular film for classroom use.

Anderson, Montgomery, and Smith examined the effectiveness of sound motion pictures in the teaching of biology.[3] Using random selection in part, three groups of students were formed: (1) a control group in which no films were shown or in which teachers showed films of their own choice; (2) an experimental group in which students saw selected films during the school year; and (3) an experimental group in which the films were bolstered by emphasizing the principles stressed in each film. Analysis of variance and covariance provided some evidence that results in the third group described above were superior. This procedure indicates also the importance of the teacher's preview of the film.

During World War II the use of motion pictures provided a popular method of instruction to the military personnel. An ef-

[3] Kenneth E. Anderson, Fred S. Montgomery, and Herbert A. Smith, "Toward a More Effective Use of Sound Motion Pictures in High School Biology," *Science Education,* vol. 40 (February, 1956), pp. 43–54.

fective technique involved three steps: (1) a suggestion by the instructor as to what the viewers should especially note in the film and also a statement that a quiz or discussion would follow the showing of the film; (2) the showing of the film; (3) the administration of the quiz or the discussion. This approach can be used with films in science classes, allowing for a discussion on what was viewed following the showing of the film. Too often the danger is that a film may be shown with no allowance for discussion or follow-up activity during a given period.

"Such projected materials as motion picture films and filmstrips have long been used by science teachers because of their promise in learning situations. The research, while of limited amount, has tended to support the use of these materials," according to a recent study[4] Wise found in his study of biology films that enrichment may take place without detracting from the normal student achievement.[5] Should a teacher demonstration be used rather than a related motion picture film? This comparison was made by Smith in testing three sections of general science in each of 5 schools.[6] The three films used were: magnetism, simple machines, and properties of water. Smith found that sound motion pictures and teacher demonstrations are equally successful in teaching and that the intelligence quotient of the students has no bearing on the effectiveness of either method.

In selecting a film, the vocabulary of narration should be carefully noted. In studying 10 science films (5 from the biological and 5 from the physical sciences), Mallinson reported that 87 words were difficult for grades above Grade 7.[7] He suggested that synonyms can be used in several places where the films are used at the junior high school level.

[4] J. S. Richardson, G. P. Cahoon, and J. A. Rutledge, "Materials in the Teaching of Science," *Review of Educational Research,* vol. 21 (October, 1951), p. 284.

[5] Harold E. Wise, "Supplementary Contributions of Sound Motion Pictures in High School Biology," *Science Education,* vol. 33 (April, 1949), pp. 206–213.

[6] Herbert A. Smith, "Determination of the Relative Effectiveness of Sound Motion Pictures and Equivalent Teacher Demonstrations in Ninth-Grade General Science," *Science Education,* vol. 33 (April, 1949), pp. 214–221.

[7] George G. Mallinson, "Narration in Films for Science," *The Science Teacher,* vol. 17 (December, 1950), pp. 220–221.

The chief values in using motion pictures are stated by Blanc as follows:

1. Motion of plants and animals in their natural environments can be shown.
2. Motion of processes too slow to be seen normally may be viewed.
3. Motion of processes too rapid to be seen normally may be viewed.
4. Motion of objects too minute to be seen without a microscope can be shown.
5. Operations and actions too complex to be understood easily may be explained by animation.[8]

Mallinson suggests that biology films be previewed to determine that they are accurate and free from error.[9] In the biological sciences it is likely that motion pictures will contain inaccuracies as a result of research. The science teacher should, therefore, bring the inaccuracies to the attention of the students before the showing of the film.

Extensive use should be made of science films which depict processes that are not easily studied. For example, important processes that are portrayed very effectively on sound motion picture film include "time-lapse" such as the growth of a seedling in four weeks, the locomotion of paramecia with ciliary activity, valve action, peristalsis, the act of swallowing, the 4-cycle engine in operation, a tornado or hurricane, and the manufacture of acid by an industrial plant.

The filmstrip should be used where visualization of a concept is not dependent upon action. Filmstrips and still pictures that show interrelationships can be helpful in identification, observation, classification, evaluation, and study of earth surfaces; showing a chemical set-up; identification of ores, plants, and animals; and comparison of structures and their functions in various species. Some of these concepts may be developed through the use of slides as well as filmstrips.

---

[8] Sam S. Blanc, "Vitalizing the Classroom: Slides, Filmstrips, and Films, *School Science and Mathematics,* vol. 53 (April, 1953), p. 257.

[9] George G. Mallinson, "Some Implications for Using Films in the Teaching of Biology," *The American Biology Teacher,* vol. 14 (February, 1952), pp. 37–40.

In using the problem-solving approach, Woodburn reports the use of 2″ x 2″ color slides as follows:

. . . Students, in general, are not accustomed to approaching a topic in science with a problem-solving attitude. In some instances they actually resent having to "think their way out" of a perplexing and frustrating circumstance. Teachers who are trying to add the problem-solving type of activity to their repertoire need every aid to learning that is available or can be made available.

The first phase of this type of teaching involves getting a specific problem identified to the students or posed before them in a realistic . . . manner. The author was able to photograph a pair of pedigreed boxer dogs and their litter which included three all-white or nearly all-white pups. The discrepancy between the coat color pattern of the parents and offspring immediately poses a problem before a group of students. . . .

In another case, the author photographed a sow with her litter of pigs. This slide immediately conflicts with the "like begets like" concept. Analysis of the facts evident in the slide and the consideration of conditions under which this litter was produced—these data practically led the students to raise the question of whether or not the litter could have been sired by more than one male hog. . . .

The 2″ x 2″ color slide is effective in aiding students to visualize the species and materials with which investigators have worked. The author has come to realize how little meaning bare words carry in attempting to describe Leghorn and White Silkie chickens to students from nonfarm backgrounds. An understanding of the inhibitor gene effect as discussed in the textbook, however, hinged on the students' conceptions of these two breeds of chickens. Exhibitors at the local State Fair cooperated in making a slide available in which these two breeds can be compared. . . .

Some of the desirable reality of slides of the actual materials used in the solution of a problem may be sacrificed at certain phases of the teaching exercise in order to save some of the time required to arrange the actual materials for satisfactory photography. The origin and testing of hypotheses may be portrayed by slides prepared from photographed diagrams and charts. . . . The problem that was involved here was sex-linkage as exemplified by the barred feather pattern in chickens. The slide contains the genes symbols that were necessary to provide a logical observation of the crosses as diagrammed. Differences between poultry and humans in respect to the transmission of the sex chromosomes create a good problem-solving situation. Given data related to the transmission of human color blindness, students who have developed the sex-linked concept as exemplified in poultry should be able to sense the genetic pattern of inheritance of color blindness.[10]

The 2″ x 2″ slides may have an advantage over the filmstrip if flexibility is needed. In commercial sets, a teacher may wish to drop one or more slides and insert a teacher- or student-made slide that may be interpolated. There are many commercial sources that supply excellent 2″ x 2″ slides.[11] Occasionally, some students who are interested in photography may be stimulated to prepare their own slides to be projected in the science classroom. Activities that are initiated by students, such as making their own slides, may do much to promote a genuine interest in science.

MICROPROJECTOR

Numerous 2″ x 2″ slides of microscopic structures or organisms can be purchased for classroom use. But often a microprojector is the most effective device for teaching a particular topic. For example, the microprojector makes it possible for the class actually to see how paramecia swim in a drop of water and how they obtain food. A biology teacher should contact several representatives from commercial sources to determine which type of microprojection equipment is suitable for a given situation.

Where the budget in a given school system does not permit the purchase of individual microscopes for each student in a biology class, the microprojector is essential. Even where there are individual microscopes, the microprojector is a most useful visual aid in magnifying the size and shapes of various structures associated with living organisms. The science and biology teacher also points

---

[10] John H. Woodburn, "Visual Aids and the Problem-solving Type of Teaching Exercise," *The Science Teacher*, vol. 20 (September, 1953), pp. 167–169.

[11] See Elsie P. Heyl's booklet, *Where to Buy 2″ x 2″ Slides: A Subject Index,* Baltimore, Md., Enoch Pratt Free Library, published annually.

to the specific structures on the screen which can be observed at the same time by all of the students in the class. This technique assures the teacher that all students observe the amoeba. Otherwise, it is possible that students may observe a speck of dirt or dust under the individual microscope and think it is an amoeba.

Not all prepared slides are identical. Thus, it is possible that some students will not see a particular part of a cell such as a nucleus under the individual microscope. But if the projection method is used, all students are given an opportunity to see particular structures. Drawings and biological charts may be prepared easily through the use of a microprojector.

Suggestions were given in Chapter 5 for the construction of a microprojector. Some students may wish to construct the instrument as a project even though a commercial microprojector is available in the classroom. When a microprojector is employed, the teacher should point to specific objects or structures to be observed on the screen. In a biology class, students may follow up this procedure in a laboratory by preparing slides or studying preserved specimens on slides under a microscope. At least, the microprojector enables the teacher to show the entire class what to look for before a laboratory period.

Some of the interesting phenomena that are made visible through microprojection of temporary wet mounts include flagellates in termites, swelling and bursting of cells, cyclosis which is a streaming of protoplasm, and the slowing down of locomotion in paramecium to show movement of cilia and trichocysts. A bioscope is a commercially made microprojector. A viewscope can be used for magnifying some prepared slides that do not need very high magnification. For example, a cross section of some roots and stems may be magnified adequately through a viewscope or a filmstrip slide projector.

PHOTOGRAPHY

Photography can be combined with microprojection by using special equipment to produce photographs of microscopic materials. Most if not all schools can afford to purchase an accessory to a standard microscope to permit students and teachers to record the observations with a photomicrography set. While the camera is in place, observations can be made and a photomicrograph taken. The film can be developed in the school darkroom and a complete series of photographs—showing mitosis in onions or in starfish eggs, for example—can be incorporated as part of the classroom instruction. Photomicrography may serve as an initial basis for stimulating some students to become very much interested in science. Photographic collections, exhibits, displays and micro materials shown in these collections are invaluable in studying several species, biological principles, and related scientific phenomena. Heredity, the nature of chromosomes and genes, the cell and its parts, mitosis, and differences of the plant and animal cell are a few items that can be studied effectively through photomicrography.

Photographs of scientific equipment, especially a setup of an experiment or a demonstration are helpful to teachers and students. Students and teachers may wish to photograph models, charts, laboratory experiments, field trip observations, and other scientific activities. In addition to supplying valuable photographs, the photographic process may be used to teach several basic principles in courses in physics, chemistry, and general science.

A unit on photography can be developed by teaching principles of light through the study of a camera and developing and printing film. The chemistry of photography can also be taught through the developing and printing of photographs. A record of progress of student projects can be photographed. Photographs of student reports and field trips will also be helpful. They represent useful tools in the teaching of science for a better understanding.

MAGNIFYING EQUIPMENT

An enlarger of photographic film is another aid to effective science teaching. A school darkroom should have an enlarger;

a camera; and developing materials such as chemicals, paper, trays, and a printing box to permit the full utilization of photographic equipment for visual science teaching. Enlarged photographs of dissections and of chemical and physical experiments may help students to evaluate their own achievements. Many phenomena and objects in science need to be magnified to be seen and understood.

For this reason many scientific supply companies offer for sale various kinds of magnifying instruments for use in the teaching of biological and physical sciences. In addition to the typical students' microscopes, there are *stereomicroscopes* for studying natural 3-dimension objects; *macroscopes* for gross studies, dissection, and field trips; *microprojectors* for projecting mounted or living organisms and for tracing on pads; *spectroscopes* for observing the spectra of elements needed in chemical analysis; and *opaque* and *transparent projectors* for magnifying and viewing slides, filmstrips, pictures, diagrams, and some chemical reactions. Science teachers should examine catalogues and ask for demonstrations of this equipment to determine which of the magnifying and viewing equipment will best serve the needs for a particular school.

MODELS AND MOCK-UPS

Models of specimens, steam engines, gasoline engines, a cross section of a leaf, the parts of a flower, and atom, and the like are replicas of the original except for size. Mock-ups are working models of an apparatus or a machine. A mock-up of an automobile engine (4-stroke cycle) may show how a piston works by pushing a button. The back and forth motion of the piston is displayed on a board in relation to the total engine which may be filled in diagrammatically. The learner actually sees the four strokes in operation in a mock-up.

An advantage of a mock-up is that one specific area—such as the 4-stroke cycle and how it works—is emphasized without interference from other parts that surround an engine. The army and navy training programs use mock-ups along with actual

Fig. 8.1. Mock-ups stress functional aspects of instruction. (Courtesy of Board of Education, Philadelphia Public Schools, Philadelphia, Pa.)

models. The Link Trainer, for example, simulates the cockpit of an airplane and is used in the training of pilots.

Although many excellent models may be purchased from scientific supply companies, some students may show much creativity by constructing their own models or mock-ups. Figures 8.1 and 8.2 illustrate a mock-up and a model that were made by students. A model that demonstrates nuclear fission can be made with a series of mouse traps.[12] However, the limitations of such demonstrations and models should be clearly stated. It is easy to help develop misconceptions as well as correct concepts through the use of models.

SUMMARY

There are many varied audio-visual aids to teaching and to learning science. They reinforce the learning of abstract concepts

[12] See W. H. Slabaugh, "A Lecture Demonstration of Nuclear Energy," *Journal of Chemical Education,* vol. 25 (December, 1948), p. 679.

Fig. 8.2. A project in geology was prepared by ninth graders. (Courtesy of Uniondale High School, Uniondale, N.Y.)

and clarify the meaning of various scientific phenomena. They should be carefully selected in terms of specific criteria and needs of the pupils and the teacher. They should be used effectively by having the teacher preview and evaluate materials to be adapted to classroom instruction. This applies to motion picture films, film-strips, slides, microprojection, charts, and models. The specific visual or audio-visual aid to be used for a given lesson should be selected wisely in terms of the aims of the lesson and the materials available at the time. The employment of these aids should be an integral part of the methods of teaching and the content of the lesson to be taught. The demonstration method, for instance, cannot be effective unless there are excellent materials (audio-visual aids) available for the demonstration. Similarly, for a problem-solving lesson other suitable materials are needed.

SOURCES FOR FILMS AND FILMSTRIPS

The following references should be consulted freely in order to keep up to date with the latest films and filmstrips:

U.S. Government Film Catalogue Number 3434, U.S. Office of Education Bulletin No. 21.

Bulletin Number 12, *A Directory of 3300 16 mm. Film Libraries, 1956,* U.S. Government Printing Office, Washington, D.C., 1958.

The current edition and supplements of the *Educational Film Guide,* H. W. Wilson Company, New York, N.Y.

The current *Educator's Guide to Free Films,* Educator's Progress Service, Randolph, Wis.

Some of the distributors listed below may have branch offices in several of the larger cities. Check the local telephone directory before writing to the main office.

Abbott Laboratories, Professional Service Dept., North Chicago, Ill.

Academy Films, 800 N. Seward St., Hollywood, Calif.

Allis-Chalmers Manufacturing Co., Films Section, Milwaukee 1, Wis.

Almanac Films, Inc., 516 5th Ave., New York 18, N.Y.

American Can Co., 100 Park Ave., New York, N.Y.

American Cancer Society, 47 Beaver St., New York 4, N.Y.

American Film Registry, 24 E. 8th St., Chicago 5, Ill.

American Guernsey Cattle Club, 70 Main St., Peterborough, N.H.

American Museum of Natural History, 79th St. and Central Park West, New York, N.Y.

Associated Films, Inc., 79 E. Adams St., Chicago 3, Ill.

Associated Films, Inc., 347 Madison Ave., New York 17, N.Y.

Athena Films, Inc., 165 W. 46th St., New York 19, N.Y.

Audio Film Center, 101 W. 31st St., New York, N.Y.

Australian News & Information Bureau, 636 5th Ave., New York 20, N.Y.

Bailey Films, Inc., 6509 DeLongpre Ave., Hollywood 28, Calif.

Arthur Barr Productions, 1265 Breese Ave., Pasadena, Calif.

Bausch & Lomb Optical Co., Film Distribution Service, 635 St. Paul St., Rochester 2, N.Y.

Brandon Films, Inc., 200 W. 57th St., New York, N.Y.

Bray Studios, 729 7th Ave., New York 19, N.Y.

British Information Service, 45 Rockefeller Plaza, New York 21, N.Y.

J. I. Case & Co., Racine, Wis.

Colonial Films, 71 Walton St. NW., Atlanta 6, Ga.

Coronet Films, Coronet Bldg., Chicago 1, Ill.

Curriculum Films, Educational Projections, Inc., 10 E. 40th St., New York 16, N.Y.

Denoyer-Geppert Co., 5235 N. Ravenswood Ave., Chicago 40, Ill.

Dow Chemical Co., Midland, Mich.

Edited Pictures System, Inc., 165 W. 46th St., New York 19, N.Y.

Encyclopaedia Britannica Films, Inc., 1150 Wilmette Ave., Wilmette, Ill.

Family Films, Inc., 5823 Santa Monica Blvd., Hollywood, Calif.

Films of the Nations Distributors, Inc., 62 W. 45th St., New York 36, N.Y.

Fish & Wildlife Service, U.S. Dept. of Interior, P.O. Box 128, College Park, Md.

Frith Films, 1816 North Highland Ave., Hollywood, Calif.

General Electric Corp., 1 River Rd., Schenectady 5, N.Y.

General Motors, Dept. of Public Relations, 3044 W. Grand Blvd., Detroit 2, Mich.

Heidenkamp Nature Pictures, 538 Glen Arden Dr., Pittsburgh 8, Pa.

Ideal Pictures Corp., 58 E. South Water St., Chicago 1, Ill.

Indiana University Films, Audio-visual Center, Bloomington, Ind.

Institute of Visual Training, 40 E. 49th St., New York 17, N.Y.

Instructional Films, Inc., 1150 Wilmette Ave., Wilmette, Ill.

International Film Bureau, Inc., 57 E. Jackson Blvd., Chicago, Ill.

International Film Foundation, Inc., 345 E. 46th St., New York 17, N.Y.

Iowa State University, Bureau of Visual Instruction, Iowa City, Iowa.

Jam Handy Organization, 2821 E. Grand Blvd., Detroit 11, Mich.

Johnson Hunt Productions, 6509 DeLongpre Ave., Hollywood, Calif.

Knowledge Builders, 525 Madison Ave., New York 22, N.Y.

Lederle Laboratories, Division American Cyanamid Co., 30 Rockefeller Plaza, New York 20, N.Y.

Library Films, Inc., 25 W. 45th St., New York 19, N.Y.

Life Filmstrips, Time and Life Building, 9 Rockefeller Plaza, New York 20, N.Y.

Mallinckrodt Chemical Works, 3600 N. Second St., St. Louis 7, Mo.

March of Time, 369 Lexington Ave., New York 17, N.Y.

McGraw-Hill Publishing Co., Films Division, 330 W. 42nd St., New York, N.Y.

Metropolitan Life Insurance Co., 1 Madison Ave., New York 10, N.Y.

Monsanto Chemical Co., St. Louis 4, Mo.

National Audubon Society, 1130 5th Ave., New York, N.Y.

National Cancer Institute, Bethesda 14, Md.

National Film Board of Canada, Suite 2307, RKO Bldg., 6th Ave., New York 20, N.Y.

National Garden Bureau, 407 S. Dearborn St., Chicago 5, Ill.

National Tuberculosis Association, 1790 Broadway, New York 19, N.Y.

New York Botanical Garden, Bronx Park, New York, N.Y.

New York State College of Agriculture, Film Library, Cornell University, Ithaca, N.Y.

New York State Society for Medical Research, 2 E. 63rd St., New York 21, N.Y.

New York University, Film Library, 26 Washington Pl., New York 3, N.Y.

North Carolina State College, Dept. of Visual Aids, Raleigh, N.C.

Ohio State University, Dept. of Photography, Columbus 10, Ohio

Popular Science Publishing Co., Inc., Audio-Visual Division, Filmstrip-of-the-Month-Club, 353 4th Ave., New York 10, N.Y.

Shell Oil Co., 50 W. 50th St., New York 20, N.Y.

Sinclair Refining Co., 155 N. Wacker Dr., Chicago 6, Ill.

Society of American Bacteriologists, Committee on Visual Aids, School of Medicine, University of Pennsylvania, Philadelphia 4, Pa.

Society for Visual Education, Inc., 1345 W. Diversey Parkway, Chicago 14, Ill.

Socony-Mobile Oil Co., 26 Broadway, New York 4, N.Y.

Teaching Films Custodians, Inc., 25 W. 43rd St., New York 18, N.Y.

Tennessee Valley Authority, Division of Agricultural Relations, Knoxville, Tenn.

U.S. Atomic Energy Commission, 1901 Constitution Ave., Washington, D.C.

U.S. Dept. of Agriculture, Washington 25, D.C.

U.S. Forest Service, U.S. Dept. of Agriculture, Washington 25, D.C.

U.S. Public Health Service, Communicable Disease Center, Atlanta, Ga.

United World Films, Inc., 1445 Park Ave., New York 29, N.Y.

University of California, University Extension, Visual Dept., 2272 Union St., Berkeley, Calif.

Ward's Natural Science Establishment, 3000 E. Ridge Rd., Rochester 7, N.Y.

Westinghouse Electric Corp., School Service, 306 4th Ave., Pittsburgh 30, Pa.

Wisconsin Alumni Research Foundation, P.O. Box 2059, Madison, Wis.

Wistar Institute, 36th St. and Woodland Ave., Philadelphia, Pa.

Young America Films, Inc., 18 E. 41st St., New York 17, N.Y.

EXERCISES

1. What are the advantages and limitations of using the chalkboard in teaching science?
2. Under what conditions should the students construct maps and posters rather than the teacher?
3. What criteria should the science teacher employ in selecting motion picture films? What are effective procedures in teaching when using motion picture films?
4. For what purpose would it be more desirable to use filmstrips or slides in place of a motion picture film?
5. Discuss the use of microprojection as compared with pupils' using individual microscopes.
6. How can the use of mock-ups in teaching science be more effective than diagrams?

SUGGESTED READINGS

Brown, James W., Lewis, R. B., and Hacleroad, F. F., *A-V Instruction Materials and Methods,* McGraw-Hill Book Company, Inc., 1959.

Burnett, R. Will, *Teaching Science in the Secondary School,* New York, Rinehart & Company, Inc., 1957.

Dale, Edgar, "Using Films for a Purpose," *The News Letter,* vol. 21 (April, 1956), pp. 1–4.

Dale, Edgar, *Audio-Visual Methods in Teaching—Revised,* New York, Dryden Press, Inc., 1954.

Heiss, E. D., Obourn, E. S., and Hoffman, C. W., *Modern Science Teaching,* New York, The Macmillan Company, 1950.

Martin, W. Edgar, *Facilities and Equipment for Science and Mathematics,* Washington, D.C., U.S. Department of Health, Education, and Welfare, 1960.

May, Mark A., and Lumsdaine, A., *Learning Through Films,* New Haven, Conn., Yale University Press, 1958.

Morholt, E., Brandwein, P. F., and Joseph A., *A Sourcebook for the Biological Sciences,* New York, Harcourt, Brace & Company, 1958.

Obourn, Ellsworth S., *et al.,* "General Facilities and Equipment," in *Science and Mathematics in Public High Schools, 1958, Part 1,* Washington, D.C., U.S. Department of Health, Education, and Welfare, 1960.

Richardson, John S., *Science Teaching in Secondary Schools,* Englewood Cliffs, N.J., Prentice-Hall, Inc., 1957.

Wittich, Walter A., and Schuller, C. F., *Audio-visual Materials: Their Nature and Use,* New York, Harper & Brothers, 1953.

9

PRINTED MATERIALS AND RE-ENFORCING LEARNING OF SCIENCE

TEXTBOOKS AND OTHER BOOKS

Criteria Used in Selecting Textbooks

Printed materials, especially textbooks, make a vital contribution to the teaching of science. Despite the charges that textbooks are misused in teaching, they are recognized as important aids to learning. They can help the teacher to individualize instruction by permitting each student to read at his own rate and comprehension; they are economical in that texts may be used for a number of years; they can help students learn how to study, to read better, and to solve problems; they promote further learning; they give unity to a course; and, finally, the printed page reinforces the learning in or out of the classroom by providing the student with reading materials to be studied at different intervals.

In many science classes more than one textbook is available to the students. In all classes at least one textbook should be available to each pupil. Frequently, the science teacher is asked to recommend a science text or several science books for purchase. In making selections it is helpful to use a set of criteria. Mallinson suggests the following criteria in selecting a textbook for junior high school science: the level of reading difficulty, the style of writing, the nature of the illustrations, the kind of supplementary activities, the provision for individual differences, and the clarity and organization of material.[1] Some science teachers may prefer

[1] George G. Mallinson, "Some Problems of Vocabulary and Reading Difficulty in Teaching Junior High School Science," *School Science and Mathematics,* vol. 52 (April, 1952), pp. 269–274.

to add the degree to which simple-to-complex materials are organized.

The level of reading difficulty especially in terms of vocabulary should be carefully evaluated for different classes. Frequently, a more advanced textbook is very much desired by a science teacher for most of her students. Yet this same text may be too advanced for one of her classes. Occasionally, it may be desirable to use more than one text within a given class to provide for the differences in individual students. Mallinson wrote:

> Once a textbook has been selected it should be examined carefully to determine whether or not the difficult terms have been defined and explained either in the text or in the footnotes when they are used for the *first* time.
>
> If the teacher finds a number of words that are likely to cause difficulty for the students, it may be wise to list them. The students should then be given specific instruction in their pronunciations, spellings, and meanings *before* the words actually appear in the text. Thus, it will not be necessary for the teacher to spend time correcting misconceptions that arise from the pupils' misunderstandings of such words.[2]

Vogel developed an evaluation scale that may be a guide to selecting a science textbook.[3] His criteria are grouped under 10 major headings: qualification of the author, organization, content, presentation, accuracy, readability, adaptability, teaching aids, illustrations, and appearance. A similar rating scale was also developed by Burr.[4]

Whether the selection is to be made by an individual science teacher or by a committee of teachers, it may be helpful to obtain answers to the following questions:

1. Are the major objectives of teaching science being considered in selecting a text?
2. How is the syllabus related in terms of content to the content in the textbook?

---

[2] *Ibid.*

[3] Louis F. Vogel, "A Spot-Check Evaluation Scale for High School Science Textbooks," *The Science Teacher,* vol. 18 (March, 1951), pp. 70–72.

[4] Samuel E. Burr, "A Rating Scale for Textbooks," *Journal of Education,* vol. 132 (May, 1949), pp. 138–139.

3. Are publishers' catalogues which list new books being examined along with the new texts?
4. What is the quality of the cover, paper, printing, binding, graphic and pictorial aids, study guides, problem-solving activities, film listings and descriptions, bibliographies, and self-evaluation devices?
5. What is the level of difficulty of reading and vocabulary?
6. Is the text attractive and readable to students?
7. Is the text accurate and up to date?

Perhaps the science teacher or committee which selects a textbook should re-examine the criteria periodically in terms of changing objectives or the change in the type of class or student body. It is possible that a text may be most suitable for one particular class and yet be unsuited to the needs of many pupils in a different class. The assumption is that a textbook is really designed for the student rather than for the teacher. Some teachers may wish to obtain pupil comments about evaluating several textbooks as part of the overall procedure.

SELECTING SUPPLEMENTARY SCIENCE BOOKS

Many science teachers, librarians, parents, and publishers are confronted with the problem of suggesting supplementary reading books in the sciences for intellectually gifted and other pupils in the junior and senior high schools. The basis for recommending such books varies considerably from one individual to another. A recent study was designed to determine criteria for selecting supplementary science readings with the help of 156 leading science educators who are members of the National Association for Research in Science Teaching. Table 4 lists the six most important criteria in two categories—effect on the reader and qualities of the book.

The tabulated results of the judgments expressed by the science educators led to the following implications and recommendations:

1. In selecting the best books for intellectually gifted students, group participation is a highly effective method. Science education

TABLE 4. Criteria for Selecting Supplementary Science Readings

Rank	Criterion	Percentage of Responses Ascribing Degree of Importance		
		Much	Crucial	Combined Score
	Category A—Effect on the Reader			
1.	It provokes thinking and discussion.	33.3	60.7	94.3
2.	It develops interest in matters of science.	43.3	44.7	88.0
3.	It stimulates further reading.	47.3	40.0	87.3
4.	It helps to articulate and elucidate scientific concepts and principles.	46.7	36.7	83.4
5.	It suggests further problems.	47.3	26.7	74.0
6.	It gives insights into social implications and contributions of science.	38.7	26.7	65.4
	Category B—Qualities of the Book			
1.	It is accurate and authoritative.	18.7	74.6	93.3
2.	It is fair and sincere in its presentation of controversial subject matter.	36.7	47.3	84.0
3.	Its enrichment material goes beyond that of secondary text books.	43.3	40.7	84.0
4.	It has good literary standards —clear style, grammatically correct, easy to read.	43.3	36.7	80.0
5.	Its general theme and tone are wholesome.	44.7	26.7	71.4
6.	It is a book of lasting value— one worth owning and going back to.	53.4	18.0	71.4

SOURCE: C. W. Barnes, A. D. Beck, W. B. Reiner, and N. S. Washton, "Criteria for Selecting Supplementary Reading Science Books for Intellectually Gifted High School Students," *Science Education*, vol. 42 (April, 1958), pp. 215–218.

specialists should also share their experiences as a group in using the 12 criteria in proposing those science books that would satisfy as many of these criteria as possible.

2. The ability of intellectually gifted high school students should not be underestimated. Their level of reading should be upgraded through a careful selection of books. Therefore, serious attention should be given to the selection of appropriate science books that challenge these bright students. Perhaps the reading of better science books may carry over into other areas of knowledge where the students will demand a higher level and a better quality book.

3. The reading of excellent science books is vital for the total development of all high school youth. The purpose is not to make scientists of all of them. However, intelligent citizens in our society need an understanding of science and its impact upon our culture. Schools and libraries, parents and teachers should make available top-notch science books to our young people.

4. There is a close relationship between student activity in science such as home laboratories, science clubs, collecting scientific materials, and the reading of science books. It is extremely difficult to determine whether the reading of science books causes students to engage in scientific hobbies or vice versa. Hence, the reading of worthwhile science books and the extracurricular science activities in the school and at home should be encouraged.

5. Teachers, administrators, librarians, and parents can use the 12 criteria in determining the degree to which a book satisfies most of these criteria before recommending such a book to the students. Wherever possible, the students should also evaluate the book after reading it and determine whether or not most of the criteria were satisfied.

6. It is important that our students be given the opportunity of reading the kind of science books that will help them develop their maximum potentiality in scholarship, extending and deepening their interests, social adjustment, understanding science, and possibly consider scientific careers.[5]

Supplementary science readings are available in paperback editions and can be purchased for classroom use or for home use.

[5] C. W. Barnes, A. D. Beck, W. B. Reiner, and N. S. Washton, "Criteria for Selecting Supplementary Reading Science Books for Intellectually Gifted High School Students," *Science Education,* vol. 42 (April, 1958), pp. 215–218.

Classical science books available in paperback for as little as 35¢ up to $2.00 per copy include: *Crucibles* by Jaffe, *Origin of the Species* by Darwin, *Bees* by von Frisch, *Biography of the Earth* by Gamow, *Atomic Age Physics* by Semat and White, *The Meaning of Evolution* by Simpson, *Readings in the Literature of Science* by Dampier, and hundreds of others.

The following publications list available paperbacks:

Paperback Books in Print, New York, R. R. Bowker, semiannual, $3.00 the year, $2.00 single copy.

Atwood, H. Townsend (ed.), *Good Reading,* New York. New American Library, 75¢.

Helen B. Hogan, *Treasures in Paperbacks,* Chapel Hill, N.C., University of North Carolina, 75¢.

Hilary J. Deason and Robert W. Lynn, *An Inexpensive Science Library; A Selected List of Paperbound Science Books,* Washington, D.C., American Association for the Advancement of Science, 25¢.

The use of supplementary science books and other reading materials should be encouraged in all science and occasionally in English classes. It is another method of introducing students to new materials and of meeting the varied needs and interests of all students in a group. Good supplementary readings in science will serve to stimulate additional reading in the same or related topic. This can develop initiative and self-direction. Students can compare different authors and readings on the same science topic and thus will be helped to evaluate what they read in a more critical or analytical fashion.

VOCABULARY STUDIES

One of the major considerations in selecting an appropriate science text or book is the degree to which the reader experiences difficulty with the vocabulary in the book. In recent years, much attention has been given to the vocabulary in science books. Yet there appear to be at least two divergent points of view as expressed in two articles that appeared in *The American Biology Teacher.* Malatesta wrote: "It [the biology textbook] consisted

mainly of difficult scientific terms with equally difficult explanations. There was little to fire the imagination of the average student and lead him in what can be the wondrous field of nature."[6]
Sister Payne, on the other hand, expresses the following point of
view: "Why should scientific terminology be simplified for him
[the student]? Why substitute simple words or slang phrases for
distinctive, scientific phraseology that is purposeful and pointed?
Why step down educational levels? We need not assume that the
present generation of students is endowed with less ability than
the parental generation who passed similar courses. Do we not
insult both parent and progeny by catering to mediocrity?"[7]

In discussing both of these viewpoints, Mallinson writes: "The
divergence of these viewpoints does not indicate lack of merit in
either. Any textbook for science must be written so that the students for whom it is designed are able to read it. But to emascu-
late the scientific terminology to such an extent that accurate
scientific meanings are not expressed would be equally unwise."[8]

Over one hundred studies of vocabulary were examined by
Curtis and Mallinson, each of whom reported that there are too
many undefined scientific terms in science textbooks and that too
many nonscientific and difficult terms are introduced in the textbook which are beyond the level of secondary school students.[9]
It was also indicated that the level of the difficulty at the beginning
of the book is the same as at the end. In other words, no provision
for improvement or pupil growth is considered in the development
of the textbook.

Investigations by Shores and by Swenson emphasize the need
for all teachers, including science teachers, to be teachers of read-

[6] Anne Malatesta, "Dry as Chalk Dust," *The American Biology Teacher,* vol. 12 (February, 1950), pp. 27–28.

[7] M. Anthony Payne, O.S.B., "Some Queries, Mr. Editor," *The American Biology Teacher,* vol. 12 (May, 1950), pp. 108–109.

[8] Mallinson, *op. cit.*

[9] Francis D. Curtis, *Investigations of Vocabulary in Textbooks of Science for Secondary Schools,* Ginn & Company, 1938, pp. 115–116; George G. Mallinson et al., "The Reading Difficulty of Textbooks in General Science," *School Review,* vol. 52 (February, 1952), pp. 94–98.

ing.[10] Unfortunately, it is frequently tempting for the science teacher to spend a classroom period emphasizing only vocabulary. The functional approach to teaching science would suggest that new scientific vocabulary should be introduced where there is a need for it in conjunction with new principles or major understandings. Science teachers should avoid making the teaching of science the teaching of a foreign language with emphasis on merely new vocabulary. Technical terms should be employed in discussions to illustrate their meanings and in making applications. For example, a major understanding or concept would be photosynthesis. If the new technical term to be introduced is *catalyst* during a discussion of *photosynthesis,* a discussion could include the roles of sunlight and chlorophyll. Applications of other catalysts or enzymes might also be introduced to assign deeper meanings and to develop a greater understanding.

FUNCTIONS OF A TEXTBOOK

Perhaps the most significant development in recent years in the use of textbooks is that the textbook now serves the purpose of assisting the teacher and the student, not the purpose of providing the teacher with all of the content needed for teaching the course. The traditional approach was to base the teaching of a science course almost completely on the contents of a textbook in science. Research in science has made it evident to science teachers that all books in science may become out of date sooner than in other subjects. For this reason, the teacher is compelled to supplement instruction which may originally have been determined by a textbook. Today's approach is usually the converse of teaching only the textbook; science textbooks are now used to supplement classroom instruction. This is especially true where a good syllabus is developed and is used as the basis for organizing and teaching

[10] J. H. Shores, "Skills Related to the Ability to Read History and Science," *Journal of Educational Research,* vol. 36 (April, 1943), pp. 584–593; Esther J. Swenson, "A Study of the Relationship Among Various Types of Reading Scores on General and Science Materials," *Journal of Educational Research,* vol. 36 (October, 1942), pp. 81–90.

a science program. Science textbooks that supplement instruction are usually employed by teachers as references or encyclopedic volumes to enable students to look up additional materials beyond classroom activity. The text used primarily as a reference is frequently employed by the student to look up specific information that may not have been understood in class. The book should have clear explanations, good illustrations, appropriate vocabulary, and a good writing style. Scientific explanations and applications should accompany scientific principles in this type of text.

One of the misuses of a textbook is to require students to read assignments because the science teacher did not have sufficient time to "cover it" in class. Homework from a textbook is done to drill or to give students practice in retaining information and being able to apply it in different situations or in solving problems. This process of reinforcing learning by reading again or repetition by seeing or hearing will become part of the pupil learning experience if it has meaning or purpose. Thus, a function of textbooks in science is to re-enforce the learning that may have originated in the science classroom or laboratory.

At the end of the twentieth century, as indicated earlier, most science textbooks contained about 200 pages. Today most of the science texts in the junior and senior high schools run from 500 to 1000 pages. Scientific developments, discoveries, and historical information are accumulated and added in the writing of new science textbooks. In many cities, this cumulative process appears in the syllabuses. Very few science teachers or curriculum specialists wish to take the initiative in deleting outdated and insignificant information. How much of Dalton's atomic theory, the Lewis and Langmuir concept of the structure of the atom, and the Bohr concept should be taught in a high school chemistry class? Perhaps a specialized course in the history of science should be designed which emphasizes the case study approach in teaching science. This may make it possible for many science educators to omit much of the historical material from a general education chemistry or science course.

Another problem is to determine who should decide what goes in or out of the syllabus and the textbook. Burnett writes: "Is it less 'fundamental,' for example, for a student to know something of the nature of histamine and the physiological effects of the action of histaminase on histamine than it is for him to know the names and actions of ptyalin, pepsin, and trypsin? The former has probably never been presented in a high school textbook, and the latter has been included in an almost identical fashion in practically all biology textbooks."[11]

Earlier research has produced the knowledge about the enzymes and digestion. This information is well imbedded in most of the textbooks. The competition for sales for textbooks which contain much of the information people are accustomed to seeing will probably serve as a continued force in selecting what should stay in the textbooks. Histamine and histaminase and their relationships to hypersensitivity and good health are relatively new to the high school biology textbooks. Therefore, it should be the function of the author to include and bring information up to date in revising all textbooks. In science, this can be done only up to a certain point since new discoveries are sure to be made shortly after a science text goes to press. Hence, it is the function of the science teacher to bring the textbook up to date by use of reports, discussions, meetings, and referring to periodicals.

Science textbooks should be used as a source of obtaining basic information considered essential in developing the objectives of science education. They can be used to re-enforce learning as well as to stimulate students to make further inquiries into science beyond the level of a given textbook. A good textbook may also be used as a reference. New learning activities such as individual projects, laboratory experiments, and demonstrations may also be suggested in the textbook. The science textbook in conjunction with other readings constitutes an important tool for teaching science.

[11] R. Will Burnett, *Teaching Science in the Secondary School,* Rinehart & Company, 1957, p. 167.

MAGAZINES AND BULLETINS

Since the latest information in scientific research cannot be made available in the textbook, many science teachers fill the gap by using several helpful periodicals to provide current reading materials. The following periodicals are available to junior and senior high school students, usually at reduced rates when ordered as a class or group subscription.

Science News Letter, Chemistry, and monthly experimental kits called *Things of Science* are available from Science Service, 1719 N St. NW., Washington 6, D.C.

Scientific American, a monthly, may be used by students who have a high interest and/or ability level in science. It is located at 415 Madison Ave., New York, N.Y.

Natural History has wide popular appeal and is published by the American Museum of Natural History, Central Park West and 79th St., New York, N.Y.

Tomorrow's Scientists is available for individual and group subscriptions from the National Science Teachers Association, 1201 16th St. NW., Washington 6, D.C. Bulletins are also available from time to time that deal with useful projects. Some titles are: "Encouraging Future Scientists: Student Projects," "If You Want To Do a Science Project," "Careers in Science Teaching." All of these bulletins may be obtained for a few cents or free of charge from the National Science Teachers Association.

Science teachers will want to be informed of much of the latest research in science and in science education. The following periodicals may prove invaluable:

American Biology Teacher, National Association of Biology Teachers, Bryan, Ohio

American Scientists, Sigma Xi, 54 Hillhouse Ave., New Haven 11, Conn.

Endeavor, North Block, Thames House, Millbank, London SW.1, England

Nature, The Macmillan Co., St. Martin's St., London, WC. 2, England

Review of Educational Research, American Educational Research Association, 1201 16th St. NW., Washington, D.C.

Science, American Association for the Advancement of Science, 1515 Massachusetts Ave. NW., Washington 5, D.C.

Science Education, National Association for Research in Science Teaching, Dr. Clarence M. Pruitt (ed.), University of Tampa, Tampa, Fla.

It is highly recommended that a school library purchase the above-listed periodicals for the pupils and the faculty. Students should be encouraged to use these periodicals for research, individual and group reports, and for general information. A stimulating article may influence many students to engage in collateral reading and develop new interests in science. These supplementary readings and assignments can help students to learn basic scientific principles as well as to keep up to date with the latest information in science.

FREE MATERIALS AND THEIR SOURCES

Science teachers and their pupils may wish to use printed materials that show applications or relationships of scientific information to specific industries, health, and consumer products or consumer services. Usually, these materials are available on request by the science teacher or perhaps on request by the pupils. They are produced in various forms such as charts, pictures, leaflets, bulletins, and comics and most often carry some advertising. The school principal should be consulted as to policy on whether the school administration allows commercial materials that contain advertising to be distributed to the students.

Assuming that there is no objection to use of such materials, a biology teacher can obtain free of charge, for example, sufficient copies of colored charts with printed descriptions that show the chambers of the human heart and the associated major blood vessels. These can be distributed to all students and used in classroom instruction to reinforce a laboratory period or demonstration or discussion lesson. The American Heart Association is the distributor and will also send additional literature upon request.

In general, most of the larger chemical and pharmaceutical manufacturing companies, engineering industries, governmental agencies (agriculture, wildlife, and geology), and aviation industries have useful and educational materials for free distribution. It is difficult to obtain a complete listing of all of these industries, but a sampling is listed as follows:

American Can Co., 100 Park Ave., New York 17, N.Y.

American Cancer Society, 47 Beaver St., New York 14, N.Y.

American Dental Association, 222 E. Superior St., Chicago 11, Ill.

American Forest Products, 1816 N St. NW., Washington 6, D.C.

American Gas Association, Educational Service, 420 Lexington Ave., New York 17, N.Y.

American Heart Association 44 E. 23rd St., New York 10, N.Y.

American Nature Association, 1214 16th St. NW., Washington 6, D.C.

American Optical Co., Instrument Division, Buffalo 15, N.Y.

American Potash Institute, 1102 16 St. N.W., Washington 6, D.C.

Bausch & Lomb Optical Co., 1635 St. Paul St., Rochester 2, N.Y.

Borden Co., Educational Service, 350 Madison Ave., New York 17, N.Y.

Bristol-Myers Co., 630 5th Ave., New York 20, N.Y.

Church and Dwight, 70 Pine St., New York, N.Y.

Cinchona Products Institute, 10 Rockefeller Plaza, New York 20, N.Y.

Corning Glass Works, Public Relations Dept., 718 5th Ave., New York 19, N.Y.

Crown Zellerbach Corp., Rincon Annex, Box 3475, San Francisco, Calif.

Diamond Crystal Salt Co., St. Clair, Mich.

Dow Chemical Co., Midland, Mich.

General Foods Corp., 250 Park Ave., New York 17, N.Y.

Johnson & Johnson Co., Education Dept., New Brunswick, N.J.

Metropolitan Life Insurance Co., School Service Dept., 1 Madison Ave., New York 16, N.Y.

National Audubon Society, 1130 5th Ave., New York 28, N.Y.

C. Pfizer Co., 11 Bartlett St., Brooklyn 6, N.Y.

Upjohn Co., Kalamazoo, Mich.

SUMMARY

Although science textbooks can be out of date in a short period of time, they are important tools of teaching. In selecting a textbook for class adoption, different criteria should be employed with an awareness of the nature of the student body and the functions of the text. In selecting supplementary readings for bright students, surveys indicate that many scientific questions may go unanswered in a given book. This may cause some students to do more reading and research and result in a greater learning of science. Printed materials such as magazines, newspapers, leaflets, and government publications should be made available in order that students may keep up to date with the latest developments in science. Scientific vocabulary should be taught as part of regular science teaching and reading unless remedial reading is indicated.

EXERCISES

1. Discuss the criteria in adopting a science text for a particular class.
2. Explain the various functions of a science textbook, and indicate how they are related to class instruction.
3. What sources are available to obtain a list of the latest supplementary reading books in science?
4. How should science vocabulary be taught to a ninth-grade science class which is two years behind in reading ability?
5. List five current periodicals used by secondary school science students and teachers.

10

EVALUATING LEARNING
OF SCIENCE

The science teacher has not taught if the student has not learned. To determine whether or not a student has learned science and to determine the effectiveness of the teaching process, the teacher uses many techniques and instruments of evaluation. Unfortunately there are too many parts of the learning of science that cannot always be measured. For example, the scientific attitudes learned by some students may never be measured or observed in class by the teacher. A negative development may occur in which a student learns to dislike science as a result of taking a specific science course.

There are different measuring techniques for determining pupil growth in scientific knowledge or information, attitudes, interests, behavior, problem-solving abilities, and related skills. The science teacher is faced with a more complex task in evaluating his success in teaching than is the shoe salesman in evaluating his success in selling—the latter can judge results by the money he produces for the shoes he sells. If the salesman cannot produce cash receipts or make a minimum number of sales he is not selling. In other words, there is no selling unless there is buying. An analogy might be made in which case it could be said that there is no teaching unless there is learning.

Evaluation is a process in which *values* of something are determined. For example, in our objectives of teaching science, pupils should learn certain understandings, skills, attitudes, and interests. Determining the degree to which pupils attain or make progress toward mastering any of these objectives is the process of measurement. Wandt and Brown wrote: "Evaluation depends upon, but is not synonymous with, measurement. Evaluation goes beyond measurement in answering the question: Is the obtained measure desirable or undesirable?"[1]

Pencil-and-paper tests are frequently employed in the process of measurement. They are usually part of the overall evaluation system in determining the values and achievements of individual students.

EVALUATION—A CONTINUOUS PROCESS

Perhaps the most significant methods of teaching science are the techniques employed by the teacher during the process of evaluation. These instructional procedures call for determining at regular and frequent intervals the degree of mastery and understanding of ideas on the pupil's part. Thus, evaluation should be a continuous process throughout the lesson, the teaching unit, and the course. During the lesson, the teacher asks questions, the students ask questions, students reply, students write on the board or in notebooks at their seats, a pencil-and-paper test is administered, the teacher observes pupil behavior, and the homework is discussed. All of these procedures make up the total evaluation process. Hence, evaluation of pupil learning is a continuous approach to the methodology of teaching.

What progress do students show they have made at any given stage of development? Do the brighter students show their ability and readiness to go on to advanced work? Do the slow learners demonstrate exactly what their difficulties have been? For example, chemistry students cannot solve weight-weight problems if they do not know how to write balanced equations. The science teacher is therefore concerned with determining whether or not all of the students can write balanced equations of the reactions involved. Such evaluations should precede instruction in weight-weight problems. This determination of how much progress has been made toward the development of objectives is a continuous evaluation procedure, and it informs the teacher of diagnostic or remedial

[1] Edwin Wandt and Gerald W. Brown, *Essentials of Educational Evaluation,* Henry Holt & Company, 1957, p. 1.

instruction that may be needed by the slow learners. It also enables the science instructor to plan the new and advanced work for the average and bright students.

Another function of evaluation as a continuous process is the determination of the effectiveness of instruction and planned activities. The science teacher is eager to learn whether or not his teaching is productive. Have the discussion, recitation, laboratory, demonstration, problem solving, case study, field trip, and projects contributed equally toward developing the objectives? Perhaps the laboratory method is more effective for teaching specific manipulative laboratory skills than the demonstration method. Research in science teaching indicates this to be a fact. But the science teacher is interested in finding out for himself if his pupils gain these skills most efficiently through the laboratory procedure. A good evaluation procedure such as a laboratory test based upon performance of skill, rather than on a pencil-and-paper test alone, will reveal the degree of gain in skill in the pupils. If certain objectives such as skills have not been obtained by the use of a specific method of teaching, either a different method should be employed or the basic objectives re-examined. Evaluation, therefore, as a continuous process is a way of enabling the science teacher to validate the objectives, content, and methods of teaching.

FACTORS AFFECTING STUDENT ACHIEVEMENT

Using experimental forms of a new chemistry examination, Anderson conducted several studies and found that students achieved significantly more when: (1) they attended large schools; (2) the class size was smaller; (3) the teacher had a smaller load and had studied chemistry for a greater number of hours while in college; (4) students were given laboratory experience rather than only demonstrations.[2] Laboratory manuals did not affect student achievement in biology classes.

[2] Kenneth E. Anderson, "A Study of Achievement in High School Chemistry in Several Eastern and Midwestern States," *Science Education,* vol. 34 (April, 1950), pp. 168–176; "The Teachers of Science in a Representative Sampling of Minnesota Schools," *Science Education,* vol. 34 (February, 1950), pp. 57–66; "Summary

Current events in science, especially as reported in advertising materials such as pamphlets and periodicals, may be employed in the teaching of high school chemistry and physics classes. Miller and Dresden found that devoting one-fifth or more of class time to the study of current materials will not lower achievement by physics and chemistry students as measured by the Cooperative Physics tests and Cooperative Chemistry tests.[3] On the *Time* Current Affairs Tests the experimental groups displayed a superior knowledge in current affairs.

Undue pressure on the part of pupils, teachers, and parents may deter the achievement of pupil's mastery of subject matter. Some students are made to feel that they must get a perfect score in science in order to maintain respect or love from parents. This frequently causes emotional problems that will not only hinder progress in learning science but make for a poorly adjusted student as well. The other extreme of setting low standards will also hinder pupil progress by not encouraging them to work to their maximum capacity. Realistic tests should be developed very carefully. Klausmeier wrote:

Testing can be made constructive in the following ways: Make sure that the purposes of the test for both student and teacher are clearly understood; give tests frequently so that each one does not become so important; give tests only as scheduled; use tests as a method by which students can measure their progress; help students recognize the factors that produce differential test scores; and finally, use the test results as a means of understanding students better and of organizing more effective learning experiences.

These elements of creating an orderly work situation—manifesting confident leadership, establishing a zest for learning, and setting reasonable levels of achievement—are related to understanding students as individuals and also to managing interpersonal group relations.[4]

---

of the Relative Achievements of the Objectives of Secondary School Science and a Representative Sampling of 56 Minnesota Schools," *Science Education,* vol. 33 (December, 1949), pp. 333–343.

[3] M. M. Miller and K. Dresden, "Current Approaches in the Teaching of Science," *School Science and Mathematics,* vol. 49 (May, 1949), pp. 359–365.

[4] Herbert J. Klausmeier, *Teaching in the Secondary School,* Harper & Brothers, 1958, p. 389.

A good test should be a good learning situation. Students can learn during the test and after the test if it is well constructed and administered. The scoring of the test should not be the end product. Students can be motivated to learn more science as a result of taking a good test, regardless of the score obtained. This should be a major criterion in the construction of teacher-made tests as well as in the selection of standardized tests. Testing, one of the many instruments for evaluation, can be used by the science teacher to make a diagnosis of pupil weaknesses and achievements and to improve the teachers techniques of teaching. If the test is a learning experience, it will not only serve as a basis for assigning a grade but will influence achievement.

DATA NEEDED FOR EVALUATION

When tests are used to obtain scores for pupils at the end of a week, month, unit, or term of instruction, it is difficult to determine how much a student has learned as a result of the teacher's instruction. Actually, unless a pretest is administered and scored, there is no valid basis for measuring pupil growth in a given course. This problem is very acute in the teaching of science since the curriculum in science is so varied in the elementary schools. Students enter the junior high school from several elementary schools with highly varied backgrounds in science. The variation may be due to the previous training in the elementary school and/or the home and to individual pupil interest and ability. If a seventh- or eighth-grade science teacher wishes to learn how much of a unit in astronomy his students have or have not covered in an earlier grade, he should administer a pretest. It is possible that most of his students have already learned much about the planets, for example, in the sixth grade. Therefore, testing at the beginning and at the end of a unit or part of instruction will give the science teacher a more accurate picture of pupil achievement.

The pretest is used not only to determine the initial status but also to diagnose pupil weaknesses in understanding science or the lack of skills in science. Frequently, a science teacher will use the results of pretests to plan a new unit. This approach is being more widely practiced today because of the very heterogeneous background of science that junior and senior high school pupils display. A high school biology teacher may find that some of his students have come from a general science teacher who emphasized blood and circulation to the exclusion of many other biological concepts. The result may be that the students in the high school biology class find the repetition of blood and circulation dull simply because they already have the necessary information. A pretest which shows initial knowledge can aid the teacher in planning any unit.

Tests, anecdotal records, observations, conferences, and expression of attitudes are all helpful as part of data needed for evaluation. The science teacher usually offers a series of applications as part of the daily instruction to reinforce the learning of scientific principles and problem solving. Organizing and teaching scientific applications or problem solving can be an important part of the evaluation process in determining pupil achievement, retention, and transfer.

The science teacher, in addition to finding out how much the student learned, should occasionally administer an opinionnaire to screen pupil thinking on what procedures or methods of teaching were effective. The science teacher can design a form in which pupils are asked to indicate their relative judgments of procedures as "most helpful," "very helpful," "helpful," "little help," or "not helpful" for each of the following 29 items:

Directions: Place an X in the circle under the appropriate column for each item which expresses your opinion about how helpful the activities listed below are in learning science.

1. If I ask questions in class
2. If I recite in class
3. If the teacher asks the questions
4. If other pupils recite
5. If the science teacher performs a demonstration
6. If the teacher conducts an experiment

7. If I write the demonstrations in my notebook
8. If the teacher explains ideas and asks questions
9. If the science teacher lectures with no discussion
10. If the teacher presents a problem followed with much discussion
11. If the class visits a museum, planetarium, or other point of scientific interest
12. If the teacher shows a good science film
13. If I make a science project
14. If I keep a good science notebook
15. If I perform a science demonstration in class
16. If I could perform experiments in class
17. If I read science texts in class
18. If I read science texts outside of class
19. If I read science books (not texts) and magazines in class
20. If I read science books (not texts) and magazines outside of class
21. If homework is given every day
22. If homework is given when I'm interested in a special topic
23. If I get science tests regularly
24. If the teacher explains the results of the tests
25. If the teacher asks my ideas about science experiments
26. If the teacher asks me to suggest various ways to solve problems
27. If I can copy in my notebook the demonstration performed by the teacher
28. If I am asked to bring in newspaper or magazine science articles
29. If I can make drawings of the things I see and make in class

Although the results of this type of questionnaire are subject to discussion in terms of validity, some ideas may develop to cause the science teacher to re-evaluate many of the classroom instructional procedures. For example, there is nothing sacred about the idea that all demonstrations or experiments must be copied in a student notebook for general science. Is this kind of activity related to the objectives? And do students perform such an activity with a positive or negative attitude?

EVALUATION FOR WHAT?

Most of the teacher-made tests in science seem to emphasize facts that may or may not be related to important ideas or scientific principles. Yet the objectives of science teaching go beyond factual knowledge when emphasis is given to scientific attitudes, understandings, skills, thinking, appreciations, and interests. In recent years, science teachers have attempted to measure attitudes and scientific thinking along with scientific principles and their applications. Anderson writes:

To get at the more important concepts or to rise above the mere testing of facts to more permanent learnings, one has to modify or adapt the usual form or type of item. To illustrate items that rise above the usual factual question and get at principles of science, may I quote from one examination?

"39. A storekeeper placed some calcium chloride between his sash and storm window during a severe cold spell. What happened?
1. The window became more heavily frosted than the nearby windows.
2. The substance became dry and powderlike.
3. The calcium chloride evaporated.
4. The windows remained almost free of frost.
5. Nothing happened.
"40. Which one of the following statements gives the principle that best explains the answer to question 39?
6. Many gases such as water vapor and carbon dioxide can be solidified.
7. Many chemical reactions depend upon the lack of or presence of moisture.
8. Many solids such as dry ice and iodine pass directly from a solid to a gaseous state.
9. Many substances readily lose their water of hydration or crystallization on exposure to air.
10. Many substances have the property of absorbing or adsorbing moisture from air or other substances."

Lest we get the idea that objective testing is the only answer to evaluation of science instruction, let us hasten to add that an important corollary of all instruction is the degree to which this instruction operates in the lives of boys and girls.[5]

[5] Kenneth E. Anderson, "Improving Science Teaching Through Realistic Research," *Science Education*, vol. 37 (February, 1953), p. 57. The examination to which Anderson refers is his *Anderson Chemistry Test, Form Am,* World Book Company, 1950, p. 4.

The Educational Testing Service recently developed a statement of the purposes of teaching and testing in science and a series of tests that measure growth in science over a period of years from elementary school through the first two years of college. Excerpts follow:

New knowledge flows fast in the field of natural science—supplementing, modifying, or replacing established ideas, practices, and materials. In this changing field, what ways of thinking and acting will help young people to live effectively and with reasonable understanding? What aspects of scientific training are essential for educational growth in science? Science teachers agree, in general, that:

The student should acquire knowledge of basic scientific concepts in each major area of science. These concepts must be thoroughly understood and retained by the student to provide adequate capacity for growth in science.

The student should acquire problem-solving skills which he needs in the application of scientific knowledge to familiar and unfamiliar situations.

The STEP (Sequential Tests of Educational Progress) science tests are designed to measure these two aspects of science education generally and are limited to the content of the "average" curriculum.

CRITERIA FOR SELECTION OF MATERIALS

Basic concepts are identified in each of several subject matter fields —biology, chemistry, physics, meteorology, astronomy, and geology. Often there are numerous understandings related to a single concept. For example, the concept of chemical change involves the law of conservation of matter and the understanding that energy changes are always involved. It was necessary, therefore, to recognize the important understandings pertinent to each concept, and to use this list as a source of things to be tested. The committee endeavored to include abilities essential to critical thinking at various stages of development. These abilities, basically the same in all branches of science at all levels of education, provide a common basis for measuring progress in the field as a whole, without regard for specific subject matter content.

Since the committee agreed that the student who is truly making progress in science is one who increasingly is able to apply knowledge in a variety of ways, basic understanding and skills should be tested in situations in which science is applied. The broad situational aspects were identified as economic, cultural, social, and science-in-the-home. Within each situational aspect, problem areas were defined; for example, areas in the economic aspect include conservation, industry, and agriculture. The tests were built around situations representative of these problems. Sets of questions were devised which would relate basic understandings and the application of specific skills to these situations. Insofar as possible, each test question measures simultaneously a specific skill and a specific concept or undertanding.

SKILLS TESTED

1. Ability to identify and define a scientific problem; to isolate a problem from a mass of given material.

2. Ability to suggest or screen hypotheses; to suspend judgment; to recognize cause and effect; to recognize the possibility of testing and hypothesis; to recognize the logical consistency and plausibility of a hypothesis and to check it with relevant laws, facts, operations, or experiments.

3. Ability to select validating procedures: to design experiments, to plan collection of appropriate data.

4. Ability to interpret data and draw conclusions: to formulate valid conclusions; to recognize or draw generalizations from data known or given.

5. Ability to evaluate critically the claims or statements of others: to evaluate advertisements, written materials, and audio-visual materials; to detect superstition and fancy; to recognize the pseudo-scientific and the use of unwarranted extrapolations or generalizations; to distinguish among fact, hypothesis, and opinion; to distinguish the relevant from the irrelevant.

6. Ability to reason quantitatively and symbolically: to understand and use numerical operations, symbolic relations, and information presented in graphs, charts, maps, and tables.

SAMPLES OF SCIENCE TEST MATERIAL

Each test consists of sets of multiple-choice objective questions, each set based on a single problem situation. The number of questions in a set depends on the length and nature of the problem situation. Within each set the various questions measure different skills and understandings.

The situational materials presented in the problems were carefully selected for their relevance to the everyday life of the students and to the interests of students at particular educational levels.

As the tests in the series progress from lower to more advanced educational levels, students are given an opportunity to demonstrate their increased competence in handling scientific skills and understandings.

The following samples of science test material illustrate at different levels the ability to select validating procedures; to design experiments; to plan collection of appropriate data.

Level 4 (Grades 4–6)

Situation: Tom wanted to learn which of three types of soil—clay, sand, or loam—would be best for growing lima beans. He found three flower pots, put a different type of soil in each pot, and planted lima beans in each. He placed them side by side on the window sill and gave each pot the same amount of water.

The lima beans grew best in the loam. Why did Mr. Jackson say Tom's experiment was NOT a good experiment and did NOT prove that loam was the best soil for plant growth?

A. The plants in one pot got more sunlight than the plants in the other pots.

B. The amount of soil in each pot was not the same.

C. One pot should have been placed in the dark.

D. Tom should have used three kinds of seeds.

Level 3 (Grades 7–9)

Situation: Tom planned to become a farmer, and his father encouraged this interest by giving Tom a part of the garden to use for studying plant life.

Tom wanted to find out what effect fertilizer has on garden plants. He put some good soil in two different boxes. To Box A he added fertilizer containing a large amount of nitrogen. To Box B he added fertilizer containing a large amount of phosphorous. In each box he planted the number 12 bean seeds. He watered each box with the same amount of water. One thing missing from Tom's experiment was a box of soil with

A. Both fertilizers added.

B. Neither nitrogen nor phosphorous fertilizers added.

C. Several kinds of seeds planted.

D. No seeds planted.

Level 2 (Grades 10–12)

Situation: You and your family are visiting the Grand Canyon National Park in Arizona. The Canyon, one of the geographical wonders of the world, is a gigantic gorge as much as 18 miles across and a mile deep. At the bottom of this gorge the Colorado River is now flowing through an inner gorge of extremely ancient metamorphic rocks which are covered by thousands of feet of varied sedimentary formations.

Upon reaching the bottom of the Canyon, you find the Colorado River extremely turbulent and muddy. To determine how much mud and other eroded material is in the water it would be best to take measured samples of the river water and

A. Determine the average molecular weight of the samples.

B. Evaporate the water and weigh the residue.

C. Add reagents to precipitate dissolved minerals, filter, and weigh the residue.

D. Filter, evaporate the water, and weigh the residue from the filtrate.

Level 1 (Grades 13–14)

Situation: The Alpha Uranium Company is organized to prospect for, obtain, and refine uranium ores.

As a protection against radiation injuries, a check is needed to determine whether plant employees have been exposed to too much radiation. Which of the following safety procedures would be best?

A. Providing each worker with a Geiger counter to be carried at all times.

B. Providing each worker with a radiation-sensitive piece of photographic film mounted in a badge.

C. Have each employee pass by a Geiger counter as he leaves the plant.

D. Taking a weekly X ray of each employee and checking for radiation bone-damage.[6]

The foregoing samples of questions that are found in several standardized tests suggest the emphasis of measuring scientific

[6] *A Brief—Cooperative Sequential Tests of Educational Progress,* Educational Testing Service, 1958, pp. 16–17.

knowledge as well as scientific thinking. A different approach to testing pupil ability in scientific method was developed by Goehring. He designed a series of film slides and used them in test items as follows:

EXPLANATION OF THE FILM SLIDE, STATEMENT OF THE PROBLEM, AND TEST QUESTIONS FOR SELECTED FILM SLIDE TEST ITEMS OF THE FINAL TRYOUT TEST OF THE SCIENTIFIC METHOD

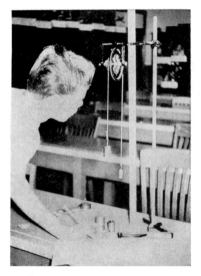

TEST ITEM NUMBER 10

This boy is doing an experiment to find out how the simple machine apparatus behaves. So far, he has not measured any distances, but he has found during several trials that a small weight attached to the larger wheel will always raise a larger weight attached to the smaller wheel. From these observations, what one general conclusion may be accepted as being true?

Fig. 10.1. Test Item Number 10. (Courtesy of Harvey J. Goehring, Jr.)

a. The output work of a machine is always less than the input work.   *a.* _____

b. The wheel-and-axle can be used as a machine to increase force.   *b.* __×__

c. When there is a game in force there is always a loss in speed.   *c.* _____

d. The small weight will move twice as far as the large weight.   *d.* _____

e. The mechanical advantage of a wheel-and-axle is less than one.   *e.* _____

TEST ITEM NUMBER 11

The car in which these boys are sitting is attached by the cables to a wheel high above the ground. When the machinery is started, the car will be whirled around at a high speed. The vane, or flap, in front of the boys (which one of them is holding) can be moved from side to side as the cars are swung around in a circle. The boys are planning to try an experiment to find out which factor has the most effect upon the distance the car swings up and down as it whirls around. Of these factors, which one will have the most effect in making the car move up and down as it whirls around?

Fig. 10.2.   Test Item Number 11. (Courtesy of Harvey J. Goehring, Jr.)

a. The position of their weight in the car.   a. ____

b. The direction the car is moving over the ground.   b. ____

c. The length of the cable suspending the car.   c. ____

d. The height of the car above the ground.   d. ____

e. The speed of the air over the vane in front.   e. __×__

TEST ITEM NUMBER 18

This boy is interested in finding out why a small metal ball swings as it does. He is going to count the swings that this metal ball makes

Fig. 10.3. Test Item Number 18. (Courtesy of Harvey J. Goehring, Jr.)

in one minute. He would like to know whether the following factors affect the swings made in one minute:

1. Length of the cord
2. Amount of weight on the cord
3. Height of the weight above the floor

After making his first trial, which of these factors should he change for his second trial?

a. Any two factors.   a. _____
b. Numbers 1 and 2.   b. _____
c. Only the first.   c. ___×___
d. Numbers 1 and 3.   d. _____
e. All three factors.   e. _____

[7] The sample test items and photographs were furnished by Dr. Harvey J. Goehring, Jr., 8239 Lincoln Road, Verona, Pa. These appear in his doctoral study, "A Film Slide Test to Measure Ability to Apply Scientific Method in the Area of Mechanics in High School Physics," University of Pittsburgh, 1956.

Although some of the laboratory situations can be set up in the school laboratory for testing purposes, a good series of film slides can present the same ideas from a different view. This approach becomes both a test and a learning experience.

Practical tests may measure knowledge, skills, such as problem solving or laboratory manipulative, attitudes, interests, and any combination of these objectives. Practical tests in the form of slides for testing scientific method have been illustrated from the field of physics.

In biology, a practical test may take the form of a series of stations where students move from one part of the room to another. At each station there is a display (perhaps under the microscope) of biological specimens in a dish or dissecting pan; students are asked to write down the identification or function of the object under display at each station. This type of practical test is actually testing information based on observation, retention, and possible association.

Some biology teachers would administer other types of practical tests such as observing pupil ability in the use of the microscope (laboratory manipulative) or observing the skill with which students make a dissection of an organism or an organ. Practical tests that are varied may have not only excellent appeal to students but also may be very instructional as a culminating experience.

In his study on "Problem-solving Techniques in Teaching Secondary School Physics," Dean gives the following illustration of a practical test:

A class had been studying magnetism, electromagnetism, and electric motors. They had investigated the magnetic effects of electric currents and the principles by which electric motors might be constructed. The problem-solving approach had been used with a liberal supplement of lecture and reading assignment. The students were given an objective test and were also instructed to pass through five stations of a practical examination.

The first station was a wire revolving about a permanent magnet standing on one end in a pool of mercury. The mercury served to conduct the current to the end of the wire. The students were instructed to explain why the wire revolved about the magnet.

The students had not previously seen such a motor. In order to correctly fulfill the instructions, they had to state: that when an electric current flows through a conductor in a magnetic field the conductor will move in a direction at right angles to the direction of the field. It sounds as if every student should see the explanation at once, having just studied the phenomena, but such was not the case. Students who had used the problem approach extensively did better than those who had not. As might have been expected, the brighter students in the group did better than the slower ones.

The second station consisted of a piece of magnetite, commonly known as lodestone, and a compass. Patches of different colored paint covered the surface of the magnetite. The students were instructed to determine the location of the poles of the lodestone and to report their answers in relation to the color, such as the south pole was red and the north pole was green, or whatever the colors were.

Students and teachers are in the habit of identifying the poles of a magnet as being at the ends and not thinking much about it. In this case, however, the magnet is irregularly shaped, and no simple relation exists between the poles and the shape of the magnet. To correctly solve this problem, the student must make use of what he knows about the shape and action of a magnetic field and the interaction of two such fields.

There is little doubt that the student had a problem; he wanted to do well in the examination, and to do so he must discover the location of the poles one way or another. He is unable to produce the answer from his memory because he has never encountered this particular situation before. If he is right, it is either because he guessed and was lucky or because he solved the problem. The chance of correctly guessing two colors out of seven or eight is small enough that the former possibility can be generally discounted.

The third station was two pieces of identical-appearing material, one of which was magnetized, the other not. The student was told what the situation was and asked to identify the magnet. Again the class had not encountered this particular problem when they were studying magnets. They supposedly knew and understood how magnetic fields acted and how a magnet attracted a nonmagnetized piece of ferromagnetic material; the problem that they faced was how to apply that knowledge to this situation. Some students were never able to discover what the problem was. Several asked if they could have a piece of string with the obvious intention of making a compass. Others played with the materials aimlessly. A few picked up one piece and began to systematically test the other to see at what locations the attraction was strongest. These students soon discovered that one bar was not attracted to the center of the other. Some obvious hypotheses were made by students as they worked on this problem. Attempts were made to hold one bar still and to see if the other bar was attracted toward it, apparently on the assumption that the magnetized bar would attract but that the non-magnetized bar would not. Other students attempted to make use of the fact that there was no mutual repulsion. Several students found that the first bar that they had picked up would be attracted to the other and immediately concluded that this one was not the magnet.

After the examination, the better part of a class period was devoted to considerations of this and other questions. Particular care was taken to emphasize the process of learning to determine which bar was which. It was felt that this was a difficult problem and that only quite skilled thinkers who also understood the basic physics required, could solve it.

The fourth station was a "St. Louis" motor with a wound field. Two dry cells provided power. The students were asked to reverse the direction of rotation of the armature.

In this instance the class had worked with permanent magnet St. Louis motors and had seen a large wound field motor demonstrated and reversed. In addition, their text discussed the problem of reversing electric motors. Nevertheless, not all of the students in the class proved able to reverse the motor. Some would reverse the polarity at the battery and then be very surprised when the motor continued to turn in the same direction. The problem in this case appears to have been quite simple; one has to only apply what he has seen and read to a real situation. The same students who failed to reverse the motor were able to answer correctly a multiple-choice test item on how to do it. It was concluded, in this instance, that the mental ability to transfer learning from one medium to another had not been gained.

The fifth station was in the nature of a review. There were two dry cells, connecting wire, and a three-volt flashlight bulb. The student was instructed to connect the batteries and the bulb in such a manner that the bulb would glow brightly. A bulb that was just glowing was not considered a correct answer. A number of students failed to accomplish this task, simple as it seems. The problem here would seem to be that of applying one's verbal knowledge of series connections to the real situations. If an individual did not have certain factual knowledge, he would not be able to solve this problem. One would have to know that it takes a greater potential to cause a bulb to glow brighter, or better yet, have a working knowledge of Ohm's Law and the heating effect of an electric current.

In review of these five tests of a student's ability to solve practical problems having to do with electricity and magnetism, a few comments may be offered. The various stations were deliberately designed to be of differing degrees of difficulty. The last item was such that most of the class was able to do what was called for. The simple motor proved to be too difficult for most of the students to explain. The other problems proved to be somewhere in between these two in difficulty.

When setting up evaluation instruments such as these, the teacher must be ready to make modifications according to the ability and attitudes of a particular class.[8]

The use of practical tests in evaluating problem-solving ability should not discourage teachers if the results are not too good. Science teachers should experiment in trying out different situations or anecdotes that lead to problem-solving activity. It will probably take some time for students either to condition their thinking or to learn to adjust to problem-solving activity. The science teacher will recognize that in many cases students may be under the impression that science is memorizing technical words and definitions. Students who enter a science class with this negative attitude or misconception need positive direction in their science

[8] Peter Dean, "Problem-solving Techniques in Teaching Secondary School Physics," a paper presented at the Thirty-second Annual Meeting of the National Association for Research in Science Teaching, Atlantic City, N.J., February 20, 1959. Also see Lester C. Mills and Peter Dean, *Problem-Solving Methods in Science Teaching,* Bureau of Publications, Teachers College, Columbia University, 1960, pp. 76–79.

activities to convince them that understanding science can be most interesting and challenging. Evaluation procedures can be used for guiding and directing learning activities in science in order that these students will want to learn science.

Attitudes, appreciations, and interests are more difficult to measure and evaluate than understandings, factual knowledge, or problem-solving skills in science. These intangible factors or objectives can be evaluated through anecdotal records and through the observation and study of individual pupil activities related to questions, answers, discussions, chalkboard activities, oral and written reports, projects, experiments, group activities, and outside classroom activities such as field trips and visits to points of scientific interest.

Anecdotal records in a science class may prove very helpful in understanding pupil attitudes and behavior. For example, a student's remark, "Knock on wood," "Where's my rabbit foot?" or other similar remarks will reveal superstitious behavior and attitudes. The science teacher may record incidents or remarks on cards or sheets of paper which become the anecdotal record of a pupil. Some teachers of science will code behavior of individual pupils where special guidance or development is wanted. Rating scales and check lists of scientific attitudes are easy to check for the following: superstitions, coincidence, use of evidence, exaggerations, sticking to facts, jumping to conclusions, tolerance of other opinions and ideas, and response to vague explanations. A mimeographed sheet which has a column for each student and a list of activities may require only a check mark when an incident or remark by a pupil is noted. Interviews with students, periodic conferences, and student diaries of learning activities will also help the science teacher guide and evaluate the students.

Although it is possible to administer interest inventories, the science teacher can determine pupil interests in science through projects, research, and the nature of pupil participation in class. Individual conferences and student diaries of learning activities can be helpful in evaluating the changes in student development. A picture test such as that designed by Read (see Figure 10.5)

Fig. 10.4. The picture test designed by John G. Read predicts future success in senior high school and college science courses. (Used with permission from John G. Read, "A Nonverbal Test of the Ability to Use the Scientific Method as a Pattern for Thinking," *Science Education,* vol. 33 [December, 1949], pp. 361–366)

can be helpful. Discussing this test, Read wrote, "Pupils in junior high school often show interest and ability in science. The picture test may be able to predict future success for these pupils in the more formal sciences of high school and college, and so fix in their minds the idea that they perhaps are potentially science majors."[9] Read warned, however, that much care should be exercised in this type of guidance since other factors should be carefully evaluated, including intelligence, mathematical ability, and science ability.

OBTAINING STANDARDIZED TESTS

The science teacher will wish to consider the purposes of administering a test. Is it administered to determine achievement, interests, problem-solving ability, laboratory skills, or attitudes? After the purposes of the test are established, the teacher may wish to list the course objectives and go over a sample or specimen test to determine if most of the objectives in the course are related to the purposes of the test. Most companies will make specimen tests available to the teacher for about thirty-five cents. The teacher's major purpose in going over the test in a systematic manner is, of course, to make his own evaluation of the test to determine its validity. Unless a standardized test actually measures what it is supposed to measure, it is invalid.

After the teacher knows the purposes for administering a test,

9 John G. Read, "A Nonverbal Test of the Ability to Use the Scientific Method as a Pattern for Thinking," *Science Education,* vol. 33 (December, 1949), pp. 361–366.

he should examine catalogues that describe standardized tests, as well as the latest *Mental Measurements Yearbook*.[10] Teachers may also wish to obtain free advice in selecting science tests and other standardized tests by writing to: Evaluation and Advisory Service, Educational Testing Service, 20 Nassau Street, Princeton, New Jersey.

Catalogues which list standardized tests may be obtained from the following:

Bureau of Educational Measurements, Kansas State Teachers College, Emporia, Kan.

Bureau of Educational Research and Service, State University of Iowa, Iowa City, Iowa

Bureau of Publications, Teachers College, Columbia University, New York 27, N.Y.

California Test Bureau, 5916 Hollywood Blvd., Los Angeles 28, Calif.

Center for Psychological Service, George Washington University, Washington, D.C.

Cooperative Test Division, Educational Testing Service, 20 Nassau St., Princeton, N.J.

Educational Test Bureau, Educational Publishers, Inc., 720 Washington Ave. SE., Minneapolis, 14, Minn.

Houghton Mifflin Co., 2 Park St., Boston 7, Mass.

Ohio Scholarship Tests, Ohio State Dept. of Education, Columbus, Ohio

Psychological Corp., 522 5th Ave., New York 36, N.Y.

Public School Publishing Co., 204 West Mulberry St., Bloomington, Ill.

Science Research Associates, Inc., 57 W. Grand Ave., Chicago 10, Ill.

Stanford University Press, Stanford, Calif.

World Book Co., 313 Park Hill Ave., Yonkers 5, N.Y.

CONSTRUCTING CLASSROOM TESTS

A good test should be a good learning experience. The degree to which learning may occur during the classroom period will be influenced by the nature of the test, including the kind of questions,

[10] O. K. Buros (ed.), *The Fifth Mental Measurements Yearbook,* Rutgers University Press, 1960.

the format, the way it is administered, and the way the results of the test are used in the classroom. For example, a short quiz is prepared by the chemistry teacher. It is a test to measure whether or not students can understand the relationship between the structure of an atom and its valence. Perhaps more learning will occur if the students evaluate or correct their own papers during the class and opportunities are provided for pupils to ask questions. Explaining the answers to student questions at the end of an examination or quiz can be an effective learning procedure. Again the following week a modified quiz measuring the same idea of valence and atomic structure is administered. Students will be able to make self-evaluations in noting their individual growth in learning this topic. It is more important to have the students evaluate their own growth or lack of it than merely to record a grade in the roll book.

It is fallacious to assume that the more students who fail in a physics or other science course, the higher or better are the class standards. For many students physics may be a difficult course. In any case, however, the science teacher should carefully evaluate his own teaching and the tests which he administers. If the majority of the students in a class fail a test, it indicates that either the test is faulty or the students have not learned what is expected of them. The teacher may or may not be at fault. Nevertheless, the test and instructional procedures should be carefully scrutinized.

Grading on a normal distribution curve does not alter the fault in a test. If the highest grade is 60, it should not necessarily be assumed that this student deserves the highest grade. If, in another class, the lowest score is 70, this does not imply that this student should fail because it is the lowest score in this class. Normal distribution curves may be helpful to teachers in tabulating test scores or student grades over perhaps a three- or five-year period where in many instances the results of the data may take the form of normal distribution curves.

In constructing a class test, the science teacher is careful to prepare questions that do not lend themselves to more than one correct response. For example, the biology teacher avoids a question such as, "One-celled animals are _____." Is the answer paramecia, amoebae, protozoa, or some other protozoan? If the biology teacher wanted to test the meaning of the word *protozoa,* the question would have read: "One-celled animals are known as phylum _____." Test items should be carefully studied for possible multiple replies, vagueness, and inaccuracies. It is not good practice to suggest to students that "The answer I wanted is _____," even though the student response is accurate. The science teacher should prepare tests and score them with much humility. Douglass wrote:

> One of the first places to which investigation should be directed in instances of more than ordinary proportions of failure is the marking practices of the teachers concerned. It has been shown in numerous studies that the percentages of failing marks assigned by different teachers in the same school and in the same subjects in different schools contain variations so great as to lie beyond all possibility of the existence of a corresponding variation in the abilities of the different groups of pupils.
>
> Careful studies by committees of teachers of the marks assigned by teachers in school may serve to attract attention to discrepancy in marking standards, and thereby reduce materially the number of failing pupils.[11]

The complete answer is not necessarily uniform departmental tests. The science teacher must be free to supplement the syllabus and be creative in his or her teaching. Standardized tests are most useful if they do not become the determinants of what to teach in science. Thus, the "homemade" classroom science test should be based on the specific learnings that are related to the course objectives.

After a student receives a mark based on one or more tests, he may come to the science teacher for a conference. Classroom tests, followed by such conferences, can contribute greatly to help-

---

[11] Harl R. Douglass, *Modern Administration of Secondary Schools,* Ginn & Company, 1954, pp. 340–341.

ing students make self-evaluations. This becomes an excellent guidance function which encourages pupils to seek help from their science teacher. Group guidance may also occur in the classroom immediately following a discussion of class marks. Study habits, pupil goals and motives, attitudes, understandings or lack of them, and skills may be discussed by pupils on a self-evaluation basis within the class. Well-constructed science tests in terms of the course objectives and their results can be used by science teachers in guiding students intellectually and vocationally.

A good science teacher not only is humble in making pupil evaluations, but is also flexible. The teacher should not discourage students from asking questions after a test. Frequently, a student may learn a concept for the first time after a class quiz if he is encouraged to ask questions.

The teacher-made test should not be stereotyped. Students should not be able to determine in advance what type of test the teacher will give. For example, the science teacher who tests only new words or vocabulary and always structures the classroom quiz along these patterns will cause the pupils merely to memorize definitions. This procedure suggests that the science teacher is teaching science like a foreign language. Teacher-made tests should be varied, interesting, and stimulating. A good science test can actually be a joy to take. It can offer a satisfaction similar to the one which comes from putting together a jigsaw puzzle.

The science teacher should ask these questions in designing classroom tests: Am I testing what I taught or what students should have read in the text? What number of my questions are related to functional scientific information, scientific attitudes, skills, or problem solving? Do I vary the nature of my test and give essay, completion, multiple-choice, modified true-false, matching, and practical quizzes? Do I make item analyses of the various questions on my test? Do I use test results to improve my teaching as well as to serve as part of the learning experience for my students? Do my tests guide me in planning lessons and in making diagnoses for remedial teaching? Do the tests help the students make self-evaluations that promote learning?

EVALUATING A SCIENCE PROGRAM

Since Sputnik many school systems have quickly installed a number of curriculum changes in the science program. A good feature of this activity is that it has caused many people and schools to take a careful look at what science is being taught. Some schools have instituted several changes for the better. But it is virtually impossible to determine whether all of the changes in a science program are for the better unless a carefully planned system of evaluation is employed.

Some schools have lengthened the school day in order to add an hour to daily instruction in science. Others have lengthened the week in order to offer science instruction on Saturdays or after regular school hours. Most of the schools in revising the science program have examined the total sequence from kindergarten through the twelfth grade rather than the junior high school science program or the elementary school science program. A few schools have recently invited outside science education consultants to evaluate the entire science program by noting faculty training, experience, recent in-service training, degrees, science courses offered, science equipment and supplies available, and related factors that make for a good science program.

Various organizations, including the Physical Science Committee at the Massachusetts Institute of Technology, the American Chemical Society, the American Physiological Society, the Manufacturing Chemists Association, the National Aviation Education Council and the National Science Foundation, are trying to develop either new materials such as workbooks, suggested experiments, and teacher training courses in sciences as institute courses or a new syllabus in science courses that will solve many problems which some people believe are related to Sputnik. Several cities have taken action in science as noted in the following pamphlets: *The Detroit Science Education Story, The Indianapolis Science Education Story, The Oklahoma Science Education Story.*[12] Many

[12] These are publications of addresses presented at the Eighth Institute of the Thomas Alva Edison Foundation, November, 1957.

of these groups are proposing various types of "crash through" programs as a result of Sputnik. While it is essential that our schools continually evaluate their program of instruction, in science and all areas, "crash through" programs like other programs should be evaluated early to determine whether any harm or good may come from them.

Many educators are showing much concern for the hasty "let's do something about it" approach. Perhaps programs of evaluation should be formulated along with the suggested "crash through" programs of science. In a recent *Saturday Review* editorial, Norman Cousins wrote:

. . . I found that most of the concern was directed not to attitudes of students but to competitive issues related to the Soviet Union; in particular, the role of the university in supplying enough scientists to give us eventual scientific supremacy.

There can be little question that our universities have had a substantial expansion in science courses. But I am not sure that this increase in emphasis is resulting in a proportionate increase in creative scientists; that is, scientists who know how to work with theory and who are capable of fresh conceptual thought. The impression I have is that we are turning out good technicians and engineers, but not necessarily original thinkers who have an urge to probe on the frontiers of scientific progress.

Even more disturbing, perhaps, was an attitude I detected here and there on campuses of schools of technology. The laboratory and everything that happened in it was sovereign. The liberal arts are taught but are more tolerated than pursued. Questions concerning human purpose and the making of a better life seem to be regarded as extraneous and rather sentimental.[13]

Although there is always some improvement to be made in a science program, changes should be instituted in terms of betterment if improvement is to take place. In making more technicians, it is possible that we may be making more monsters than men. Therefore, the editor's concern expressed above is a realistic one. The high school science teacher is not concerned with making

---

[13] "Stroll on the American Campus," an editorial, *Saturday Review*, April 30, 1960.

scientists out of all of his pupils. He is, of course, concerned with inspiring and nourishing those students who are interested and capable of becoming scientists. But for the majority of students the science teacher is concerned with teaching science for purposes of general education stated in Chapter 2.

The following criteria for evaluating a secondary school science program were proposed by Rarick and Read:

1. Do the courses offered satisfy the personal-social needs of the pupils?
2. Does the functional information assist the students in applying practical scientific principles which will be helpful in their lives?
3. Is the scientific method constantly brought to the attention of the students as they study scientific principles?
4. Is opportunity given for further exploration in the realm of science?
5. Are science principles used in the solution of problems which are challenging, pertinent, and timely?
6. Do the teacher and the pupils know what the purpose of the day's work is?
7. Do the pupils know why the subject matter is being considered at that time?
8. Is everything being done to encourage the students to further a science hobby or to work on some science project in which they are interested? (This can be done by means of a science fair in your school, which will prepare students to participate in regional and state-wide fairs).[14]

Many school systems have at regular intervals employed criteria such as these suggested by Rarick and Read, and as a result many new programs have been developed.[15] Determining whether or not the criteria have been used effectively is a next step that can

[14] G. L. Rarick and J. G. Read, "Criteria for Evaluating a Secondary School Science Program," *Educational Administration and Supervision,* vol. 36, (May, 1950), pp. 313–314.

[15] For descriptions of new programs and sources for requesting additional information, see *New Developments in High School Science Teaching,* published by National Science Teachers Association, Washington, D.C., 1960, $1.50; and the March, 1960, issue of *Science Education News* published by American Association for the Advancement of Science, Washington, D.C.

be accomplished through a series of valid tests and measurements. An evaluation program of these new science developments instituted in many schools throughout the country is called for to determine whether or not the desired objectives are being developed.

SUMMARY

Evaluation is a continuous process. The evaluation procedures are an integral part of instruction. Student achievement, remedial teaching, placement, attitudes, and diagnostic work in science are accomplished by various instruments such as tests, conferences, observations, anecdotal records, and reports. Student achievement in science is related to class and school size, the type of laboratory experience, and the training and personality of the teacher. Standardized tests should be used in terms of the objectives of the science course. Classroom tests should be a good learning experience for the students. Evaluation techniques should be explored at the same time that changes in curriculum are anticipated.

EXERCISES

1. Discuss the differences between evaluation and measurement.
2. What characteristics should a science teacher look for in selecting a standardized test?
3. What are the problems in evaluating attitudes, appreciations, and interests in science?
4. Explain how a good testing program can help a science teacher identify the talented pupil in science.
5. How can pupil opinions be used in evaluating a science program of instruction?
6. Discuss how the classroom teacher can use item analyses of tests in improving science instruction.

SUGGESTED READINGS

Adams, G. S., and Torgerson, T. L., *Measurement and Evaluation for the Secondary School Teacher,* New York, Dryden Press, 1956.

Anastasi, A., *Psychological Testing,* New York, The Macmillan Company, 1954.

Bean, K. L., *Construction of Educational and Personnel Tests,* New York, McGraw-Hill Book Company, Inc., 1953.

Berberich, J. R., *Specimen Objective Test Items,* New York, Longmans, Green & Company, Inc., 1956.

Buros, O. K., (ed.), *The Fifth Mental Measurements Yearbook,* Highland Park, N.J., Gryphon Press, 1960.

Cronbach, L. J., *Essentials of Psychological Testing,* 2nd ed., New York, Harper & Brothers, 1960.

Dressel, Paul L., and Mayhew, L. B., *General Education, Explorations in Evaluation,* Washington, D.C., American Council on Education, 1954.

Dressel, Paul L., and Nelson, Clarence R., *Questions and Problems in Science, Test Item Folio 1,* Princeton, N.J., Educational Testing Service, 1956.

Freeman, F. S., *Theory and Practice of Psychological Testing,* (rev.), New York, Henry Holt & Company, Inc., 1955.

Green, H. A., Jorgensen, A. N., and Gerberich, J. R., *Measurement and Evaluation in the Secondary School,* New York, Longmans, Green & Company, Inc., 1954.

Henry, N. B. (ed.), *Measurement of Understanding,* Forty-fifth Yearbook, Part I, National Society for the Study of Education, Chicago, University of Chicago Press, 1946.

Lindquist, E. F. (ed.), *Educational Measurement,* Washington, D.C., American Council on Education, 1951.

Remmers, H. H., Gage, N. L., and Rummel, J. F., *A Practical Introduction to Measurement and Evaluation,* New York, Harper & Brothers, 1960.

Ross, C. C., and Stanley, J. C., *Measurement in Today's Schools,* 3rd ed., Englewood Cliffs, N.J., Prentice-Hall, Inc., 1954.

Thomas, R. M., *Judging Student Progress,* New York, Longmans, Green & Company, Inc., 1954.

Travers, R. M. W., *Educational Measurement,* New York, The Macmillan Company, 1955.

Vernon, P. E., *Personality Tests and Assessments,* New York, Henry Holt & Company, Inc., 1954.

11

ESTABLISHING A NEW SCIENCE CLASSROOM

In view of the fact that student enrollments have increased and will continue to do so for many years in the secondary schools, it is not uncommon for a science teacher to be asked to design and plan for the establishment of a science room in the new junior-senior high school building. If possible, it is best to meet with the architect before the building is constructed and go over such details as electrical outlets, gas and water facilities, light, ventilation and hoods to accommodate fumes, and the location of built-in cabinets, storage, preparation and darkrooms. For existing buildings, science teachers may wish to determine how to modernize the science laboratories and to call upon various service representatives as well as consultants in science education.

In the previous chapter, reference was made to new science programs and the importance of evaluation. To determine the type of science laboratories to be recommended for a junior or senior high school, a wise first step is to examine the science programs carefully for needs expected to continue for several years as well as for probable changes that may occur in order to allow for accommodations without drastic structural changes in the science room. Actually, the science laboratory—which includes the furniture, equipment, and supplies—should permit a degree of flexibility to meet the changing needs of the community. Paul deH. Hurd writes: "Modern practices in science teaching suggest that a single room of great flexibility is the most appropriate for achieving the results desired. Outstanding science facilities would be characterized as learning areas with a high degree of adjustable and adaptable working space. This is imperative in order to accommodate a science curriculum that is more fluid today than at any time within the past twenty years."[1] Hurd lists several criteria in determining flexibility as follows:

Is the room flexible enough to provide for the many kinds of learning activities essential in modern science instruction? This means, among other things:

1. Desirable learning activities are not restricted or inhibited in any way by the physical environment.
2. The learning environment makes it possible for many activities, related to the gathering and verification of data, to be carried on at the same time.
3. Group problem-solving activities are not restricted by immovable or unwieldy furniture. Individual and group arrangements are possible within the classroom at the same time.
4. Many learning resources are conveniently located within the classroom, such as reference books, current materials, magazines, models, charts, specimens, and commonly used equipment.
5. Auxiliary facilities in terms of segregated work areas are available for students with special interests and skills. These areas should provide facilities for long-term experiments and for the preparation of projects.[2]

The following questions can serve as a guide in determining if the room is flexible from the point of view of instruction:

1. Can students move easily from class to laboratory activities within a single room and from one work area to another room without any difficulty?
2. Can demonstration setups be established in several areas throughout the room?
3. Does the layout of the room enable the science teacher to move about the room freely, thus permitting effective guidance and instruction to individuals?
4. Are doors and aisles constructed and located to permit instant use of mobile laboratory tables?

---

[1] Paul deH. Hurd, "How to Achieve Outstanding High School Science Facilities," *American School and University* (1956–1957).
[2] *Ibid.*

5. Are laboratory facilities available and ready for use whenever needed? (laboratory equipment, projection machines, library resources, tape recordings, films, aquarium, charts, and models)

6. Do students have sufficient display areas to present their visual ideas in cabinets, project tables, chalk, magnetic and peg boards? Are they located in the laboratory and in nearby halls?

7. Is there a minimum of stationary equipment, and are the tables movable to permit various class arrangements for group work and other methods?

8. Can the tables be used for laboratory and class work?

9. Is there sufficient storage space for living and nonliving materials?

10. Are there darkrooms and preparation, growing, and project rooms?

There are two types of science rooms: (1) the multipurpose which has laboratory and classroom facilities for more than one science, and (2) the single-purpose room which is used for the teaching of one specific science such as biology, physics, or chemistry. It is desirable that most rooms be designated for multipurpose use. However, the student enrollment and the objectives of teaching science should be the determining factors. Where there are 500 or less students in a school it is most advantageous to have a multipurpose science room where general science or any of the basic sciences can be taught. Science rooms should provide 35 to 40 square feet per student. If darkrooms and preparation and storage rooms are included, the total area required per student may be at least 50 square feet. It is suggested that the science teacher obtain a master check list of science facilities at the time a new science laboratory classroom is planned.[3]

Serious consideration should be given to the use of a multipurpose science room. It should have adequate space for demonstrations, discussions, display, laboratory, projects, and reading.[4]

[3] "A Guide for Evaluating Your Science Facilities," from Scientific Apparatus Makers Association, 20 N. Wacker Drive, Chicago 6, Ill.

[4] Illustrations and descriptive material of science laboratories that appear in this chapter were furnished through the courtesy of E. H. Sheldon Equipment Company, Muskegon, Mich.

A MULTIPURPOSE SCIENCE CLASSROOM FOR JUNIOR AND SENIOR HIGH SCHOOLS

LECTURE-DEMONSTRATION-DISCUSSION AREA

All students should be able to hear each other throughout the room. The distance between the instructor and the students should be less than 16 feet. Tablet arm chairs are desirable for writing notes and for temporary storage of books and accessories.

DISPLAY AREA

Sufficient display area is essential for charts, models, and projects to enrich science instruction. Space should also be available for an accumulation of display materials and exhibits.

LABORATORY AREA

The design of furniture and its placement in the laboratory area should permit laboratory stations for individual students, for pairs, and for groups of students. Supply cabinets, fumehoods, and instrument stations should be directly accessible to the students. The work areas in the laboratory should keep all traffic lanes clear.

FUMEHOOD

For the junior high school multipurpose science room, one large size fumehood is very satisfactory for demonstrations in the laboratory. It is most desirable to have visibility on two or three sides of the fumehood.

LIGHT AND DARKROOM AREA

The darkroom in a laboratory can enrich the teaching of several scientific principles in physics as well as biology. Running water, a basin, electrical outlets, and a double door should be carefully planned for the darkroom.

PROJECT AREA

Appropriate space for projects or special repairs on equipment will improve the efficiency of the multipurpose science room. This area is frequently located away from chemicals or corrosive materials. Exhibits may be placed in the project area on a temporary basis.

READING AND REFERENCE AREA

To encourage student research and projects, a reference library of handbooks, records, and other research materials should be avail-

Fig. 11.1. Instructor's table. (Courtesy of E. H. Sheldon Equipment Company)

able near the project area. One or more tables may be used for reading and reference.

PROJECT-MAINTENANCE-DISPLAY AREA

Item 1. Wood and Metalworking Bench—drawer and cupboard storage for raw materials and temporary projects.

Items 2, 4, 7. Display Panels—shelves, hooks, rings, spotlights, etc., for current display or permanent use.

Item 3. Tools and Raw Materials Storage Case—for wood-metalworking and chemistry maintenance areas.

Item 5. Chemistry Maintenance Bench—drawers and cupboards for burners, blowpipes, molds, trays, shapers, raw materials, patterns, and temporary project storage. Fireproof Sheldine top for glass blowing, etc.

Item 6. Projects Bench—bench and overhead cabinet providing storage for paper, wood, plastics, finishing materials.

READING AND REFERENCE AREA

Item 8. Display and Storage—science unit demonstration equipment; illustrative materials and teaching aids.

Fig. 11.2. Special Projects Area. (Courtesy of E. H. Sheldon Equipment Company)

Item 10. Display and Storage—science unit demonstration equipment.

LECTURE AND DEMONSTRATION AREA

Item 14. Sliding Chalkboard—Display and Storage—permanent and temporary demonstration materials, current chemicals, science unit demonstration equipment, visual aid equipment.

Item 15. Lecture and Demonstration Table—storage for table accessories, small tools, and demonstration apparatus.

STUDENT LABORATORY AREA

Item 17. Student Tables—slide-away units for student chemistry and/or physics apparatus. Two cupboards providing locked storage for apparatus tote trays or miscellaneous equipment; open storage compartment provided above cupboards will accept tote tray.

Item 18. Annex Section—providing locked cupboards, and eight

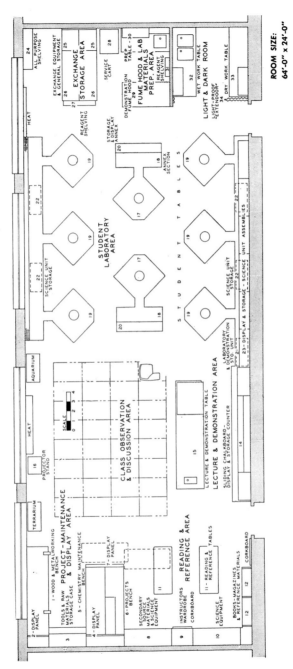

ROOM SIZE:
64'-0" x 24'-0"

Fig. 11.3. Total Experience Science Laboratory. (Courtesy of E. H. Sheldon Equipment Company)

tote trays for storage of chemistry, physics, and biology kits for experiments such as Mechanics of Solids, Fluorescence, Soil Test, etc. Four compartments for microscopes, portable D.C. power or table meter assemblies.

Item 19.   Student Table and Annex Section—composed of Items 17 and 18 in assembly.

Item 20.   Storage and Display Annex—open shelving and counter with meter rods for laboratory display, materials distribution, titration setups and other laboratory work.

Item 21.   Laboratory-Demonstration Storage Unit—counter and cupboard base cabinet with pegboard back, hooks, and shelves; or three full length adjustable shelves.

Item 22.   Science Unit Storage—counter and cupboard base cabinet same as Item 21. For storage of apparatus such as condenser or burette, and equipment used in Mechanics of Liquids, or Dissection.

Item 23.   Display and Storage Assembly—suspended cabinets above counter for storage or display of science unit assemblies.

EXCHANGE STORAGE AREA

Item 26.   Storage Case—miscellaneous supplies and/or apparatus tote trays.

DEMONSTRATION FUMEHOOD AND LABORATORY MATERIALS DISTRIBUTION AREA

Item 29.   Demonstration Fumehood—providing demonstration and/ or experimentation area; ventilated storage in base cabinet for acids and fuming chemicals.

Item 30.   Preparation Table—with sink and services; provides storage for miscellaneous supplies. Serves as laboratory preparation table or extra student work table.

LIGHT AND DARKROOM AREA

Item 32.   Wet Work Table—provides sink, services and storage for all photographic work.

Item 33.   Dry Work Table—provides counter and storage for equipment used in light-sound experiments and dry photographic work.

Item 34.   Light-proof Extendoor—provides an efficient means of light-proofing the room when needed, and when open allows the area to function effectively as a part of the student laboratory area.

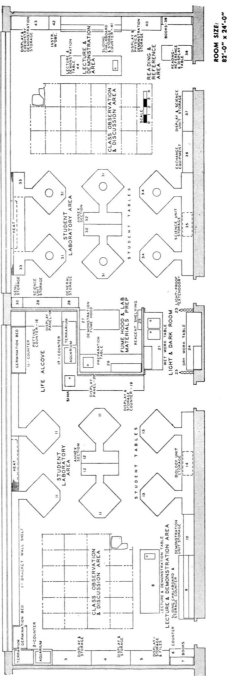

ROOM SIZE:
82'-0" x 24'-0"

Fig. 11.4. Total Experience Biological-Physical Science Laboratories Plan. (Courtesy of E. H. Sheldon Equipment Company)

BIOLOGY AND PHYSICAL SCIENCE ROOM

This two-room suite shows one method by which the total experience features of the modern science room may be provided in a limited space. The usual plan with two ordinary 40′ rooms and a common 12′ storage room gives way to one with life and really functional use.

Figure 11.4 illustrates a combination biology and physical science room which would be very suitable in a smaller senior high school or a junior high school. For the senior high schools of modest size, separate laboratory rooms may be provided for chemistry and physics.

CHEMISTRY LABORATORY

One of the advantages of the chemistry laboratory illustrated below is that there is no need for a separate storage room with a preparation counter. The instructor is in a position to exercise the necessary control and supervision and the handling of stored materials. Services and materials are within equal distance of all students.

PHYSICS LABORATORY

One of the interesting features of the physics laboratory plan illustrated below is that an electronics-sound room and an electronics area have been added in addition to the basic laboratory areas. These will enable students to construct, test, study, and experiment with electronic equipment in an efficient manner. Many sound projects such as radio, television, tape recording, and broadcasting may be conducted in the sound-proof electronics-sound room. There are sufficient areas for display, work counter, storage, and demonstration.

SUMMARY

In planning a new science classroom, the design of furniture and its placement should be flexible. The laboratory furniture and

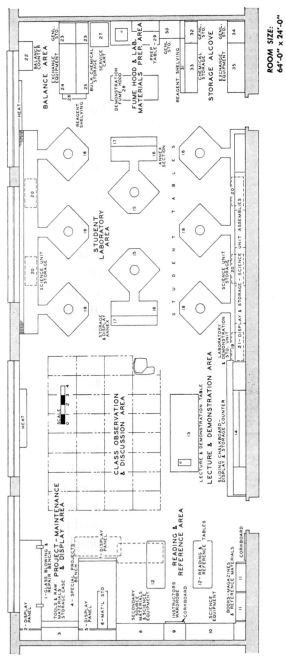

Fig. 11.5. Total Experience Chemistry Laboratory Plan. (Courtesy of E. H. Sheldon Equipment Company)

ROOM SIZE:
64'-0" x 24'-0"

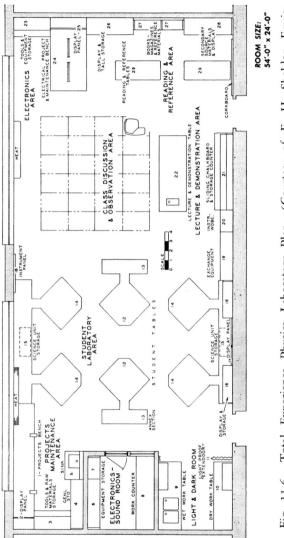

Fig. 11.6. Total Experience Physics Laboratory Plan. (Courtesy of E. H. Sheldon Equipment Company)

equipment should not be restricted within the physical environment. Several types of individual and group arrangements of furniture will enable variations in instruction to accommodate changing enrollments. For smaller junior and senior high schools, the multipurpose science classroom can meet the needs of most science courses. It is desirable to have well-equipped physics and other science laboratories as well as the multipurpose room.

EXERCISES

1. What is meant by a flexible science room?
2. Discuss the advantages and disadvantages of a multipurpose versus a single-purpose science room for a senior high school.
3. Explain the functions of the following areas in a science laboratory classroom: display and storage, tools, project, light and darkroom, fumehood, and reading.

SUGGESTED READINGS

Hurd, Paul deH., "How to Achieve Outstanding High School Science Facilities," *American School and University*, 1956–1957, New York, American School Publishing Corporation, 1956.

Hurd, Paul deH., *Science Facilities for the Modern High School,* Stanford, Calif., Stanford University Press, 1954.

Richardson, John S. (ed.), *School Facilities for Science Instruction,* Washington, D.C., National Science Teachers Association, 1954.

12

PROFESSIONAL GROWTH OF THE SCIENCE TEACHER

STUDENT TEACHER, COOPERATING TEACHER, AND COLLEGE SUPERVISOR

Usually the prospective science teacher receives an introduction to the teaching profession through a good student teaching experience. It has been said, "One of the best ways of learning to teach is by teaching." Student teaching is supervised both by the regular science teacher on an everyday basis and by the college supervisor on scheduled, periodic visits. Both kinds of supervision can serve as effective procedures and experiences in introducing the beginning teacher to a school system and to the teaching profession without unnecessary pitfalls. The major function of the cooperating teacher is to show the student teacher by demonstration and practice the effective methods of teaching specific kinds of lessons in science. The cooperating teacher is usually an experienced, master teacher. Within a short period of time, the student teacher begins to teach under the guidance of the master teacher. Care should be exercised that a student teacher does not feel that he or she must follow only the patterns or methods of teaching that are employed by the cooperating teacher. The cooperating teacher should encourage the student teacher to use his or her own ingenuity, initiative and resourcefulness in developing the daily lesson.

In the beginning, the student teacher should observe at least two or three science teachers as well as two or three different sciences such as general science, earth science, biology, chemistry, or physics. This variation will influence the student teacher to explore different types of procedures as well as to organize and plan a lesson in several ways. Student teachers in science have an opportunity to observe and practice-teach in several sciences and should be permitted to work with laboratory materials and equipment for demonstration and laboratory teaching. After a short period of observations, student teachers should begin teaching at least one class daily for a period of several weeks or for the duration of a teaching unit.

The big difference between the cooperating teacher and the college supervisor with reference to the student teacher is that the cooperating teacher usually "looks at the student teacher" as though he or she were teaching the class. In other words, the cooperating teacher may be thinking, "If I were teaching this lesson, would I be doing what this student teacher is teaching at this moment?" This can be a most helpful approach to the student teacher; but it can also be a limiting factor. Hence, the college supervisor should compare the student teacher with other student teachers, not with experienced or master teachers. The college supervisor should, with the help of the cooperating teacher, encourage the student teacher to experiment with many procedures and materials in teaching science. Some of the procedures may work most effectively in one class but not in another. Actually both the cooperating teacher and the college supervisor can work as a team in making worthy contributions to the development of a future science teacher.

How does the cooperating teacher contribute to the success of the student teacher? One of the student teachers in a class report suggested the following ideas:

1. The cooperating teacher provides the student teacher with information concerning the school and the individual pupils (records, test scores, pupil background, and personality problems).
2. The cooperating teacher shows the student teacher how to use certain audio-visual aids (motion picture films, filmstrips, projectors, laboratory materials, and other resource materials that are available in the school).
3. The cooperating teacher offers many constructive suggestions which are carefully evaluated by the student teacher.

4. The cooperating teacher helps the student teacher learn how to assume responsibility for the attendance records and other clerical duties required by all schools.

5. The cooperating teacher helps the student teacher learn how to manage a class and to develop effective lesson plans and procedures for teaching different lessons in science.[1]

It should also be recognized that a student teacher does enter a school and a science class with a good background of more than 30 credits in the college sciences and about 18 credits in education courses which include psychology of adolescence, methods, and student teaching. Usually, the student teacher has completed at least 24 college credits in one specific science. The student teacher also knows how to make a lesson plan, organize materials for instruction, and has a general idea about the art of questioning and evaluating a lesson. Before student teaching, or at the very beginning, he was taught to observe the following in a science class:

1. Were there any signs of stimulating or motivating learning such as science demonstrations, experiments, personal anecdotes, or the use of special audio-visual aids?

2. Is there a good social climate in the science class? Are the pupil-teacher rapport and the pupil-pupil rapport good? Are there wholesome attitudes toward the subject?

3. Does the science teacher ask thought-provoking questions which do not always necessarily call for a complete yes or no?

4. To what degree do the pupils show interest in the classroom activity—discussion, demonstrations, experiments, chalkboard work, pupil reports, or projects?

5. How does the science teacher direct pupil participation so that it does not become a teacher-pupil question-answer period?

6. In the course of a lesson, does the science teacher use more than one method of teaching? Over a period of several lessons, are varieties of instructional procedures employed?

7. Can the student teacher visualize a lesson plan as the master or cooperating teacher is being observed in the course of a lesson?

[1] Rhona Rubin, at the time a student teacher in science while a student at Queens College, New York, N.Y.

To assist both the student teacher and the cooperating teacher in understanding their relationship to each other, the following functions of the cooperating teacher may be helpful.

The cooperating teacher:

1. Is legally in control of and responsible for the science class (health, welfare, and safety).
2. Meets the student teacher as a co-worker and elevates the esteem of the class for the student teacher.
3. Provides a relaxed atmosphere and encourages a friendly working relationship with the student teacher.
4. Truly cooperates in feeling a sense of professional obligation in assisting in training future teachers of science. In return, the student teacher will assist the cooperating teacher with many classroom chores such as records, bookkeeping and related non-instructional activities.
5. Gives the student teacher an opportunity to teach the science classes regularly for at least a teaching unit as soon as the student teacher is ready.
6. Is willing to meet in a three-way conference with the student teacher and the college supervisor if the schedule permits.
7. Offers constructive suggestions in content and methodology to the student teacher who should make a serious attempt to follow them.
8. Emphasizes preparation of the student teacher before teaching a daily lesson.
9. Encourages pupil teacher to be creative and flexible in executing daily lesson plans.
10. Discusses the overall plan of the course for the semester or for the year with the student teacher, to permit more effective plans in daily instruction.
11. Provides the student teacher with necessary background information about individual pupils in the class so that the student teacher has more insight in teaching all members of the science class.
12. Solicits the help of student teachers in grading pupil examination papers and other class routines without "dumping" all of the menial tasks on the student teacher.
13. Accepts conflicting criticisms from the college supervisor with

diplomacy and maintains a professional friendly relationship with the supervisor.[2]

The responsibilities of the college supervisor will vary from one institution to another. In most universities, the college supervisor of science student teaching has formerly taught science in the secondary schools and has usually had some supervisory or administrative experience. It is desirable that a college supervisor visit student teachers at least four or five times during the semester to assist the student teacher in evaluating his or her own development as a science teacher. At the end of each visit or observation, the supervisor should confer with the student teacher and, if possible, also with the cooperating teacher. The major function of the conference is to guide, reassure, and help the student teacher evaluate his or her own instruction. Self-evaluation is the most important part of student teaching experience in science. It is most desirable that a beginning teacher know exactly what to analyze and what proper steps to take if a lesson does not materialize as originally planned. For this reason, self-evaluation on the part of the student teacher should be stressed by the college supervisor.

According to several sources the college supervisor performs the following duties:

1. Assigns and places the student teacher in a suitable school situation
2. Assists the student teacher with any problems in schedules or related administrative matters that may arise in the secondary school
3. Reassures the student teacher to enable him or her to show minimum tension and to direct the lesson to the class, not to the supervisor
4. Emphasizes the strengths in a student teacher during the conference and helps the student teacher make a self-evaluation in terms of constructive criticism following the teaching situation

[2] See the following: D. K. Curtis and L. O. Andrews, *Guiding Your Student Teacher,* Prentice-Hall, 1954, pp. 13–16; P. R. Grim and J. U. Michaelis, *The Student Teacher in the Secondary School,* Prentice-Hall, 1953, p. 27; L. Nelson and B. McDonald, *Guide to Student Teaching,* William C. Brown Company, 1958, pp. 26 and 32.

5. Is available to the student teacher for help in planning a lesson, examining the nature of the content and methodology, and locating sources of various scientific materials that may strengthen a science lesson
6. Conducts self-evaluation of supervision and a periodic examination of the student teaching and teacher training program
7. Acts as a source of information for publications, research studies, and standardized tests as well as new ideas and successful techniques used by other student teachers and regular teachers
8. Conducts seminars with student teachers in science to share experiences and provide for new information
9. Assumes responsibility for final grades and evaluation and writes letters of recommendation to assist student teachers in locating teaching positions[3]

THE SCIENCE TEACHER AND THE SCHOOL SUPERVISOR

In the previous section it was noted that the cooperating science teacher in a secondary school and a college supervisor make a very significant contribution toward the development of a student teacher and ultimately a regular science teacher. Good supervisory practices will help a beginning science teacher become a master teacher. The science teacher may have problems of classroom management, discipline, the location of audio-visual aids, scientific apparatus and materials, and motivating pupil interests and learning in science. Usually there is always someone available in a secondary school such as a principal, a curriculum coordinator, an assistant principal, or a departmental chairman who can assist the beginning science teacher in solving most of these problems. There should be freedom of communication between the supervisor and the beginning science teacher. It frequently takes a few years before a beginning science teacher becomes a master in the use of demonstrations, problem-solving techniques, laboratory, and developmental methods of teaching. Continued supervision to help the teacher achieve self-evaluation without developing any

[3] See W. T. Gruhn, *Student Teaching in the Secondary School*, The Ronald Press Company, 1954; and S. P. Wiggins, *The Student Teacher in Action*, Allyn & Bacon, 1957.

fears or anxieties will help make the science teacher a master teacher.

During the probationary period of the teacher, the superintendent of schools or supervisor in the junior and senior high school will observe a beginning teacher. The following items are usually included in the report form on a class visit: name of teacher, class, type of class, room, date, a brief description of class activities, title of lesson, motivation, aim, questioning, teaching devices and methods, group procedures, individualization of instruction, materials of instruction, budgeting of time, tempo, drill, chalkboard work, class management, evaluation, and summary. This report should be used by the science teacher to improve his teaching. Usually a conference is scheduled between the supervisor and the teacher to discuss this report.

THE SCIENCE TEACHER ALWAYS A STUDENT

The effective science teacher remains always a student of science and human behavior. He attempts to keep up with the latest research in science and in education. The greatest occupational hazard of a science teacher is to be out of date with the latest scientific and teaching developments. Hence, the science teacher, throughout his teaching experience will engage in at least one or more of the following activities to maintain his professional growth.

Graduate Study

For several years the trend has been to require a master's degree as minimum education for secondary school teachers. It is not uncommon to find many communities throughout the United States giving additional compensation to teachers who have earned additional college credits beyond the master's degree. In some school communities, teachers of science holding a doctorate or its equivalent receive at least one thousand dollars above the salary of a teacher who holds only the bachelor's degree.

Science teachers are motivated to pursue their studies in graduate colleges and universities not only because of the extra pay but also because of the need to learn of the latest developments in science and in teaching. In a few school districts, the tuition of graduate study for teachers is paid for by the board of education.

The nature of the graduate program will vary according to the preparation of the science teacher, the certification requirements of the state, and the requirements for a higher degree at a given university. For example, a student who graduated from a liberal arts college with an excellent background in the natural sciences will probably need a full year of professionalized courses in education including student teaching or internship teaching. On the other hand, a student teacher who has graduated from a college with a baccalaureate and has satisfactorily completed all of the education courses will want to continue in one of the specific sciences and related sciences. Many of the better teaching requirements in several states recommend that a science teacher in the fifth year of graduate work pursue courses in the natural sciences, education, and liberal arts other than science. A prospective science teacher should consult the state education department or the superintendent of public instruction in the state in which he intends to teach.

Summer and Year-Round Institutes

Regardless of whether or not a science teacher wants another degree, he finds a great need to continue to study science as he continues to teach. The National Science Foundation in Washington, D.C., under appropriations by the Federal government has been awarding thousands of fellowships and tuition-free scholarships with all expenses paid to thousands of science teachers throughout America. This program was instituted a few years ago with the sole purpose of upgrading the background of science teachers in order to improve the teaching of science in the secondary schools. Each year the National Science Foundation prepares a list of all of the colleges and universities that offer summer institutes and year-round science institutes for science and mathematics teachers.

Recently, Dr. John R. Mayor, Director of Education of the

American Association for the Advancement of Science, helped establish summer fellowships for science and mathematics teachers that were valid for up to three years of graduate work. It is possible for some science teachers to plan their graduate studies so as to earn a higher degree. The level of course instruction in the various sciences varies with the institution and the nature of the course and ranges from a college freshman review to a high-powered graduate course for the Ph.D. Each science teacher should select the appropriate instruction to meet his needs.

In-Service Training and Extensive Reading

Not all of the improvement of teaching science is due to the teacher's taking courses at college. A group of science teachers in a school system or local community can meet regularly with a few science and education consultants or experts to learn how to improve their own program of science. In-service training which is usually sponsored by the local school system can be a most efficient way to promote the professional development of the science teacher. Teacher exchanges in neighboring communities can likewise be explored during in-service training.

It is impossible to expect a science teacher to keep up to date in his scientific knowledge by pursuing all of the graduate courses in the natural sciences. Hence, a conscientious science teacher who seeks to grow professionally will continually read new textbooks, scientific journals and related periodicals.

Professional Organizations and Publications

Most of the professional organizations publish periodicals that are automatically sent to the members. It is highly desirable that science teachers join at least one national or one regional and/or local science teachers group to maintain a higher professional standard. Attending conferences, exchanging ideas and latest developments in science and in the teaching of science are other advantages of participating as members of a science teachers association.

A junior-senior high school library should have the following periodicals for the science faculty and the students: *Scientific*

American, Science, The Quarterly Review of Biology, The Journal of Chemical Education, Physics Today, Tomorrow's Scientist, The Science Teacher, Science Education, Popular Science, and other journals of a technical nature that some of the science faculty may want. These periodicals are essential not only for the science teachers to keep abreast with the latest information but also for the student who will soon find his textbook out of date. Suggested reading assignments should be given from periodicals as well as textbooks.

The following list includes professional associations dedicated to science teachers, with the titles of the magazines published by each:

Central Association of Science and Mathematics Teachers, P.O. Box 408, Oak Park, Ill., *School Science and Mathematics.*

Metropolitan Detroit Science Teachers Club, 3437 Oakman Blvd., Detroit 4, Mich., *Metropolitan Detroit Science Review.*

National Association of Biology Teachers, 110 E. Hines St., Midland, Mich., *The American Biology Teacher.*

National Association for Research in Science Teaching, Howard University, Washington, D.C., *Science Education.*

National Council for Elementary Science, University of Tampa, Tampa, Fla., *Science Education.*

National Science Teachers Association, 1201 16th St. NW, Washington 6, D.C.

Many of the secondary school science teachers in America belong to at least one or more of the above science teachers associations. In the interests of the profession and for the professional development of science teachers, support of these organizations is needed. In most instances the dues to the organization will include a subscription to the periodical which is invaluable to the science teacher.

Community Activities

The science teacher is an active citizen of his or her community and should provide leadership for appropriate community problems. For example, the questions of adding fluorides to a drinking water supply, pasteurization of milk, purification of water, spraying of insects, and other related technical problems can be solved through the cooperative leadership furnished by the science teacher and the community. Community forums, discussions, and round table meetings may serve as important places for the science teacher to give counsel.

After-school and Saturday-morning science programs are gaining favor in many communities. Although this type of activity does not necessarily promote the professional development of the science teacher, it does help young people decide on possible careers in science and in the extension of their interests in and knowledge of science. These services by the science teacher will improve public relations and make worthy contributions to the community.

Several communities through a number of scientific and technical industries have established recognition awards for science teachers. It is a forward step to note that prizes of $500, $1000, and medals are awarded to outstanding science teachers. A few industries have employed science teachers during the summer months in order that they obtain a firsthand knowledge of the utilization of science by the industries. Both the firm and the science teacher benefit from this experience. The student in the high school receives the real benefit of the enthusiasm and added knowledge and experience that the science teacher brings to class. The National Science Teachers Association obtained contributions from many industries for outstanding science teaching techniques. The STAR (Science Teacher Achievement Recognition) awards program conducted by the National Science Teachers Association and sponsored by the National Cancer Institute and the U.S. Public Health Service attracts many science teachers each year to submit ideas for making science instruction more inspirational and efficient.

Evaluation and Experimentation

In Chapter 10 it was suggested that evaluation should be a continuous process of teaching and learning. The science teacher, like all scientists, will experiment with new procedures or methods of teaching science. It will not be determined whether or not some of the experimental innovations are for the better until the science teacher evaluates by testing, observing, studying, and follow-up work. For some objectives of science education, it may be more effective to use the case study approach rather than a listing of historical material in science. For developing scientific attitudes and skills, the problem-solving method of teaching science may be most effective for some science teachers. The demonstration and laboratory methods are almost universal in their appeal, depending upon the stress of the objectives. Group work, pupil research and projects, supervised student study, discussions and recitations will also be used by the science teacher from time to time. If each science teacher would establish an experiment of teaching science by using one method at a given time and evaluating the same, we should all learn more about the more effective practices of teaching science to our youth. A vast number of hypotheses concerning teaching and learning need to be tested.

SUMMARY

The professional growth of a science teacher begins when he is a college student and continues when he becomes a student teacher. Student teaching is an invaluable experience to the prospective science teacher in helping him to learn the necessary attitudes, skills, and knowledge. The beginning teacher learns that he must evaluate his own instruction. He should learn to accept constructive criticism and how to use it for better teaching.

The real science teacher is always a student because he keeps up to date with the latest developments in science and education. Hence, he attends graduate classes, institutes, and in-service classes. He is active in one or more professional societies that contribute to the advancement of science teaching. He participates in community activities as a citizen as well as a science teacher.

EXERCISES

1. Discuss the role of the cooperating teacher and the college supervisor with respect to the student teacher in science.

2. How can the school supervisor help the beginning science teacher?
3. What opportunities are available to science teachers who wish to continue their advanced studies?
4. In what kinds of professional organization activities can a science teacher participate?
5. How can a science teacher serve as a consultant in his community?

SUGGESTED READINGS

Brown, Thomas J., *Student Teaching in a Secondary School,* New York, Harper & Brothers, 1960.

Curtis, D. K., and Andrews, L. O., *Guiding Your Student Teacher,* Englewood Cliffs, N.J., Prentice-Hall, Inc., 1954.

Grim, P. R., and Michaelis, J. U., *The Student Teacher in the Secondary School,* Englewood Cliffs, N.J., Prentice-Hall, Inc., 1953.

Gruhn, W. T., *Student Teaching in the Secondary School,* New York: The Ronald Press Company, 1954.

McGuire, V., Myers, R. B., and Durrance, C. L., *Your Student Teaching in the Secondary School,* Boston, Allyn & Bacon, Inc., 1959.

Nelson, L., and McDonald, B., *Guide to Student Teaching,* Dubuque, Iowa, William C. Brown Company, Publishers, 1958.

Wiggins, S. P., *The Student Teacher in Action,* Boston, Allyn & Bacon, Inc., 1957.

INDEX